APPLIED MATHEMATICS

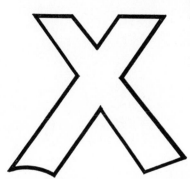

Applied Mathematics

JAMES F. JOHNSON

Revised by
PETER ANDRIS

THE BRUCE PUBLISHING COMPANY

Milwaukee

Library of Congress Catalog Card Number: 65–23745

Copyright © 1965 THE BRUCE PUBLISHING COMPANY
MADE IN THE UNITED STATES OF AMERICA

(21/68)

Preface

APPLIED MATHEMATICS is intended to supply a basic working knowledge of practical mathematics for students in junior and senior high schools and vocational schools, for workers in the trades and in industry, and for others who desire an introduction to the topics that are treated. The book is not intended as a complete, rigorous treatise or handbook. Those seeking such a treatment should consult the references in the bibliography.

In this revision, the following points have been kept in mind:

1. To bring costs, prices, and wages, and related material up to date;
2. To keep the problems practical and meaningful in terms of today's world;
3. To treat the material in such a way as to encourage the reader to do his work in as systematic a manner as possible.

Although the general format used by the original author has been retained, the book has been largely rewritten, and many sections have been enlarged, especially those dealing with the mathematics of the trades. Readers of the book are strongly encouraged to consult the references in the bibliography, and to study the U. S. Government Standards and Publications and the ASA Standards.

The reviser wishes to express his gratitude to Professor John T. Dygdon of the Illinois Institute of Technology, Mr. Phil M. Spink of The Bankers Print, Mr. Thomas Baacke of the Chicago Vocational High School, Mr. Norman Figatner, and Professor Frank Moore of Chicago Teachers' College South for their suggestions, help, and advice. Many organizations have very kindly supplied photographs, which are gratefully acknowledged.

He is likewise grateful to Mr. Albert Kosloff, to Professor Howard James of the Wright Branch of the Chicago City Junior College, and Mrs. James for typing; to Mr. Robert Bruce and Mr. Bruno Wolff of The Bruce Publishing Company for their patience and help in seeing the book through the press, and to his wife and three sons for their extraordinary patience and understanding.

PETER ANDRIS
Chicago City Junior College
Southeast Branch

Contents

Unit IV
TRADE MATHEMATICS

Unit V
SHOP FORMULAS

Unit I
FRACTIONS

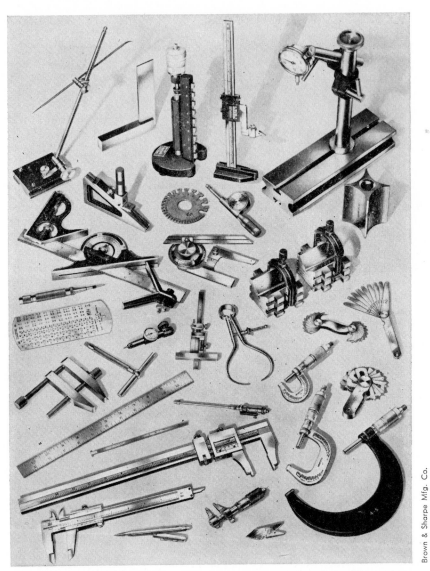

In addition to the precision measuring tools of industry, the tradesman must be able to understand and apply the principles of mathematics.

CHAPTER 1

Understanding Fractions

1.1 Introduction

We can obtain a clear understanding of what a fraction is by carefully examining the marks on an ordinary 12-in. rule.

Fig. 1.

The enlargement in Figure 2 shows that each inch is divided into 16 equal parts. Each of these parts or divisions equals one sixteenth of an entire or whole inch.

Fig. 2.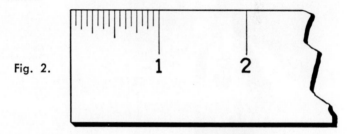

We can write this amount as a number in the form $\frac{1}{16}$.

This kind of a number is called a *fraction*. It represents, in this case, one of the sixteen equal parts into which the unit, one inch, has been divided. If we took three of these divisions, that is, three-sixteenths, we could express them in fractional form as $\frac{3}{16}$ of an inch. In the same way, five of these equal divisions could be expressed as $\frac{5}{16}$ of an inch.

1.2 Definition of a Fraction

This brief explanation shows us that *a fraction of an inch is one or more of the equal parts into which an inch is divided*. Other units, such as feet, yards, miles, acres, pounds, and so on could be divided into fractional parts also. If we examine each of the fractions, $\frac{1}{16}$, $\frac{3}{16}$, $\frac{5}{16}$ we notice that they are made up of two parts, or terms, separated by a line called a fraction line. The term below the fraction line tells us into how many equal parts the unit (here one inch) has been divided. This term is called the *denominator*.

3

The great strides in space technology such as the launching of Saturn I are made possible by the careful application of the principles of mathematics.

National Aeronautics and Space Administration

The term above the fraction line tells us how many of the equal parts we are taking in forming the fractions. This term is called the *numerator*. In the fraction $\frac{1}{16}$, the number 1 is the numerator; the number 16 is the denominator. The number 1 tells us that we are taking 1 of the equal parts into which the unit has been divided. The number 16 tells us that the unit has been divided into 16 equal parts.

In the fraction $\frac{3}{16}$, the number 3 is the numerator; the number 16 is the denominator. The fraction $\frac{3}{16}$ tells us that a unit was divided into 16 equal parts and that we are considering 3 of these equal parts. We may put this in another way. Suppose that we had a unit which was

American astronauts
like L. Gordon Cooper
rely on the technical
skill of the men who
build and launch their
space vehicles.

National Aeronautics and
Space Administration

divided into 16 equal parts and we wanted to take 3 of these equal parts. Then we would represent these 3 sixteenths as $\frac{3}{16}$ in fractional form.

The sign separating the numerator of a fraction from its denominator is called a *fraction line* and *indicates division*.

A fraction can thus be considered as the indicated division of two whole numbers, and this fact will be used later in dealing with certain processes involving fractions.

1.3 Proper Fractions

Fractions like $\frac{1}{16}$, $\frac{5}{16}$, $\frac{3}{8}$, $\frac{7}{9}$, and so on, whose numerators are *smaller* than their denominators are called proper fractions. Proper fractions always indicate or represent amounts which are less than 1.

1.4 Improper Fractions

Fractions like $\frac{4}{3}$, $\frac{17}{8}$, $\frac{18}{15}$, $\frac{13}{6}$, $\frac{9}{5}$, and so on, whose numerators are *larger* than their denominators, are called *improper fractions*. Fractions of this kind indicate or represent amounts which are always greater than 1.

Fractions like $\frac{2}{2}$ (read "two halves"), $\frac{4}{4}$ (read "four fourths"), $\frac{8}{8}$ (read "eight eighths"), whose numerators are *equal* to their denominators are also called *improper fractions*.

Since the line separating the numerator and denominator of a fraction indicates division, the improper fraction $\frac{3}{3}$ can be thought as representing $3 \div 3$, which equals 1. Thus $\frac{3}{3} = 3 \div 3 = 1$. Likewise, $\frac{4}{4} = 4 \div 4 = 1$, and the same is true for any improper fractions whose numerator and denominator are the same.

The above procedure may be reversed, and we can write 1 as an improper fraction whose numerator and denominator are equal. For example, we may change 1 to such fractional forms as $\frac{15}{15}$, $\frac{27}{27}$, $\frac{121}{121}$, $\frac{356}{356}$, and so on. Improper fractions whose numerators are larger than their denominators can be changed to a combination of a whole number and a fraction by performing the indicated division.

Thus $\frac{19}{8} = 19 \div 8 = 2\frac{3}{8}$ (read "two and three eighths")

$\frac{22}{5} = 22 \div 5 = 4\frac{2}{5}$ (read "four and two fifths")

1.5   Mixed Numbers

A number which is made up of a whole number and a proper fraction is called a mixed number. For example $5\frac{3}{16}$ or $4\frac{1}{2}$ are examples of mixed numbers.

A mixed number may be changed to an improper fraction by:

a) Multiplying the whole number by the denominator of the proper fraction.

b) Adding to this product the numerator of the proper fraction. This will be the numerator of the improper fraction.

c) Writing this new numerator over the denominator of the proper fraction. The fraction thus obtained is an improper fraction equivalent to (having the same value as) the mixed number.

For example, to change $2\frac{5}{8}$ to an improper fraction:

a) Multiply the whole number 2 by 8, the denominator of the fraction, obtaining 16.

b) Add 5, the numerator of the fraction, to 16 obtaining 21.

c) Write 21 over 8, yielding the improper fraction $\frac{21}{8}$. This improper fraction tells us that $2\frac{5}{8}$ is the same as or is equal to $\frac{21}{8}$, or that in the mixed number $2\frac{5}{8}$ there are 21 eighths.

The following example will illustrate the application of this rule.

■ **EXAMPLE 1:**

Change $9\frac{13}{16}$ to an improper fraction.

Solution and Explanation:

Using the above rule, we first find the numerator of the equivalent improper fraction. This is done by (*a*) multiplying 9 by 16 and (*b*) adding 13 to this product.

a) $9 \times 16 = 144$ *b*) $144 + 13 = 157$

c) We next write 157 over the original denominator 16, getting $\frac{157}{16}$, the desired equivalent improper fraction.

Therefore: $9\frac{13}{16} = \frac{157}{16}$ **answer.**

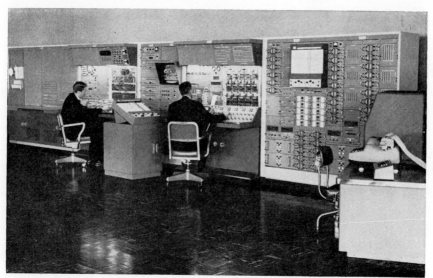

Electronic Associates, Inc.

One of the most amazing developments in the last few years is the analog/digital computer, which is able to calculate, analyze, remember, and predict.

■ **EXAMPLE 2:**

How many $\frac{1}{16}$ inches are there in the measurement $7\frac{5}{16}$ inches?

Solution and Explanation:

We can determine the number of $\frac{1}{16}$ inches in $7\frac{5}{16}$ inches by changing $7\frac{5}{16}$ to an improper fraction. The numerator of the improper fraction will indicate the number of $\frac{1}{16}$'s of an inch in the original mixed number.

Using the rule for changing a mixed number to an improper fraction, we multiply the whole number 7 by 16, obtaining 112. To this we add 5, obtaining 117. We then write 117 over the denominator 16, obtaining $\frac{117}{16}$. This is the improper fraction equivalent to the mixed number $7\frac{5}{16}$. The numerator, 117, of the improper fraction $\frac{117}{16}$ tells us that in the measurement $7\frac{5}{16}$ inches there are 117 one-sixteenth inches.

1.6 Problems Involving Proper and Improper Fractions and Mixed Numbers

1. Determine which of the following are mixed numbers, proper fractions or improper fractions:

$$\frac{3}{16}, \quad \frac{17}{32}, \quad 5\frac{3}{8}, \quad \frac{15}{15}, \quad \frac{23}{7}, \quad 8\frac{3}{4}, \quad \frac{37}{50}, \quad \frac{72}{72}, \quad 11\frac{7}{8}, \quad \frac{75}{76}$$

2. Change the following fractions to mixed numbers:

$$\frac{7}{2}, \quad \frac{13}{8}, \quad \frac{19}{16}, \quad \frac{37}{12}, \quad \frac{23}{10}, \quad \frac{45}{32}, \quad \frac{27}{4}, \quad \frac{73}{64}$$

3. How many eighths are there in each of the following measurements?

$$9\tfrac{3}{8} \text{ in.,} \quad 3\tfrac{7}{8} \text{ in.,} \quad 6\tfrac{1}{4} \text{ in.,} \quad 1\tfrac{5}{8} \text{ in.,} \quad 11\tfrac{3}{8} \text{ in.}$$

NOTE: The word *inch* and its plural *inches* are indicated by the abbreviation *in.,* or by the symbol *"*. For example, a length of five inches is expressed as 5 in. or 5".

4. How many pieces $\frac{1}{2}$ in. long can be cut from a strip of aluminum that measures $11\frac{1}{2}$ in. long?

5. It is desired to divide a line $4\frac{1}{4}$ in. long *into equal spaces each $\frac{1}{4}$ in. long*. How many such spaces are there in this line?

6. Change the following to improper fractions:

$$5, \quad 43\tfrac{1}{16}, \quad 15\tfrac{3}{15}, \quad 8, \quad 10\tfrac{3}{4}, \quad 17\tfrac{1}{2}, \quad 18\tfrac{1}{12}, \quad 62\tfrac{7}{8}, \quad 27\tfrac{4}{15}, \quad 12\tfrac{5}{64}$$

7. What fractional part of 9 is 5? What fractional part of 64 is 45?

8. By changing the mixed numbers to improper fractions, tell which of the following is greater:

$$3\tfrac{1}{8} \text{ or } \tfrac{27}{8}; \quad 3\tfrac{3}{5} \text{ or } \tfrac{19}{5}; \quad 8\tfrac{3}{16} \text{ or } \tfrac{129}{16}; \quad 7\tfrac{3}{4} \text{ or } \tfrac{31}{4}$$

9. In measuring the width of a strip of wood, a student counts the divisions on his rule and finds that the piece is $\frac{15}{8}$ in. wide. Express this width as a mixed number.

10. The width of the flange of a steel beam was given as $\frac{63}{8}$ of an inch. Express this dimension as a mixed number.

11. How many 32nds are there in each of the following dimensions?

$$3\tfrac{7}{32} \text{ in.;} \quad 9\tfrac{19}{32} \text{ in.;} \quad 17\tfrac{3}{32} \text{ in.;} \quad 1\tfrac{3}{32} \text{ in.;} \quad 24\tfrac{31}{32} \text{ in.}$$

12. There are 36 in. in one yard. What fractional part of a yard is 15 in., 9 in., 32 in., 18 in., 24 in., 30 in.?

1.7 Reduction of Fractions

Proper fractions like $\frac{1}{16}, \frac{3}{4}, \frac{5}{32}, \frac{7}{8}, \frac{11}{12}$ are said to be in their *lowest terms*. We say these fractions are in their lowest terms because it is impossible to find a whole number (other than 1) which will divide exactly the numerator and denominator of each of these fractions. Consider the fraction $\frac{5}{32}$. There is no whole number (other than 1) which will divide *exactly* the numerator 5, and the denominator 32. Hence it is impossible to reduce this fraction further. Proper fractions which meet this condition are said to be in their simplest form or in their lowest terms.

Such fractions as $\frac{6}{8}, \frac{28}{64}, \frac{16}{36}, \frac{40}{144}$ are not in their lowest terms nor in their simplest form. Each of them may be reduced by dividing both terms by a number (other than 1) which is an *exact* divisor of their numerator and denominator. This exact divisor is also called a *factor* and because it is common to both terms it is a common factor or common divisor.

> **If both terms of a fraction are divided by the same number (except zero), the value of the fraction is not changed, although its form is changed.**

Consider the fraction $\frac{6}{8}$. We can divide the numerator and denominator of this fraction by 2. When we perform this division the original fraction will become $\frac{3}{4}$. The terms of the fraction $\frac{3}{4}$ have no common divisor. Hence $\frac{3}{4}$ is a fraction in its lowest terms. *This process is called reduction to lowest terms.* It is important to notice that although the form of the fraction $\frac{6}{8}$ was changed, its value was *not* changed, since $\frac{6}{8}$ and $\frac{3}{4}$ have exactly the same value.

The fractions $\frac{28}{64}$, $\frac{16}{36}$, $\frac{40}{144}$, can be reduced to $\frac{7}{16}$, $\frac{4}{9}$, $\frac{5}{18}$, respectively. The form of each fraction has been changed, but its value has not been changed.

A fraction should always be given in its lowest terms, that is, the numerator and denominator should be divided by their *largest common divisor*. For example, the fraction $\frac{30}{168}$ can be reduced to $\frac{15}{84}$; $\frac{15}{84}$ can be reduced to $\frac{5}{28}$. When reduced this far, we say that the reduction is complete. If we were asked to reduce $\frac{30}{168}$ to lowest terms we would say it was $\frac{5}{28}$, *not* $\frac{15}{84}$. This reduction could have been accomplished in one step by dividing each term of $\frac{30}{168}$ by 6, their largest common divisor.

■ EXAMPLE:

Redraw the sketch (Fig. 3, p. 10) giving all dimensions in their lowest terms.

Solution and Explanation:

NOTE: Dimensions are placed on shop drawings and sketches in order to specify sizes, distances between lines, surfaces, and holes in such a way that the objects shown can be manufactured and assembled without any doubt on the part of the workmen involved in these processes. Dimensions are shown in different ways in the various fields of engineering, but the same fundamental procedures are used in these fields. Dimension lines are used to show distances on drawings. These dimension lines are thin solid lines with a break in the center and an arrowhead at each end. The particular distance indicated is usually placed in the gap at the center of the dimension line.

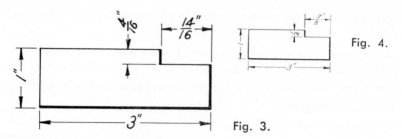

Fig. 4.

Fig. 3.

By examining the measurements in Figure 3 it may be seen that both $\frac{14}{16}$ in. and $\frac{4}{16}$ in. are not in their lowest terms.

Both the numerator and the denominator in the fraction $\frac{14}{16}$ may be divided by the common factor 2. This reduces it to $\frac{7}{8}$. The result, $\frac{7}{8}$, cannot be further reduced. Hence, $\frac{14}{16}$ in. expressed in simplest form, or lowest terms, becomes $\frac{7}{8}$ in.

In the fraction $\frac{4}{16}$, both the numerator 4 and the denominator 16 may be divided by 2, which reduces the fraction to $\frac{2}{8}$. Now 2 is a factor of both the numerator 2 and the denominator 8, so that each may be divided by 2 again. The result is the fraction $\frac{1}{4}$, which cannot be reduced further. The measurement $\frac{4}{16}$ in. thus becomes $\frac{1}{4}$ in. when reduced to its simplest form.

Hence the measurement $\frac{14}{16}$ in. expressed in its lowest terms is $\frac{7}{8}$ in., while the measurement $\frac{4}{16}$ in. in its lowest terms equals $\frac{1}{4}$ in. These measurements should be used in the redrawn sketch (Fig. 4).

NOTE: The reduction of the fraction $\frac{4}{16}$ might have been accomplished in one operation by dividing both terms by 4, the largest (highest) common factor. When the highest common factor cannot be determined readily, it is satisfactory to use other common factors to reduce a given fraction to its lowest terms.

1.8   Problems Involving Reduction of Fractions

1. Express in simplest form:

$\frac{14}{16}$ of an inch; $\frac{4}{12}$ of a yard; $\frac{9}{12}$ of a foot; $\frac{26}{32}$ in.; $\frac{24}{64}$ in.

2. The distance between rivet holes on a steel I beam was measured and given at $4\frac{6}{8}$ in. What should this dimension read when properly expressed?

3. Reduce to lowest terms:

$\frac{125}{325}$; $\frac{64}{120}$; $\frac{12}{84}$; $8\frac{14}{32}$; $3\frac{96}{144}$; $34\frac{12}{32}$; $19\frac{36}{48}$; $21\frac{48}{64}$

4. Redraw the sketch in Figure 5, giving dimensions in lowest terms.

5. Which of the following are *not* in their lowest terms? Why not? Express them in their lowest terms.

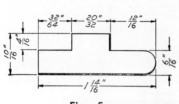

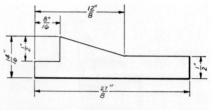

Fig. 5.   Fig. 6.

$$\frac{7}{8};\ \frac{18}{32};\ 4\frac{28}{64};\ 10\frac{15}{16};\ \frac{24}{64};\ 6\frac{3}{4}$$

6. Redraw Figure 6 and reduce all dimensions to lowest terms.

7. Is $\frac{28}{32}$ greater than $\frac{7}{8}$? Is $\frac{159}{24}$ greater than $6\frac{1}{2}$? Is $5\frac{7}{8}$ greater than $\frac{95}{16}$? Prove each answer.

8. Redraw the sketch in Figure 7 giving all dimensions in their lowest terms.

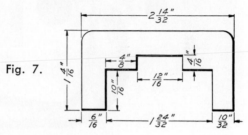

Fig. 7.

9. Reduce to lowest terms:

$$\frac{24}{56};\ \frac{96}{18};\ \frac{144}{60};\ \frac{48}{70};\ \frac{120}{32};\ \frac{34}{64};\ \frac{64}{96};\ \frac{72}{132}$$

10. Which of the following is the larger?

$\frac{40}{32}$ in. or $1\frac{1}{4}$ in.; $\frac{65}{8}$ or $7\frac{3}{4}$; $8\frac{11}{16}$ or $\frac{137}{16}$; $\frac{23}{4}$ in. or $5\frac{3}{4}$ in.; $\frac{46}{8}$ or $5\frac{3}{4}$

1.9 Changing Fractions to Equivalent Fractions Having a Given Denominator

In the preceding problems it was seen that when both terms of a fraction were divided by the same number (except zero) the form of the fraction was changed but its value was not changed. Similarly, if both terms of a fraction are multiplied by the same number (except zero), the form of the fraction is changed but its value is not changed. Consider the fraction $\frac{2}{5}$. If both terms of this fraction are multiplied by 12, for example, the fraction changes to:

$$\frac{2}{5} = \frac{2 \times 12}{5 \times 12} \text{ or } \frac{24}{60}$$

Now $\frac{24}{60}$ does not look like $\frac{2}{5}$. However, it has the same value as $\frac{2}{5}$. We can see this by reducing $\frac{24}{60}$ to its lowest terms. We do this in three steps.

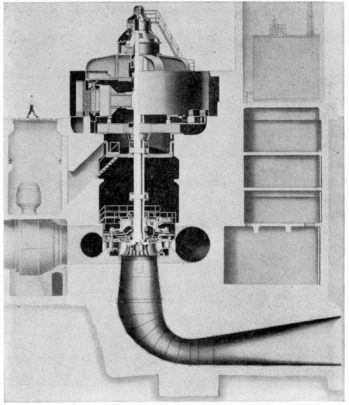

Allis-Chalmers

Sectional view of one of the hydro-electric turbines used to generate power at the Hoover Dam.

Step 1: Dividing both terms of $\frac{24}{60}$ by 2, we get $\frac{12}{30}$.

Step 2: Dividing both terms of $\frac{12}{30}$ by 2, we get $\frac{6}{15}$.

Step 3: Now dividing both terms of $\frac{6}{15}$ by 3, we get $\frac{2}{5}$, the original fraction.

Thus: $\frac{24}{60} = \frac{12}{30} = \frac{6}{15} = \frac{2}{5}$.

This reduction could have been carried out in one step by dividing both terms of $\frac{24}{60}$ by 12, getting $\frac{2}{5}$ as before.

If both terms of a fraction are multiplied by the same number (except zero), the value of the fraction is not changed, although its form is changed.

Allis-Chalmers

A powerhouse with six turbines. Compare this with the sectional view of a similar turbine on the opposite page.

This important rule is used in changing fractions so as to have the same denominators as other fractions. We can think of this as changing a given fraction to an equivalent fraction, of a different denomination, and we will be using this principle when we study the addition and subtraction of fractions having different denominators.

■ EXAMPLE 1:

Change the fraction $\frac{5}{8}$ to an equivalent fraction having the denominator 32.

Solution and Explanation:

To find the number by which both terms of the fraction $\frac{5}{8}$ must be multiplied in order to change it to an equivalent fraction with denominator 32, we proceed as follows:

1. We divide 32 by 8, the original denominator. The quotient is 4.

2. We now multiply *both* terms of the original fraction by 4, getting a new, equivalent fraction $\frac{20}{32}$.

Thus: $\frac{5}{8} = \frac{5 \times 4}{8 \times 4} = \frac{20}{32}$.

The fraction $\frac{20}{32}$ is of a different denomination than the fraction $\frac{5}{8}$, but the two fractions have the *same* value, that is, they are equivalent.

If we have whole numbers which we wish to change to a given fractional denomination, we can use a similar procedure.

■ EXAMPLE 2:

Determine how many 64ths of an inch there are in 3 in.

Solution and Explanation:

Any whole number may be written in fractional form by writing it as the numerator of a fraction whose denominator is 1.

Thus: $2 = \frac{2}{1}$; $6 = \frac{6}{1}$; $125 = \frac{125}{1}$; and so on.

In our case $3 = \frac{3}{1}$. Since we want to write this as an equivalent fraction with denominator 64, we divide 64 by 1, the denominator of the fraction $\frac{3}{1}$, and get 64. We now multiply both terms of $\frac{3}{1}$, by 64 obtaining $\frac{3 \times 64}{1 \times 64} = \frac{192}{64}$. Thus we have:

$$3 = \frac{3}{1} = \frac{3 \times 64}{1 \times 64} = \frac{192}{64}$$

That is, in 3 in. there are $\frac{192}{64}$ in. or 192 sixty-fourths of an inch.

If we work backwards we will find that if we divide both terms of the fraction $\frac{192}{64}$ by 64, their highest common divisor, we will get $\frac{3}{1}$ or 3.

If we wish to change a mixed number to a fraction of a given denomination, we first change the mixed number to an improper fraction, and then proceed as illustrated above.

■ EXAMPLE 3:

How many 32nds of an inch are there in $7\frac{5}{8}$ in.?

Solution and Explanation:

Step 1: We change $7\frac{5}{8}$ to an improper fraction:

$$7\frac{5}{8} = \frac{61}{8}$$

Step 2: We now change $\frac{61}{8}$ to an equivalent fraction with 32 as its denominator. Dividing 32 by 8, we obtain the quotient 4. Multiplying both terms of $\frac{61}{8}$ by 4, we obtain $\frac{244}{32}$.

Thus:
$$7\frac{5}{8} = \frac{61}{8}$$
$$\frac{61}{8} = \frac{61 \times 4}{8 \times 4} = \frac{244}{32}$$

Thus we see that $7\frac{5}{8}$ in. is equivalent to $\frac{244}{32}$ in., and that there are 244 thirty-seconds of an inch in $7\frac{5}{8}$ in. A good understanding of this process

A transformer which is rated at 220,000 and 115,000 volts.

will be of great help in the solution of problems involving the addition and subtraction of fractions and mixed numbers.

1.10 Problems Involving Changing Fractions to Equivalent Fractions of Another Denomination

1. Change: $\frac{5}{16}$ to 64ths; $1\frac{3}{8}$ to 32nds; $23\frac{1}{4}$ to 64ths; $5\frac{1}{4}$ to 16ths; $13\frac{1}{2}$ to 8ths.

2. Change: $3\frac{1}{5}$ to 20ths; $\frac{3}{4}$ to 60ths; $\frac{14}{15}$ to 120ths; $6\frac{3}{7}$ to 42nds; $4\frac{3}{4}$ to 100ths.

3. Change each of the following fractions to equivalent fractions having 48 for their denominator:

$$\frac{3}{8}; \ \frac{11}{16}; \ \frac{1}{2}; \ \frac{7}{4}; \ \frac{9}{6}$$

4. What is the equivalent number of 16ths of an inch in $1\frac{5}{8}$ in.; $\frac{6}{32}$ in.; $5\frac{3}{4}$ in.; 5 in.; $7\frac{1}{2}$ in.; $9\frac{7}{8}$ in.; 6 in.?

5. How many 64ths of an inch are there in $\frac{7}{8}$ in.; $11\frac{3}{4}$ in.; $20\frac{1}{2}$ in.; $2\frac{3}{16}$ in.; 14 in.; $\frac{11}{32}$ in.; $4\frac{7}{8}$ in.?

6. Change each of the following to an equivalent number of 30ths:

$$\frac{9}{15}; \ 14\frac{5}{6}; \ \frac{13}{15}; \ 5\frac{1}{3}; \ 2\frac{1}{2}; \ 8\frac{3}{10}$$

7. A flat steel bar is $2\frac{7}{8}$ in. wide. Express this width in 32nds of an inch.

8. A young man spent twenty-three and one-half dollars for tools to be used in his workshop. This is equivalent to how many quarters?

9. Change each of the following to an equivalent number of 64ths of an inch:

$$8 \text{ in.; } 10\frac{3}{4} \text{ in.; } \frac{15}{16} \text{ in.; } 7\frac{14}{32} \text{ in.}$$

10. How many 32nds of an inch are there in $3\frac{5}{8}$ in.; $30\frac{1}{2}$ in.; $\frac{7}{8}$ in.; $10\frac{1}{4}$ in.; $24\frac{3}{16}$ in.?

11. How many pieces of copper $\frac{1}{2}$ in. long may be cut from a strip of copper $17\frac{1}{4}$ in. long?

12. Convert $9\frac{1}{2}$ to 10ths; $7\frac{2}{3}$ to 15ths; $6\frac{1}{7}$ to 35ths; $9\frac{1}{4}$ to 32nds.

1.11   Review Problems Involving Expression and Reduction of Fractions

1. Change $4\frac{5}{7}$ to 63rds; $5\frac{1}{5}$ to 25ths; $\frac{7}{8}$ to 56ths; $7\frac{1}{4}$ in. to 8ths of an inch.

2. How many 16ths of an inch are there in $8\frac{1}{8}$ in.? How many 32nds of an inch in $25\frac{1}{2}$ in.?

3. Determine which of the following are in their simplest form:

$$\frac{21}{4}; \ 20\frac{38}{32} \text{ in.; } \frac{63}{72}; \ 5\frac{7}{19}; \ \frac{33}{18}$$

4. Is $\frac{24}{32}$ larger than $\frac{12}{18}$? Is $1\frac{5}{8}$ larger than $\frac{65}{40}$? Is $2\frac{15}{40}$ larger than $\frac{35}{16}$?

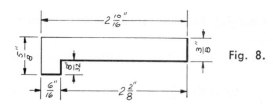

Fig. 8.

5. Some of the dimensions in Figure 8 are not correctly expressed because they are not in their simplest form. Make a new drawing giving all dimensions in their simplest form.

6. Of the following numbers, list those which are improper fractions and those which are mixed numbers:

$$8\frac{7}{32}; \ \frac{18}{15}; \ \frac{17}{19}; \ 14\frac{3}{4}; \ \frac{16}{8}; \ 1\frac{4}{5}$$

7. A strip of thin brass $7\frac{1}{2}$ in. wide is to be cut into pieces that measure $1\frac{1}{2}$ in. wide. How many pieces can be cut from this strip?

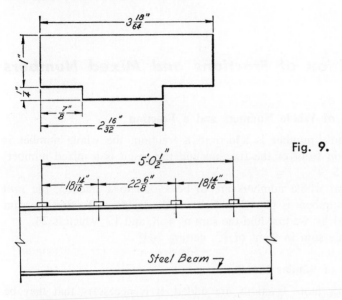

Fig. 9.

8. Redraw the sketches in Figure 9 giving all dimensions in their lowest terms.

CHAPTER 2

Addition of Fractions and Mixed Numbers

2.1 Addition of Whole Numbers and a Fraction

When a whole number is added to a fraction, the whole number is simply placed in front of the fraction and the result is a mixed number. For example, $8 + \frac{9}{16} = 8\frac{9}{16}$.

When several whole numbers are to be added to a fraction, the *sum* of the whole numbers is placed in front of the fraction. To find the sum of 4, 8, 12, and $\frac{15}{16}$, we first find the sum of 4, 8, and 12, which is 24.

We write this sum in front of $\frac{15}{16}$, getting $24\frac{15}{16}$.

2.2 Addition of Similar Fractions

When two or more fractions are added, it is necessary that they be of the same denomination, that is, that they all have the same denominator. Fractions like $\frac{1}{8}$, $\frac{3}{8}$, and $\frac{7}{8}$ are fractions having the same denominator. Fractions having the same denominator are called *similar* fractions.

Fractions having the same denominator are added by adding their numerators and writing this sum over the common denominator. To add $\frac{7}{16}$, $\frac{3}{16}$, and $\frac{1}{16}$ we add the numerators, obtaining 11. We write 11 over 16, $\frac{11}{16}$ and obtain the sum of the three fractions.

Thus: $\qquad \frac{7}{16} + \frac{3}{16} + \frac{1}{16} = \frac{7 + 3 + 1}{16} = \frac{11}{16}$

If we are asked to find the sum of $\frac{15}{64}$, $\frac{13}{64}$, $\frac{19}{64}$, and $\frac{27}{64}$ we write:

$$\frac{15}{64} + \frac{13}{64} + \frac{19}{64} + \frac{27}{64} = \frac{15 + 13 + 19 + 27}{64} = \frac{74}{64}$$

Since this fraction is not in its lowest terms, we reduce it to $\frac{37}{32}$, which we then change to the mixed number $1\frac{5}{32}$.

2.3 Addition of Mixed Numbers

We shall first consider the addition of mixed numbers whose fractional parts have the same denominator. To find the sum of such mixed numbers we first add the fractional parts as explained above. We then add the whole number parts and write this sum in front of the sum of the fractional parts.

The following example will illustrate the procedure.

■ EXAMPLE 1:

What is the sum of $5\frac{3}{16}$, $9\frac{7}{16}$, and $11\frac{5}{16}$?

A girder cantilever bridge on the New York Thru-way. From ancient Roman times building bridges has been a sign of the technological ability of a civilization.

Solution and Explanation:

The addition of these mixed numbers is best carried out by arranging them in a column thus:

$$
\begin{array}{r}
5\tfrac{3}{16} \\
9\tfrac{7}{16} \\
11\tfrac{5}{16} \\
\hline
25\tfrac{15}{16} \quad \textbf{ans.}
\end{array}
$$

The sum, $25\tfrac{15}{16}$, was obtained by first finding the fractional part, $\tfrac{15}{16}$, and then the whole number part, 25. The fractional part $\tfrac{15}{16}$, was obtained by adding the numerators of the fractional parts $(3 + 7 + 5 = 15)$ and writing this over the common denominator, 16, getting $\tfrac{15}{16}$. The whole number 25 was obtained by adding the whole numbers $(5 + 9 + 11 = 25)$ and writing this sum in front of the fraction $\tfrac{15}{16}$. Thus the sum of the three mixed numbers is $25\tfrac{15}{16}$.

■ **EXAMPLE 2:**

What is the sum of $3\frac{3}{8}$, $12\frac{7}{8}$, $22\frac{1}{8}$, $6\frac{1}{8}$?

Solution and Explanation:

Proceeding as in Example 1, we write the mixed numbers in a column:

$$3\frac{3}{8}$$
$$12\frac{7}{8}$$
$$22\frac{1}{8}$$
$$6\frac{1}{8}$$
$$\overline{43\tfrac{12}{8}} = 44\tfrac{1}{2} \quad \textbf{ans.}$$

Adding the fractional parts, we obtain $\frac{12}{8}$, which we write under the addition line and in the same column as the fractional parts of the mixed numbers. We next add the whole number parts, obtaining 43. This we write in front of $\frac{12}{8}$. Our sum this far is $43\frac{12}{8}$. Since $\frac{12}{8}$ is an improper fraction, we reduce it first to $1\frac{4}{8}$ and then to $1\frac{1}{2}$. We place the $\frac{1}{2}$ as shown, add the 1 from the $1\frac{1}{2}$ to 43, obtaining 44. Thus our final sum is $44\frac{1}{2}$.

2.4   Addition of Whole Numbers, Mixed Numbers, and Similar Fractions

In adding whole numbers, mixed numbers, and fractions having the same denominator, the same procedure is used as explained in Section 2.3. The final sum is always expressed in simplest form.

■ **EXAMPLE 1:**

Find the sum of $3\frac{13}{64}$ in., $7\frac{11}{64}$ in., 8 in., $4\frac{27}{64}$ in., $\frac{21}{64}$ in.

Solution and Explanation:

Step 1: Arranging the addends in a column we obtain:

$$3\frac{13}{64}$$
$$7\frac{11}{64}$$
$$8$$
$$4\frac{27}{64}$$
$$\frac{21}{64}$$
$$\overline{22\tfrac{72}{64}} = 23\tfrac{1}{8}$$

Step 2: Adding the fractional parts, we obtain $\frac{72}{64}$, which we place in the same column as the fractional parts whose sum this is.

Step 3: We next add the whole numbers, obtaining 22. This we write in front of the fractional part $\frac{72}{64}$. The sum so far is $22\frac{72}{64}$.

Step 4: We reduce $\frac{72}{64}$ to lowest terms, first obtaining $1\frac{8}{64}$ and then $1\frac{1}{8}$.

Step 5: Adding $1\frac{1}{8}$ to 22, we get $23\frac{1}{8}$ as the final sum of the five numbers whose sum we were to find.

2.5 Problems Involving the Addition of Whole Numbers, Mixed Numbers, and Fractions

1. What is the sum of the following?
   a) $4\frac{3}{16}$, $1\frac{3}{8}$, $4\frac{3}{4}$, $16\frac{3}{16}$, 3
   b) $2\frac{1}{4}$, $4\frac{5}{8}$, $1\frac{1}{2}$, $5\frac{7}{8}$, $3\frac{1}{8}$
   c) $1\frac{1}{4}$ in., $\frac{31}{32}$ in., $1\frac{15}{16}$ in., $10\frac{9}{16}$ in., $8\frac{5}{8}$ in.
   d) 15, 7, 8, $\frac{3}{4}$, $2\frac{1}{4}$, $4\frac{3}{4}$
   e) $4\frac{7}{16}$, $5\frac{7}{16}$, $3\frac{13}{16}$, $\frac{1}{8}$, $7\frac{5}{8}$
   f) $8\frac{3}{4}$ in., $7\frac{3}{16}$ in., 3 in., $10\frac{3}{4}$ in., $30\frac{1}{4}$ in.

2. To obtain the total width of a metal plate it was necessary to add the following dimensions: $2\frac{3}{16}$ in., $1\frac{1}{16}$ in., $3\frac{5}{16}$ in. What was the width of the plate?

3. Compute the total length and the total width of the piece illustrated in Figure 10. Redraw the piece, replacing the question marks by the dimensions you have computed.

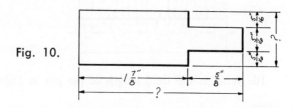

Fig. 10.

4. Four steel plates measure $\frac{3}{8}$ in., $\frac{7}{8}$ in., $1\frac{1}{8}$ in., and $1\frac{7}{8}$ in. in thickness. What is the total thickness of these plates?

5. In repairing a damaged "oil line" on an automobile, the mechanic uses three pieces of copper tubing. One of these measures $\frac{3}{4}$ ft., another 1 ft., and the other measures $1\frac{1}{4}$ ft. What was the total length of tubing used on this particular repair job?

6. In wiring a control board, No. 16 wire was cut into lengths measuring 5 ft., $8\frac{3}{4}$ ft., $7\frac{1}{2}$ ft., and $12\frac{3}{4}$ ft. What was the total length of these pieces of wire?

7. Calculate the total length of the handle illustrated in Figure 11.

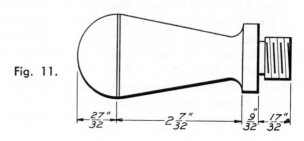

Fig. 11.

8. Determine the total length of the special link that is illustrated in Figure 12.

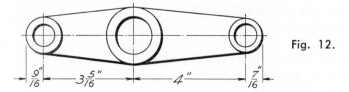

Fig. 12.

9. A special type of partition has the cross-section shown in the drawing (Fig. 13). Compute the dimension marked *W*.

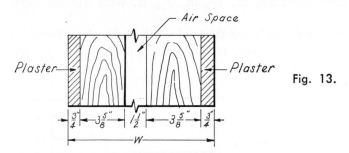

Fig. 13.

10. What is the total length of the pin in Figure 14?

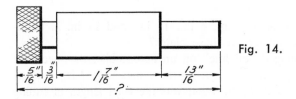

Fig. 14.

2.6 Least Common Denominator

The sum of similar fractions or fractions having the same denominator can be readily found. The numerators are added together, and this sum is written over the common denominator. The resulting fraction is reduced to lowest terms if necessary to give the sum in simplest form.

When fractions are to be added whose denominators are not the same, the given fractions must be changed to equivalent fractions having the same common denominator. This common denominator should be the smallest or *least* whole number which is exactly divisible by each of the denominators of the given fractions. Such a denominator is called the *least common denominator* and is abbreviated LCD.

When the given fractions have been changed to equivalent fractions having the least common denominator they are then similar fractions and can then be added as described in Section 2.2. If the denominators of the several fractions to be added are small numbers, the least common denominator can be found by inspection of the denominators of the fractions to be added.

Consider the fractions $\frac{1}{2}$, $\frac{1}{4}$, and $\frac{3}{8}$. Examination shows that 8 is the *least* (smallest) number that is exactly divisible by 2, 4, and 8. Hence 8 is the least common denominator of the fractions $\frac{1}{2}$, $\frac{1}{4}$, and $\frac{3}{8}$.

To add the fractions $\frac{1}{2}$, $\frac{1}{4}$, and $\frac{3}{8}$ we change each to an equivalent fraction having 8 as the common denominator, and after that proceed as in Section 2.2. When the least common denominator cannot be readily determined, a systematic procedure can be used to find it.

■ EXAMPLE 1:

What is the least common denominator of the fractions $\frac{5}{8}$, $\frac{1}{6}$, $\frac{4}{9}$, $\frac{7}{12}$?

Solution and Explanation:

Step 1: Write the denominators of the given fractions in a row, with a space between each and place a division sign around them as in short division.

$$\underline{|\ 8\quad 6\quad 9\quad 12}$$

Step 2: Now find the smallest prime number (a number which has no divisors except itself and 1) which will divide *exactly* any two of the numbers 8, 6, 9, 12. The first ten prime numbers are:

$$
\begin{array}{cc}
2 & 13 \\
3 & 17 \\
5 & 19 \\
7 & 23 \\
11 & 29
\end{array}
$$

Of these, 2 will divide 8, 6, and 12. We place it in front of the 8 and divide it into 8, 6, and 12, putting the respective quotients, 4, 3, 6 under the 8, 6, and 12. The work looks thus so far:

$$
\begin{array}{r|cccl}
2 & 8 & 6 & 9 & 12 & \leftarrow \text{line 1} \\
\hline
  & 4 & 3 & 9 & 6 & \leftarrow \text{line 2}
\end{array}
$$

Notice that the 9, which was not exactly divisible by the 2, was written below itself in line 2.

Step 3: The smallest prime number which will exactly divide at least two of the numbers in line 2 is 2. We draw another division sign, place a 2 in front of it and again write down any exact quotients. Our work will then look like this:

1st division	2	8	6	9	12	← line 1

1st division   2 | 8   6   9   12   ← line 1

2nd division   2 | 4   3   9   6   ← line 2

                  2   3   9   3   ← line 3

Notice again that the numbers 3 and 9, which cannot be exactly divided by 2, were carried down into line 3.

Step 4: The smallest prime number that exactly divides at least two of the numbers in line 3 is 3. We draw a division line around the numbers in line 3, place a 3 in front of it and perform the divisions. The work looks like this so far:

1st division   2 | 8   6   9   12   ← line 1

2nd division   2 | 4   3   9   6   ← line 2

3rd division   3 | 2   3   9   3   ← line 3

                  2   1   3   1   ← line 4

NOTE: The series of division stops when a line is reached which contains all prime numbers.

We are ready to write down the least common denominator.

Step 5: We now multiply the divisors 2, 2, and 3 and the numbers in line 4 (except the ones) together to get the LCD.

Thus: LCD $= 2 \times 2 \times 3 \times 2 \times 3 = 72$.

Now 72 is the least whole number that is *exactly* divisible by 8, 6, 9, and 12. We check this

$$\frac{72}{8} = 9 \qquad \text{(no remainder)}$$
$$\frac{72}{6} = 12 \qquad \text{(no remainder)}$$
$$\frac{72}{9} = 8 \qquad \text{(no remainder)}$$
$$\frac{72}{12} = 6 \qquad \text{(no remainder)}$$

We cannot find any other *smaller* whole number which is exactly divisible by each of the denominators. Hence this number, the *least whole number,* is the required LCD of the given fractions.

■ EXAMPLE 2:

Find the LCD of the fractions $\frac{5}{12}, \frac{4}{15}, \frac{7}{8}, \frac{9}{20}$.

Solution and Explanation:

Step 1: Write the denominators in a row with a space between each and a division sign around them:

$$| \; 12 \quad 15 \quad 8 \quad 20$$

Step 2: The smallest prime number which divides at least two of these numbers is 2. Place it in front of the 12 and perform the divisions. We get:

$$2 \; | \; 12 \quad 15 \quad 8 \quad 20$$
$$6 \quad 15 \quad 4 \quad 10$$

Step 3: The next prime number we use for a divisor is 2 again:

$$
\begin{array}{r|cccc}
2 & 12 & 15 & 8 & 20 \\
\hline
2 & 6 & 15 & 4 & 10 \\
\hline
& 3 & 15 & 2 & 5
\end{array}
$$

Step 4: The next divisor is 3:

$$
\begin{array}{r|cccc}
2 & 12 & 15 & 8 & 20 \\
\hline
2 & 6 & 15 & 4 & 10 \\
\hline
3 & 3 & 15 & 2 & 5 \\
\hline
& 1 & 5 & 2 & 5
\end{array}
$$

Step 5: The final divisor is 5:

$$
\begin{array}{r|cccc}
2 & 12 & 15 & 8 & 20 \\
\hline
2 & 6 & 15 & 4 & 10 \\
\hline
3 & 3 & 15 & 2 & 5 \\
\hline
5 & 1 & 5 & 2 & 5 \\
\hline
& 1 & 1 & 2 & 1
\end{array}
$$

Step 6: The LCD is $2 \times 2 \times 3 \times 5 \times 2 = 120$.

■ **EXAMPLE 3:**

Find the sum of $9\frac{1}{2}$ in., $1\frac{3}{16}$ in., and $7\frac{15}{32}$.

Solution and Explanation:

We notice that these mixed numbers have fractional parts of different denominations. The first step is, then, to find the LCD of the fractional parts.

Step 1:

$$
\begin{array}{r|ccc}
2 & 2 & 16 & 32 \\
\hline
2 & 1 & 8 & 16 \\
\hline
2 & 1 & 4 & 8 \\
\hline
2 & 1 & 2 & 4 \\
\hline
& 1 & 1 & 2
\end{array}
$$

The LCD is $2 \times 2 \times 2 \times 2 \times 2 = 32$

Step 2: We now write the mixed numbers as follows:

$$
\begin{aligned}
9\tfrac{1}{2} &= 9\tfrac{}{32} \\
1\tfrac{3}{16} &= 1\tfrac{}{32} \\
7\tfrac{15}{32} &= 7\tfrac{}{32}
\end{aligned}
$$

Step 3: We now determine the *new* numerators for each of the equivalent fractional parts. To find the new numerator for the first

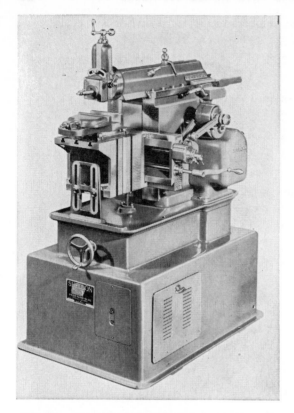

The machines of modern industry like the shaper require mechanical skill and mathematical ability on the part of the operator.

Sheldon Machine Co.

fraction, we divide 32 by 2, the old denominator, obtaining 16. We multiply the old numerator, 1, by 16, obtaining 16. The new mixed number equivalent to $9\frac{1}{2}$ is $9\frac{16}{32}$. Similarly, dividing 32 by 16, we get 2. Multiplying 3 by 2 we obtain 6. The new mixed number equivalent to $1\frac{3}{16}$ is $1\frac{6}{32}$. We now notice that the denominator of the fractional part of the mixed number $7\frac{15}{32}$ is the same as the LCD. Hence there is no need to make any change in $7\frac{15}{32}$ so we write it equal to $7\frac{15}{32}$.

Step 3 completed appears thus:

$$9\frac{1}{2} = 9\frac{16}{32}$$
$$1\frac{3}{16} = 1\frac{6}{32}$$
$$7\frac{15}{32} = 7\frac{15}{32}$$

Step 4: Now adding the fractional parts we obtain $\frac{37}{32}$, and adding the whole number parts we get 17. The sum this far is $17\frac{37}{32}$. Reducing this to simplest terms gives $18\frac{5}{32}$, the final sum.

The complete solution will appear thus:

$$9\tfrac{1}{2} = 9\tfrac{16}{32}$$
$$1\tfrac{3}{16} = 1\tfrac{6}{32}$$
$$7\tfrac{15}{32} = 7\tfrac{15}{32}$$
$$17\tfrac{37}{32} = 18\tfrac{5}{32} \text{ ans.}$$

2	2	16	32
2	1	8	16
2	1	4	8
2	1	2	4
	1	1	2

$$\text{LCD} = 2 \times 2 \times 2 \times 2 \times 2 = 32$$

2.7 Addition of Fractions and Mixed Numbers

People working in the various trades are frequently called on to determine total lengths and distances from subsidiary lengths and distances, especially when they are working from erection drawings, architect's drawings, and other types of drawings.

The processes used in such cases have already been explained. The student will find it very helpful if he will make a sketch or a neat rough diagram involving the dimensions in question, unless they may already be shown on the drawing he is using.

■ **EXAMPLE 1:**

Determine the total length of the plate in Figure 15.

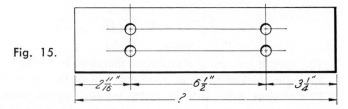

Fig. 15.

Solution and Explanation:

It is clear that the total length of the plate is equal to the sum of the separate lengths, $2\tfrac{11}{16}$ in., $6\tfrac{1}{2}$ in., and $3\tfrac{1}{4}$ in. This length is frequently referred to as the overall length.

From the dimensions given in the drawing, we see that the fractional parts do not have the same common denominator.

The LCD of the fractional parts is seen to be 16. Hence we change the fractional parts of the mixed numbers to 16ths. We then have:

$$2\tfrac{11}{16} = 2\tfrac{11}{16}$$
$$6\tfrac{1}{2} = 6\tfrac{8}{16}$$
$$3\tfrac{1}{4} = 3\tfrac{4}{16}$$
$$\text{Sum} = 11\tfrac{23}{16} \text{ or } 12\tfrac{7}{16}$$

Therefore, the total length of this plate is $12\tfrac{7}{16}$ in.

A further application of the addition of fractions may be seen in the method of determining the length of bent metal.

In calculating the total length of such pieces the *sum* of the *inside* dimensions of the finished piece is first determined. To this is added an allowance for each square corner. This varies for different kinds of material, but for the problems in this book, add half the thickness of the metal for each square corner.

How this is done is shown in the following problem.

■ EXAMPLE 2:

Calculate the length of the iron strip that is to be bent according to the shape in Figure 16.

Fig. 16.

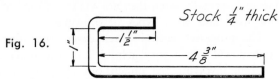

Stock $\frac{1}{4}''$ thick

$-1\frac{1}{2}''-$

$-4\frac{3}{8}''-$

Solution and Explanation:

The inside dimensions of this piece are $1\frac{1}{2}$ in., 1 in., $4\frac{3}{8}$ in.

Adding these dimensions in the usual manner the sum becomes:

$$
\begin{aligned}
1\frac{1}{2} &= 1\frac{4}{8} \\
1 &= 1 \\
4\frac{3}{8} &= 4\frac{3}{8} \\
\hline
\text{Sum} &= 6\frac{7}{8}
\end{aligned}
$$

The sum of the inside dimensions therefore is $6\frac{7}{8}$ in.

Since the thickness is $\frac{1}{4}$ in. then one half of this measures $\frac{1}{8}$ in.

This amount, $\frac{1}{8}$ in., is to be added for each square corner bend. There being two such bends the total amount to be added equals $\frac{1}{8} + \frac{1}{8}$, or $\frac{1}{4}$ in.

Adding this amount, $\frac{1}{4}$ in., to the sum of the inside measurements, $6\frac{7}{8}$ in., the result becomes:

$$
\begin{aligned}
6\frac{7}{8} &= 6\frac{7}{8} \\
\frac{1}{4} &= \frac{2}{8} \\
\hline
\text{Sum} &= 6\frac{9}{8} \text{ or } 7\frac{1}{8} \quad \textbf{ans.}
\end{aligned}
$$

That is, the total length of the above piece before bending to the shape noted should be $7\frac{1}{8}$ in.

2.8 Problems Involving Addition of Fractions and Mixed Numbers Whose Fractional Parts Have Different Denominators

1. *a*) Find the sum of $7\frac{1}{4}$ in., $2\frac{3}{4}$ in., $7\frac{3}{8}$ in., and $11\frac{5}{16}$ in.
   b) Find the sum of $3\frac{1}{16}$ in., $9\frac{1}{2}$ in., $5\frac{5}{8}$ in., $6\frac{1}{16}$ in.
   c) Find the sum of $1\frac{1}{3}$, $8\frac{5}{6}$, $15\frac{3}{4}$, $12\frac{1}{2}$.
   d) Find the sum of $14\frac{2}{5}$, $4\frac{1}{2}$, $8\frac{1}{8}$, $16\frac{1}{4}$.

2. On an architect's drawing, the following dimensions were given:
  1¾ in., 2 ft. 10½ in., 1½ in., 2 ft. 10½ in., 2 ft. 10½ in.
What is the total length represented by these dimensions?

3. Find the total length of the material used in making the template (Fig. 17).

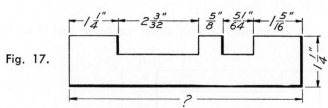

Fig. 17.

4. A boy is given a drawing (Fig. 18) of a tool rack and is asked to build one for his workbench. What is the length of the material needed?

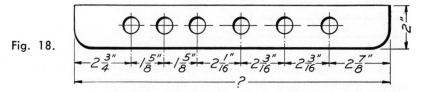

Fig. 18.

5. What is the total length of the bolt illustrated in Figure 19?

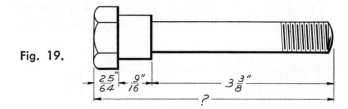

Fig. 19.

6. To complete a rush job, three draftsmen worked the following hours overtime in the course of a two-week period: 22½ hr., 19½ hr., and 17 hr. What was their combined overtime?

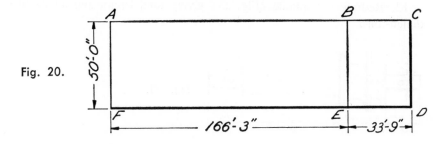

Fig. 20.

7. A manufacturing plant fenced into two sections of property having the dimensions shown (Fig. 20). How many yards of fence were used?

8. Find the sum of the following:

    a) $2\frac{3}{5}$, $4\frac{5}{3}$, $\frac{7}{5}$, $9\frac{3}{4}$, $15\frac{7}{12}$

    b) $1\frac{7}{8}$, $8\frac{1}{4}$, $12\frac{1}{8}$, $9\frac{1}{2}$

    c) $2\frac{1}{7}$, 5, $\frac{7}{10}$, $\frac{13}{35}$, $15\frac{4}{5}$

9. Determine the dimensions marked L and W in Figure 21.

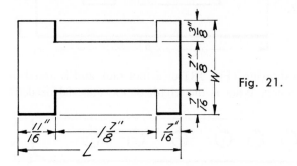

Fig. 21.

10. A college student worked the following hours in the cafeteria of a college residence hall: Monday, $2\frac{1}{2}$ hr.; Tuesday, $2\frac{1}{4}$ hr.; Wednesday and Thursday, $3\frac{3}{4}$ hr. each; Friday, $2\frac{3}{4}$ hr.; and Saturday, $5\frac{3}{4}$ hr. How many hours did he work altogether?

11. Redraw the sketch in Figure 22 of a steel stud shaft, giving all dimensions in their lowest terms. Find the total length L of the shaft.

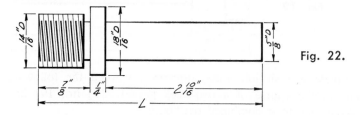

Fig. 22.

12. Redraw the spindle (Fig. 23) giving total length and all detailed dimensions.

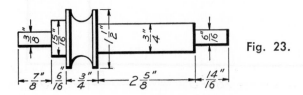

Fig. 23.

13. The total height from the first floor to the roof of a building can be found by adding 10 ft. 6 in., 4 ft. 0 in., 11 ft. 8 in., 2 ft. 6 in., 12 ft. 10 in. and 3 ft. 0 in. What is the total height?

14. What is the length of the gauge illustrated in Figure 24?

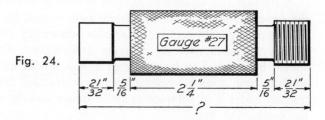

Fig. 24.

15. An architect's drawing shows the total height from the foundation footing to the finish first floor line of a small home to be 9 ft. 3 in. This is made up of the following heights: 1 ft. 10 in., 5 ft. 5 in., $3\frac{5}{8}$ in., 1 ft. $6\frac{5}{8}$ in., $11\frac{3}{4}$ in. Is the total height correct?

16. A rectangular plot of ground has a length of 112 ft. 4 in. and a width of 100 ft. 2 in. How many feet of fencing will be needed to enclose this plot?

17. In making telephone repairs in a large city, cable ducts were run for 445 ft. 0 in., 57 ft. 8 in., and 114 ft. 6 in. What is the total length of the ducts?

18. Determine the width, also the length, of the piece shown in Figure 25.

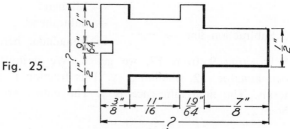

Fig. 25.

19. Five sheets of steel have the following thicknesses: $\frac{3}{16}$ in., $\frac{3}{8}$ in., $\frac{1}{2}$ in., 1 in., and $\frac{1}{4}$ in. What is the total thickness of these five sheets?

20. A detail drawing of a steel beam showed that the total length of the beam could be found by adding these three dimensions: 3 ft. $0\frac{11}{16}$ in., 22 ft. $4\frac{1}{2}$ in., and 3 ft. $0\frac{11}{16}$ in. What was the total length of the beam?

CHAPTER 3

Subtraction of Fractions and Mixed Numbers

3.1 Subtraction of Fractions

A fraction can be subtracted from another fraction if the fractions have the same denominator. If this requirement is met, the subtraction may be performed by subtracting the *smaller* numerator from the *larger,* and writing the result over the common denominator. The resulting fraction should be reduced to lowest terms if it is not in its simplest form. The work is best done by writing the larger fraction first, then the smaller fraction under it. A subtraction line is drawn and the remainder put under the subtraction line.

The larger fraction is called the minuend. The smaller fraction is called the subtrahend, and the result of subtraction is called the remainder or difference.

■ EXAMPLE 1:

Subtract $\frac{9}{32}$ from $\frac{17}{32}$.

Solution and Explanation:

In this example, the two fractions have the same denominator, 32. To perform the subtraction, we set the minuend and subtrahend under each other thus:

Step 1:   *Step 2:*

$$\frac{17}{32} \leftarrow \text{Minuend}$$
$$- \frac{9}{32} \leftarrow \text{Subtrahend}$$
Subtraction line $\rightarrow$ ——— $\leftarrow$ Remainder here

$$\frac{17}{32}$$
$$- \frac{9}{32}$$
$$\frac{8}{32} = \frac{1}{4} \textbf{ ans.}$$

Subtracting 9 from 17, we get 8. We write this over the common denominator, 32, obtaining $\frac{8}{32}$. This fraction is then reduced to lowest terms. The final difference is $\frac{1}{4}$. The entire work would appear as in Step 2.

■ EXAMPLE 2:

What is the remainder when $\frac{73}{144}$ is subtracted from $\frac{121}{144}$?

Solution and Explanation:

Step 1:   *Step 2:*

$$\frac{121}{144}$$
$$- \frac{73}{144}$$
———

$$\frac{121}{144}$$
$$- \frac{73}{144}$$
$$\frac{48}{144} = \frac{1}{3} \textbf{ ans.}$$

In Step 2, 73 is subtracted from 121. The result is 48. The number 48 is written over 144, the common denominator. The resulting fraction is $\frac{48}{144}$. When this is reduced by dividing both of its terms by 48, the result is $\frac{1}{3}$. Hence the remainder, when $\frac{73}{144}$ is subtracted from $\frac{121}{144}$ is $\frac{1}{3}$. Again, the work needed is as shown in Step 2, and this is all that need be shown in doing such problems.

3.2 Problems Involving Subtraction of Fractions Having Common Denominators

1. Subtract $\frac{19}{50}$ from $\frac{37}{50}$.
2. What is the remainder when $\frac{15}{64}$ is subtracted from $\frac{53}{64}$?
3. Subtract $\frac{19}{32}$ from $\frac{31}{32}$.
4. $\frac{79}{144}$ minus $\frac{23}{144}$ equals what?
5. Subtract $\frac{47}{60}$ from $\frac{59}{60}$.
6. What number added to $\frac{125}{144}$ equals $\frac{143}{144}$?
7. After clipping $\frac{7}{32}$ in. from a polished strip of aluminum $\frac{29}{32}$ in. wide, what is the width of the piece remaining?
8. Four brass spacers, or shims, measure a total of $\frac{11}{64}$ in. thick. After removing one shim, which measures $\frac{3}{64}$ in. thick, what is the combined thickness of the three remaining shims?
9. If the minuend is $\frac{97}{125}$ and the subtrahend is $\frac{62}{125}$, what is the remainder?
10. What is the remainder when $\frac{27}{125}$ is subtracted from $\frac{77}{125}$?
11. Find the difference between:

$\frac{33}{144}$ and $\frac{7}{144}$; $\frac{19}{35}$ and $\frac{4}{35}$; $\frac{24}{25}$ and $\frac{7}{25}$; $\frac{43}{60}$ and $\frac{17}{60}$; $\frac{683}{1728}$ and $\frac{241}{1728}$

12. In order to use a mahogany board that measures $\frac{15}{16}$ in. thick, a young man is obliged to plane $\frac{3}{16}$ in. off one side. What is the final thickness after this planing is done?

3.3 Subtraction of Fractions Not Having a Common Denominator

Fractions that do not have a common denominator must be changed to similar fractions (fractions having a common denominator) before they can be subtracted. After they have been changed so as to have a common denominator, they can then be subtracted as explained in Section 3.1.

■ EXAMPLE 1:

Subtract $\frac{11}{16}$ from $\frac{7}{8}$.

Solution and Explanation:

The common denominator of these two fractions is seen to be 16.

When each of the given fractions is changed to equivalent fractions they become $\frac{11}{16}$ and $\frac{14}{16}$ respectively. To perform the subtraction we write:

$$\frac{7}{8} = \frac{14}{16}$$
$$\frac{11}{16} = \frac{11}{16}$$
$$\text{Difference} = \frac{3}{16} \textbf{ ans.}$$

The difference of the numerators is 3. This written over 16 gives the remainder or difference, $\frac{3}{16}$. Notice carefully that the fractions are written in columns, and that the equal signs are also written in a column. This makes for neat, blunder-free work, the value of which can never be overemphasized.

■ **EXAMPLE 2:**

What is the value of the missing dimension in Figure 26?

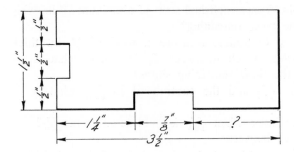

Fig. 26.

Solution and Explanation:

The three dimensions marked $\frac{1}{2}$ in. and the dimensions marked $1\frac{1}{4}$ in. and $\frac{7}{8}$ in. are called *detail dimensions*. The dimensions marked $1\frac{1}{2}$ in. and $3\frac{1}{2}$ in. are called *overall dimensions*.

In order to determine the missing dimension, we see that we must subtract the sum of $1\frac{1}{4}$ in. and $\frac{7}{8}$ in. from $3\frac{1}{2}$ in. We do this in two steps.

Step 1:

$$1\frac{1}{4} = 1\frac{2}{8}$$
$$\frac{7}{8} = \frac{7}{8}$$
$$\text{Sum} = 1\frac{9}{8} = 2\frac{1}{8}$$

Step 2:

$$3\frac{1}{2} = 3\frac{4}{8}$$
$$2\frac{1}{8} = 2\frac{1}{8}$$
$$\text{Difference} = 1\frac{3}{8} \text{ in. } \textbf{ans.}$$

Hence the missing dimension is $1\frac{3}{8}$ in.

As a check on our work, we can add $1\frac{1}{4}$ in., $\frac{7}{8}$ in., and $1\frac{3}{8}$ in.

$$1\tfrac{1}{4} \; = \; 1\tfrac{2}{8}$$
$$\tfrac{1}{8} \; = \; \tfrac{1}{8}$$
$$1\tfrac{3}{8} \; = \; 1\tfrac{3}{8}$$

Sum $= 3\tfrac{1}{2}$ in., which checks with the overall dimension.

3.4 Problems in Subtraction of Fractions Having Different Denominators

1. From $\tfrac{15}{16}$ in. take $\tfrac{3}{8}$ in.; from $\tfrac{43}{64}$ take $\tfrac{7}{16}$; from $\tfrac{3}{4}$ in. take $\tfrac{7}{32}$ in.; from $\tfrac{9}{32}$ in. take $\tfrac{1}{8}$ in.

2. Subtract $\tfrac{17}{32}$ in. from $\tfrac{3}{4}$ in.; $\tfrac{8}{15}$ from $\tfrac{7}{12}$; $\tfrac{1}{12}$ from $\tfrac{31}{144}$.

3. If $\tfrac{1}{16}$ in. was removed from a bar $\tfrac{15}{16}$ in. thick, what was the resulting thickness of the bar?

4. Find the difference between $\tfrac{5}{14}$ and $\tfrac{1}{21}$; $\tfrac{29}{36}$ and $\tfrac{1}{4}$; $\tfrac{8}{9}$ and $\tfrac{3}{4}$; $\tfrac{7}{24}$ and $\tfrac{9}{40}$; $\tfrac{19}{20}$ and $\tfrac{8}{15}$.

5. Compute the dimension marked L on the drawing (Fig. 27).

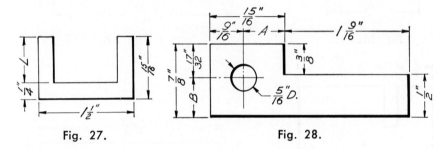

Fig. 27.   Fig. 28.

6. Compute the dimensions marked A and B in the drawing (Fig. 28).

7. Compute the dimension marked A in the drawing (Fig. 29).

8. Subtract $\tfrac{7}{128}$ from $\tfrac{3}{4}$; $\tfrac{5}{32}$ from $\tfrac{3}{8}$; $\tfrac{7}{12}$ from $\tfrac{17}{18}$; $\tfrac{1}{3}$ from $\tfrac{11}{24}$.

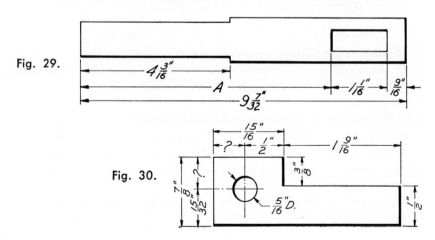

Fig. 29.

Fig. 30.

9. A surface grinder removes $\frac{7}{64}$ in. from a piece of steel which is $\frac{7}{8}$ in. thick. What is the resulting thickness of the steel?

10. In the drawing in Figure 30 locate how far the center of the hole lies from the left side, and from the top.

11. A bronze bushing has an outside diameter of $\frac{1}{2}$ in. The thickness of the metal is $\frac{3}{32}$ in.; what is the inside diameter of the bushing?

12. What is the thickness of the screw head in Figure 31?

13. The dimension indicating the width of the slot in the block as shown in the illustration (Fig. 32) is missing. What should it be?

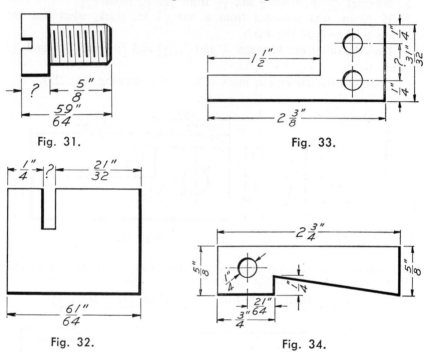

Fig. 31.

Fig. 33.

Fig. 32.

Fig. 34.

14. Supply the missing measurement in Figure 33.

15. In checking the exact location of the hole in the piece shown in Figure 34, how far should it be from the left end?

3.5 Subtraction of Fractions and Mixed Numbers

When a fraction is to be subtracted from a mixed number, the *fraction* is first subtracted from the fractional part of the mixed number. The whole number part that is left is placed *in front* of the fraction to give the final remainder or difference.

Two common situations arise in actual practice and each will be explained in detail.

The milling machine is used to make many precise cuts in metal.

Clausing

■ **EXAMPLE 1:**

An apprentice machinist takes off $\frac{3}{16}$ in. from a steel plate measuring $1\frac{3}{4}$ in. thick. What is the final thickness of the plate?

Solution and Explanation:

In this example the minuend is $1\frac{3}{4}$ and the subtrahend is $\frac{3}{16}$. The problem is set up as follows:

Step 1:

$$
\begin{array}{rcll}
1\frac{3}{4} & = & 1\frac{12}{16} & \leftarrow \text{ minuend} \\
-\frac{3}{16} & = & \frac{3}{16} & \leftarrow \text{ subtrahend}
\end{array}
$$

In this step, the minuend and subtrahend are written under each other and the subtraction line is drawn. Since the fractional part of the mixed number and the fraction to be subtracted have different denominators, they are changed to equivalent fractions having a common denominator. Thus we get $1\frac{12}{16}$ for the new minuend and $\frac{3}{16}$ for the new subtrahend. (The new subtrahend and the old subtrahend are the same since they have the same LCD, 16).

Step 2:

$$1\tfrac{3}{4} = 1\tfrac{12}{16}$$
$$- \quad \tfrac{3}{16} = \quad \tfrac{3}{16}$$
$$\text{Difference} = 1\tfrac{9}{16} \textbf{ ans.}$$

In Step 2 we subtract $\tfrac{3}{16}$ from $\tfrac{12}{16}$, obtaining $\tfrac{9}{16}$. We place the whole number 1 in front of this. The final answer is then $1\tfrac{9}{16}$. In actually doing this problem the entire work is shown in Step 2.

The final thickness of the steel plate is $1\tfrac{9}{16}$ in.

■ **EXAMPLE 2:**

What is the remainder when $\tfrac{3}{4}$ is subtracted from $7\tfrac{3}{32}$?

Solution and Explanation:

As in the previous example, we write:
Step 1:

$$7\tfrac{3}{32} = 7\tfrac{3}{32}$$
$$- \quad \tfrac{3}{4} = \quad \tfrac{24}{32}$$

In this step we write the numbers to be subtracted as shown, changing the fractions to equivalent fractions having 32 for their LCD.

Since we cannot subtract $\tfrac{24}{32}$ from $\tfrac{3}{32}$, we borrow 1 from the whole number part of the mixed number. This unit we change to $\tfrac{32}{32}$ and mentally add it to the fractional part of the mixed number. We then write:
Step 2:

$$7\tfrac{3}{32} = 7\tfrac{3}{32} = 6\tfrac{35}{32}$$
$$- \quad \tfrac{3}{4} = \quad \tfrac{24}{32} = \quad \tfrac{24}{32}$$
$$\text{Difference} = 6\tfrac{11}{32} \textbf{ ans.}$$

We see that $7\tfrac{3}{32}$ has been changed to an equivalent mixed number, $6\tfrac{35}{32}$. We now can perform the subtraction, and we obtain $6\tfrac{11}{32}$ for the remainder. Again, all the work necessary to solve this type of problem is what is shown in Step 2.

3.6 Subtraction of Mixed Numbers

Mixed numbers can be subtracted directly from each other if their fractional parts have the same denominator. If the fractional parts do not have the same denominator, they must be changed to equivalent fractions having the same common denominator. The fractional parts are then subtracted. The whole number parts are subtracted next and their difference is written in front of the fractional parts. In all cases the final answer should be reduced to its simplest form.

■ **EXAMPLE 1:**

Subtract $6\frac{1}{2}$ from $8\frac{3}{16}$.

Solution and Explanation:

We write the problem as in previous examples:
Step 1:

$$8\frac{3}{16} = 8\frac{3}{16}$$
$$- \ 6\frac{1}{2} = 6\frac{8}{16}$$

Here the subtrahend is changed from $6\frac{1}{2}$ to $6\frac{8}{16}$.
Step 2:

$$8\frac{3}{16} = 8\frac{3}{16} = 7\frac{19}{16}$$
$$- \ 6\frac{1}{2} = 6\frac{8}{16} = 6\frac{8}{16}$$
$$\text{Difference} \ = 1\frac{11}{16} \ \textbf{ans.}$$

In Step 2 the subtraction is shown in its completed form.

3.7 Problems Involving Subtraction of Fractions and Mixed Numbers

1. *a*) What length added to $5\frac{3}{16}$ in. equals $19\frac{7}{8}$ in.?
   b) After subtracting $1\frac{3}{5}$ from $6\frac{1}{3}$ what remains?
   c) Subtract $2\frac{1}{4}$ from $3\frac{1}{3}$; $8\frac{1}{8}$ from $10\frac{1}{3}$; $15\frac{1}{9}$ from $20\frac{1}{2}$.
   d) What number added to $1\frac{1}{5}$ equals $13\frac{1}{7}$?

Fig. 35.

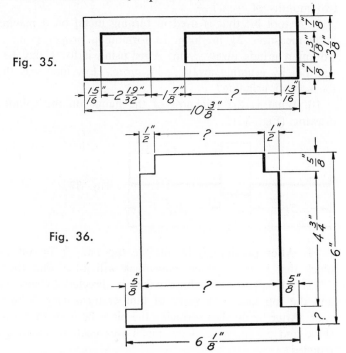

Fig. 36.

2. Figure 35 was sent to a machinist to be used in making the piece illustrated. He finds there is one important measurement missing. What should it be?

3. To make two copper pins, one piece $2\frac{13}{16}$ in. long, and another piece $2\frac{3}{32}$ in. long are cut from a rod $13\frac{1}{8}$ in. long. How much of the rod remains after this cutting?

4. In the drawing of a bookrack end (Fig. 36), determine the missing dimensions as indicated by the question marks.

5. From a bundle of paper containing 5 reams, a printer uses $1\frac{1}{2}$ reams in one day, $\frac{1}{2}$ ream on another day, and $\frac{3}{4}$ of a ream on another day. How many reams were there left in the original bundle?

6. A board measuring 4 in. wide is dressed by planing $\frac{3}{8}$ in. off one side and $\frac{3}{16}$ in. off the other side. What is the resulting width of this board?

7. From a coil of copper tubing 50 ft. in length, a plumber uses at different times pieces measuring $6\frac{1}{4}$ ft., $\frac{3}{4}$ ft., $8\frac{1}{2}$ ft., 4 ft., and $9\frac{3}{4}$ ft. How many feet of tubing are left in this coil?

8. A grindstone 14 in. in diameter is used in grinding chisels. After one month's use the diameter wears down $\frac{7}{16}$ in. After another month's use it wears down $\frac{5}{8}$ in. more. What is the diameter of the wheel after two months of wear?

9. A tool bit that is used in turning metal on a machine-shop engine lathe measures $2\frac{1}{2}$ in. long. In forming a proper point on this bit the workman grinds away $\frac{3}{16}$ in. After using it for a day he again repoints the tool by grinding away $\frac{5}{32}$ in. more. How long was the tool bit after the second grinding?

10. What is the thickness of the flange on the spindle shown in the drawing (Fig. 37)?

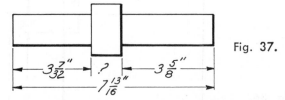

Fig. 37.

11. After planing $\frac{3}{16}$ in. off the top and $\frac{3}{16}$ in. off the bottom of a block that is $1\frac{1}{4}$ in. thick, how thick will it be after the operation?

12. An apprentice cabinetmaker is directed to surface one side face and the top face of a piece of lumber measuring 3 in. thick and 6 in. wide. After he finishes surfacing the piece he finds that it measures $2\frac{13}{16}$ in. thick and $5\frac{7}{8}$ in. wide. How much was each of the original dimensions reduced?

13. Redraw the sketch in Figure 38 putting in all dimensions including the ones indicated by the question marks.

Fig. 38.

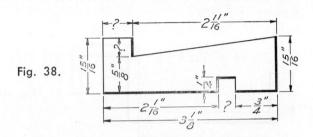

14. The weight of kerosene oil is listed as being $\frac{4}{5}$ that of water. At that rate what would be the weight of 1 gal. of kerosene when 1 gal. of water weighs $8\frac{1}{3}$ lb.?

15. From a strip of copper $10\frac{1}{2}$ ft. long the following lengths are cut at various times: $1\frac{1}{4}$ ft.; $\frac{1}{2}$ ft.; $1\frac{1}{2}$ ft.; $2\frac{3}{4}$ ft.; 2 ft. What is the length in feet of the piece remaining?

16. A casting weighs $36\frac{1}{2}$ lb. before it is worked upon in the machine shop. When all operations were completed the finished pieces weighed $21\frac{3}{4}$ lb. How much metal was machined from this casting in these operations?

17. Determine the length of the part as indicated by the question mark in the drawing (Fig. 39).

Fig. 39.

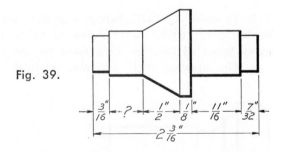

18. After withdrawing $14\frac{3}{4}$ gal. of oil from a tank containing $27\frac{1}{2}$ gal., how much remains in the tank?

3.8 Review Problems on Addition and Subtraction of Fractions

1. What number added to $17\frac{15}{35}$ equals $35\frac{8}{21}$?

2. What is the difference between $18\frac{15}{16}$ in. and $16\frac{3}{8}$ in.; between $42\frac{17}{64}$ in. and $13\frac{13}{64}$ in.; between $15\frac{19}{32}$ in. and $11\frac{13}{16}$ in.?

3. A steel block $1\frac{11}{64}$ in. thick has $\frac{9}{32}$ in. removed during a shaping operation. What is the resulting thickness after this operation?

4. Determine the length of metal needed to bend the piece in the drawing (Fig. 40).

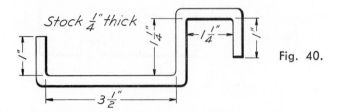

Fig. 40.

5. From a sheet of brass $11\frac{5}{8}$ in. wide, there is cut a strip $4\frac{3}{4}$ in. wide. What is the width of the sheet that remains?

6. Determine the length of the special screw shown in Figure 41.

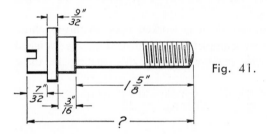

Fig. 41.

7. To paint a small kitchen, a pantry, and a back hall, four boys worked 5 hr., $6\frac{1}{4}$ hr., $4\frac{1}{3}$ hr., and $8\frac{3}{4}$ hr. respectively on the job. How many hours all together were spent on the work?

8. The drawing (Fig. 42) was returned to the drafting room by

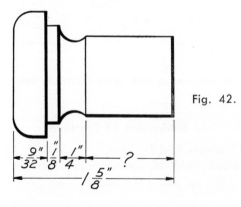

Fig. 42.

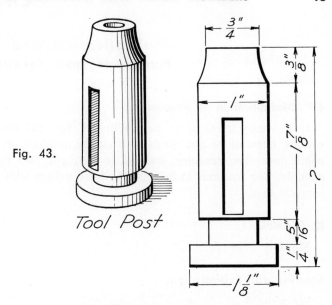

Fig. 43.

Tool Post

the foreman of the toolroom because an important dimension was missing. Check it over and redraw it, giving all dimensions.

9. To turn out a certain job on a lathe, the workman is supplied with four bars of stock weighing $19\frac{3}{4}$ lb., $17\frac{3}{4}$ lb., $20\frac{1}{2}$ lb., and $28\frac{1}{4}$ lb. After the job is completed he finds that he has $9\frac{1}{2}$ lb. of stock left. How much did he use?

10. The dimension giving the total height of the tool post shown in Figure 43 is missing. What should it be?

CHAPTER 4

Multiplication and Division of Fractions and Mixed Numbers

4.1 Multiplication of Fractions

If we have fractions to be multiplied, we find the product of the various numerators and write it over the product of the various denominators. The resulting fraction is then put into the simplest form possible. The fractions to be multiplied are written with a times sign ($\times$) between them.

■ **EXAMPLE 1:**

Multiply $\frac{3}{8}$ by $\frac{7}{16}$.

Solution and Explanation:

We write $\frac{3}{8} \times \frac{7}{16}$ or $\frac{3 \times 7}{8 \times 16} = \frac{21}{128}$.

The product of the numerators is 3×7 or 21. The product of the denominators is 8×16 or 128. Writing $\frac{21}{128}$ we have the required product. If the numerators and denominators contain common factors, we divide the numerators and denominators by these common factors replacing each by a 1. Then we write the product of the remaining numerator factors over the product of the remaining denominator factors to obtain the final product.

■ **EXAMPLE 2:**

Find the product of $\frac{15}{16} \times \frac{4}{9} \times \frac{7}{8}$.

Solution and Explanation:

Here we notice that we can divide 15 by 3, obtaining 5, and 9 by 3, obtaining 3.

Thus far our work appears thus:

Step 1:

$$\overset{5}{\cancel{15}}_{16} \times \frac{4}{\underset{3}{\cancel{9}}} \times \frac{7}{8}$$

We also see that 4 can be divided by 4, and 8 can be divided by 4. Our work would look like this then:

Step 2:

$$\overset{5}{\cancel{15}}_{16} \times \overset{1}{\underset{3}{\cancel{\frac{4}{9}}}} \times \frac{7}{\underset{2}{\cancel{8}}}$$

44

The world's largest sphere, 225 feet in diameter, required highly accurate mathematics.

Now multiplying the numerators that are left, we obtain $5 \times 1 \times 7 = 35$. Writing this over $16 \times 3 \times 2$, or 96, we obtain $\frac{35}{96}$ for the final product. Thus all our work would appear as in:

Step 3:

$$\frac{\cancel{16}^{5}}{16} \times \frac{\cancel{4}^{1}}{\cancel{9}_{3}} \times \frac{7}{\cancel{9}_{2}} = \frac{35}{96}$$

It may happen that the product of two or more fractions may be a fraction, a whole number or a mixed number, as seen in the following examples:

$$\frac{3}{4} \times \frac{1}{2} = \frac{3 \times 1}{4 \times 2} = \frac{3}{8}$$

$$\frac{7}{8} \times \frac{32}{21} \times \frac{3}{2} = 2$$

$$\frac{5}{8} \times \frac{7}{2} \times \frac{3}{4} = \frac{105}{64} = 1\frac{41}{64}$$

The operation of multiplication is indicated by the multiplication sign ($\times$). It is also indicated by the words *times, product of,* or *of.* Thus we say $\frac{5}{8}$ *times* $\frac{3}{4}$, or *the product of* $\frac{5}{8}$ by $\frac{3}{4}$, or $\frac{5}{8}$ *of* $\frac{3}{4}$.

4.2 Multiplication of Mixed Numbers

Mixed numbers are multiplied together by first changing each of them to an improper fraction. When this has been done, they can then be multiplied together by the methods of Section 4.1.

■ **EXAMPLE 1:**

Find the product: $6\frac{7}{8} \times 2\frac{1}{4} \times \frac{4}{5}$

Solution and Explanation:

As remarked above, we change the mixed numbers to improper fractions: $6\frac{7}{8}$ becomes $\frac{55}{8}$; $2\frac{1}{4}$ becomes $\frac{9}{4}$. We then have:

$$\frac{55}{8} \times \frac{9}{4} \times \frac{4}{5}$$

$$= \frac{\overset{11}{\cancel{55}} \times 9 \times \cancel{4}}{8 \times \underset{1}{\cancel{4}} \times \underset{1}{\cancel{5}}} = \frac{99}{8} = 12\frac{3}{8}$$

In doing our work, we would write the following:

$$6\frac{7}{8} \times 2\frac{1}{4} \times \frac{4}{5}$$

$$= \frac{\overset{11}{\cancel{55}}}{8} \times \frac{9}{\underset{1}{\cancel{4}}} \times \frac{\overset{1}{\cancel{4}}}{\underset{1}{\cancel{5}}}$$
$$\;\; {}_{9}$$

$$= \frac{99}{8}$$

$$= 12\frac{3}{8}, \text{ the required product.}$$

■ **EXAMPLE 2:**

A power shovel uses $3\frac{9}{10}$ gal. of gasoline per hour. How many gallons of gasoline does it consume in a working day of $7\frac{1}{2}$ hr.?

Solution and Explanation:

Here we must multiply $3\frac{9}{10}$ by $7\frac{1}{2}$. We write:

$$3\frac{9}{10} \times 7\frac{1}{2}$$

Changing the mixed numbers to improper fractions we get:

$$3\frac{9}{10} \times 7\frac{1}{2}$$

$$= \frac{39}{\underset{2}{\cancel{10}}} \times \frac{\overset{3}{\cancel{15}}}{2}$$

$$= \frac{117}{4} = 29\frac{1}{4}$$

Therefore, the power shovel would consume $29\frac{1}{4}$ gal. of fuel in $7\frac{1}{2}$ hr.

■ **EXAMPLE 3:**

Galvanized pipe 2 in. in diameter weighs $2\frac{3}{4}$ lb. per foot of length. What is the weight of a length of this pipe measuring $10\frac{1}{2}$ ft.? Since 1 ft. of this pipe weighs $2\frac{3}{4}$ lb., a $10\frac{1}{2}$-ft. length of it will weigh $10\frac{1}{2}$ times as much.

Solution and Explanation:

We then have:

$$2\tfrac{3}{4} \times 10\tfrac{1}{2}$$

$$= \tfrac{11}{4} \times \tfrac{21}{2} = \tfrac{11 \times 21}{4 \times 2}$$

$$= \tfrac{231}{8} = 28\tfrac{7}{8}$$

The weight of $10\tfrac{1}{2}$ ft. of this kind of pipe is $28\tfrac{7}{8}$ lb.

4.3 Multiplication of Mixed Numbers or Fractions by Whole Numbers

When a fraction or a mixed number is to be multiplied by a whole number, the whole number may be considered as the numerator of a fraction which has 1 for its denominator. The multiplication is then carried out in the same manner as the multiplication of fractions.

■ **EXAMPLE 1:**

A 15-gal. can is full of water. If 1 gal. of water weighs $8\tfrac{1}{3}$ lb., what is the weight of the water in the can?

Solution and Explanation:

Following the above procedure, we write:

$$8\tfrac{1}{3} \times \tfrac{15}{1}$$

Changing $8\tfrac{1}{3}$ to an improper fraction, we get $\tfrac{25}{3}$. We then have:

$$8\tfrac{1}{3} \times \tfrac{15}{1}$$

$$= \tfrac{25}{\cancel{3}_1} \times \tfrac{\cancel{15}^5}{1} = 125$$

Therefore, the weight of water is 125 lb.

■ **EXAMPLE 2:**

The material from which the piece in Figure 44 is made weighs $\tfrac{1}{16}$ lb. per inch of length. In making each piece $\tfrac{1}{4}$ in. is to be added to the length for cutting and finishing. What is the weight of the material required to make up 32 such pieces?

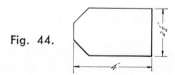

Fig. 44.

Solution and Explanation:

In working out problems of this kind the weight of the material required to make one piece should first be determined. The total weight can then be found by multiplying the weight of one piece by the number of pieces required.

The length of the piece as shown is 4 in. To this is added $\frac{1}{4}$ in. for cutting and finishing. This makes the total length of material needed for one piece equal to 4 in. $+$ $\frac{1}{4}$ in. or $4\frac{1}{4}$ in.

Since the weight of the material is $\frac{1}{16}$ lb. per inch, a piece $4\frac{1}{4}$ in. long would weigh $4\frac{1}{4} \times \frac{1}{16}$ or $\frac{17}{4} \times \frac{1}{16}$ or $\frac{17}{64}$ lb.

The weight of 32 such pieces would be 32 times the weight of one piece, or $32 \times \frac{17}{64}$ lb. Proceeding according to the rule for multiplying fractions by whole numbers, we have:

$$\frac{\overset{1}{\cancel{32}}}{1} \times \frac{17}{\underset{2}{\cancel{64}}} = \frac{17}{2} \text{ or } 8\frac{1}{2} \text{ lb.}$$

Therefore the weight of material needed to make 32 pieces is $8\frac{1}{2}$ lb.

The method used in Sections 4.2 and 4.3 is called *cancellation*. In using this method, *care* must be taken in the various division steps. The cancellation signs should be clearly drawn through the respective numerators and denominators as the cancellation progresses.

The following examples will illustrate this method further.

■ EXAMPLE 1:

Find the product $\frac{4}{5} \times \frac{15}{32} \times \frac{7}{12}$.

Solution and Explanation:

If this product were to be obtained in the usual method of multiplication of fractions, we would write:

Step 1:

$$\frac{4}{5} \times \frac{15}{32} \times \frac{7}{12}$$

$$= \frac{4 \times 15 \times 7}{5 \times 32 \times 12} = \frac{420}{1920}$$

Since $\frac{420}{1920}$ is not in its lowest terms, we would reduce it by dividing numerator and denominator by those factors of 420 and 1920 which are common to both of them. Then we would have:

Step 2:

$$\frac{420}{1920} = \frac{42}{192} = \frac{21}{96} = \frac{7}{32}$$

That is:

$$\frac{4}{5} \times \frac{15}{32} \times \frac{7}{12} = \frac{7}{32}$$

It should be noticed that in this method, we multiplied the numerators and the denominators to get $\frac{420}{1920}$. The numbers 420 and 1920 are considerably larger than any of the individual numerators or denominators. After we found the product $\frac{420}{1920}$ we reduced it to lowest terms.

■ **EXAMPLE 2:**

The amount of work can be reduced if the individual numerators and denominators of the fractions in the product are *first divided* by their common factors. The final product can then be obtained much more easily, since smaller numbers will be handled. Using this method to find the product $\frac{4}{5} \times \frac{15}{32} \times \frac{7}{12}$ we write:

Step 1:

$$\frac{4}{5} \times \frac{15}{32} \times \frac{7}{12}$$

Now, remembering that if the terms of these fractions are divided by any common factor, the value of the fractions is unchanged, we divide 4 by 4, obtaining 1 and 32 by 4, obtaining 8. This we show in

Step 2:

$$\frac{\overset{1}{\cancel{4}}}{5} \times \frac{15}{\underset{8}{\cancel{32}}} \times \frac{7}{12}$$

where we have drawn a line through the 4 and the 32 and have written the quotients 1 and 8 as shown.

We now notice that 5 divides the 5 in the denominator and the 15 in the numerator. Performing this division, we obtain:

Step 3:

$$\frac{\overset{1}{\cancel{4}}}{\underset{1}{\cancel{5}}} \times \frac{\overset{3}{\cancel{15}}}{\underset{8}{\cancel{32}}} \times \frac{7}{12}$$

Here we drew a line through the 5 in the denominator and wrote the quotient 1 below it. We also drew a line through the 15 in the numerator and wrote the quotient, 3, above it.

We now see that 3 divides 3 in the numerator and 12 in the denominator. Carrying out this division we obtain:

Step 4:

$$\frac{\overset{1}{\cancel{4}}}{\underset{1}{\cancel{5}}} \times \frac{\overset{\overset{1}{\cancel{3}}}{\cancel{15}}}{\underset{8}{\cancel{32}}} \times \frac{7}{\underset{4}{\cancel{12}}}$$

Here we drew a line through the 3 in the numerator and wrote the quotient 1 above it. We drew a line through the 12 in the denominator and wrote 4, the quotient, below it.

We now notice that the remaining numerators and denominators do not have any common factors. We then multiply the remaining numerators together to obtain the numerator of the product, which is $1 \times 1 \times 7$ or 7. We multiply the remaining denominator factors together to obtain the denominator of the product, which is $1 \times 8 \times 4$ or 32. Writing $\frac{7}{32}$ we obtain the final product.

The entire work would be shown as follows:

$$\frac{\cancel{1}}{\cancel{4}} \times \frac{\overset{1}{\cancel{\cancel{16}}}}{\cancel{32}} \times \frac{7}{\cancel{12}} = \frac{7}{32}$$

It is necessary that the lines be drawn through the numerators and denominators neatly and carefully, and the quotients written above the numerators and below the denominators. This will make the work easy to read and will reduce blunders.

■ EXAMPLE 3:

A third example, involving the product of fractions and mixed numbers, is given to clarify this procedure further.

Find the product:

$$4\frac{2}{3} \times 1\frac{31}{56} \times \frac{5}{19} \times \frac{20}{29}$$

Changing the mixed numbers to improper fractions, we write

Step 1:

$$\frac{14}{3} \times \frac{87}{56} \times \frac{5}{19} \times \frac{20}{29}$$

We now notice that 14 divides 14 in the numerator exactly, the quotient being 1. And 14 also divides 56 in the denominator, the quotient being 4. Performing this division, our work appears as in:

Step 2:

$$\frac{\overset{1}{\cancel{14}}}{3} \times \frac{87}{\underset{4}{\cancel{56}}} \times \frac{5}{19} \times \frac{20}{29}$$

We notice, at this stage, that 29 in the denominator divides itself once, and 87 in the numerator three times. We also see that 4 in the denominator divides itself once, and 20 in the numerator five times. Performing these divisions we obtain:

Step 3:

$$\frac{\overset{1}{\cancel{14}}}{3} \times \frac{\overset{3}{\cancel{87}}}{\underset{1}{\cancel{56}}} \times \frac{5}{19} \times \frac{\overset{5}{\cancel{20}}}{\underset{1}{\cancel{29}}}$$

At this stage we divide numerator and denominator by 3, and get:

Step 4:

$$\frac{\overset{1}{\cancel{14}}}{\underset{1}{\cancel{3}}} \times \frac{\overset{\overset{1}{\cancel{3}}}{\cancel{87}}}{\underset{\underset{1}{\cancel{4}}}{\cancel{56}}} \times \frac{5}{19} \times \frac{\overset{5}{\cancel{20}}}{\underset{1}{\cancel{29}}}$$

Now the product of the factors left in the numerator is $1 \times 1 \times 5 \times 5$ or 25. The product of the denominator is $1 \times 1 \times 19 \times 1$ or 19.

The final product, is $\frac{25}{19}$, which, when converted to a mixed number, is $1\frac{6}{19}$.

Therefore:

$$4\tfrac{2}{3} \times 1\tfrac{31}{56} \times \tfrac{5}{19} \times \tfrac{20}{29} = \tfrac{25}{19}$$
$$= 1\tfrac{6}{19}$$

The work that was shown in the various steps will appear this way when it is completed:

$$4\tfrac{2}{3} \times 1\tfrac{31}{56} \times \tfrac{5}{19} \times \tfrac{20}{29} = \tfrac{\cancel{14}}{\cancel{3}} \times \tfrac{\cancel{87}}{\cancel{56}} \times \tfrac{5}{19} \times \tfrac{\cancel{20}}{\cancel{29}}$$
$$= \tfrac{25}{19}$$
$$= 1\tfrac{6}{19}$$

and this is actually all that needs to be done in finding the product.

4.4 Problems Involving Multiplication of Fractions

1. Find the product: $4\tfrac{2}{17} \times 8 \times 6\tfrac{2}{5} \times \tfrac{3}{64} \times 1\tfrac{23}{28}$.

2. $2\tfrac{5}{8} \times 3\tfrac{3}{4} \times 2\tfrac{4}{5} \times 1\tfrac{1}{7} = ?$

3. $\dfrac{5 \times 9 \times 32}{25 \times 64 \times 18} = ?$

4. $\dfrac{28 \times 12 \times 55}{24 \times 36 \times 66} = ?$

5. What is the total weight of 8 cast-iron gear blanks each weighing $6\tfrac{3}{4}$ lb.?

6. Water weighs $62\tfrac{1}{2}$ lb. per cubic foot. What is the weight of 6 tanks each containing $5\tfrac{1}{3}$ cu. ft.?

7. There are $7\tfrac{1}{2}$ gal. of water in 1 cu. ft. If each gallon weighs $8\tfrac{1}{3}$ lb., what is the weight of $4\tfrac{1}{5}$ cu. ft. of water?

8. If a standard barrel contains $31\tfrac{1}{2}$ gal., what is the weight of oil in such a barrel that is $\tfrac{2}{3}$ full? The oil weighs $7\tfrac{3}{4}$ lb. per gallon.

9. If there are $7\tfrac{1}{2}$ gal. in 1 cu. ft., how many gallons of oil will 4 tanks hold, if each tank contains $4\tfrac{1}{2}$ cu. ft.?

10. Calculate the weight of 16 bars of cold-rolled steel, each bar being $11\tfrac{1}{2}$ ft. long. Each of these steel bars weighs $2\tfrac{1}{4}$ lb. per foot of length.

11. What is the total weight of 74 steel rods each 76 in. long and $\tfrac{3}{4}$ in. in diameter if each weighs $\tfrac{1}{8}$ lb. per inch of length?

12. Eight steel plates (Fig. 45) were needed for use on a steel staircase in a building. What is the total weight of these plates if each weighs $22\tfrac{1}{8}$ lb. per foot of length?

Fig. 45.

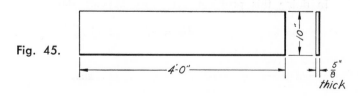

$4'\text{-}0''$

$\tfrac{5}{8}''$ thick

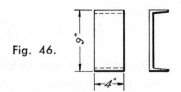

Fig. 46.

13. Four hangers are made by cutting a channel iron to the size shown in the drawing (Fig. 46). If the weight of the channel iron is $1\frac{1}{4}$ lb. per inch of length (that is, in the direction of the 4-in. dimension), what is the total weight of the four hangers?

14. Steel bars $\frac{1}{4}$ in. thick by $2\frac{1}{2}$ in. wide are listed as weighing $2\frac{1}{8}$ lb. per foot of length. What is the weight of 20 such bars each 12 ft. long?

15. A steel floor plate $\frac{1}{4}$ in. thick has a width of 4 ft., a length of 12 ft., and weighs 45 lb. per foot of length. What is the weight of the floor plate?

4.5   Division of Fractions

Division of a fraction by another fraction is performed by inverting (turning upside down) the divisor fraction and changing the sign of division to multiplication. The resulting problem is then exactly like the problem of the multiplication of two fractions and is handled as explained in Section 4.1.

■ **EXAMPLE 1:**

Divide $\frac{15}{16}$ by $\frac{3}{8}$.

Solution and Explanation:

Step 1:

The divisor fraction is $\frac{3}{8}$. When it is inverted (turned upside down) it becomes $\frac{8}{3}$. We then write:

Step 2:

$$\frac{\overset{5}{\cancel{15}}}{\underset{2}{\cancel{16}}} \times \frac{\overset{1}{\cancel{8}}}{\underset{1}{\cancel{3}}} = \frac{5}{2}$$

$$= 2\frac{1}{2}$$

Hence:

$$\frac{15}{16} \div \frac{3}{8} = 2\frac{1}{2}$$

In doing this problem, our work appears thus:

$$\frac{15}{16} \div \frac{3}{8} = \frac{\overset{5}{\cancel{15}}}{\underset{2}{\cancel{16}}} \times \frac{\overset{1}{\cancel{8}}}{\underset{1}{\cancel{3}}}$$

$$= \frac{5}{2}$$

$$= 2\frac{1}{2} \quad \textbf{ans.}$$

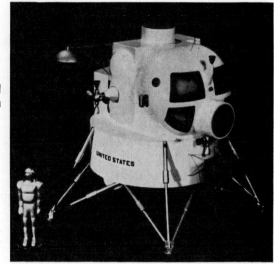

American astronauts will land on the moon in a vehicle such as this.

National Aeronautics and Space Administration

■ **EXAMPLE 2:**

Find the value of $\dfrac{\frac{25}{32}}{\frac{35}{68}}$.

Solution and Explanation:

Step 1:

We turn the divisor fraction upside down and change the sign of division to multiplication. We get:

$$\frac{25}{32} \times \frac{68}{35}$$

We now divide the numerators and the denominators by the factors common to both. We obtain:

Step 2:

$$\frac{\overset{5}{\cancel{25}}}{\underset{8}{\cancel{32}}} \times \frac{\overset{17}{\cancel{68}}}{\underset{7}{\cancel{35}}} = \frac{5 \times 17}{8 \times 7}$$
$$= \frac{85}{56}$$
$$= 1\frac{29}{56}$$

Hence, the quotient is $1\frac{29}{56}$.

Again, in the actual solution of this problem, all we would write would be:

$$\frac{\frac{25}{32}}{\frac{35}{68}} = \frac{\overset{5}{\cancel{25}}}{\underset{8}{\cancel{32}}} \times \frac{\overset{17}{\cancel{68}}}{\underset{7}{\cancel{35}}}$$
$$= \frac{5 \times 17}{8 \times 7} = \frac{85}{56}$$
$$= 1\frac{29}{56}$$

4.6 Division Involving Mixed Numbers

In dividing a mixed number by a mixed number, each mixed number is first changed to an improper fraction. The divisor fraction is next inverted, and the sign of division is changed to multiplication. The resulting problem is then handled as in the multiplication of two fractions.

■ **EXAMPLE 1:**

Divide $12\frac{3}{4}$ by $8\frac{5}{8}$.

Solution and Explanation:

As before, we perform the division in steps.

Step 1:

Each of the mixed numbers is changed to an improper fraction:

$$12\frac{3}{4} \div 8\frac{5}{8} = \frac{51}{4} \div \frac{69}{8}$$

Step 2:

In this step, we invert the divisor and change the sign from division to multiplication. We obtain:

Step 3:

$$\frac{\overset{17}{\cancel{51}}}{\underset{1}{\cancel{4}}} \times \frac{\overset{2}{\cancel{8}}}{\underset{23}{\cancel{69}}} = \frac{34}{23}$$

$$= 1\frac{11}{23}$$

Although the work above has been shown in steps, when it is actually performed, it looks thus:

$$12\frac{3}{4} \div 8\frac{5}{8} = \frac{51}{4} \div \frac{69}{8}$$

$$= \frac{\overset{17}{\cancel{51}}}{\underset{1}{\cancel{4}}} \times \frac{\overset{2}{\cancel{8}}}{\underset{23}{\cancel{69}}}$$

$$= \frac{34}{23}$$

$$= 1\frac{11}{23}$$

Thus $12\frac{3}{4} \div 8\frac{5}{8} = 1\frac{11}{23}$.

■ **EXAMPLE 2:**

How many pieces $\frac{9}{16}$ in. long can be cut from a strip $6\frac{3}{4}$ in. long?

Solution and Explanation:

To find the number of pieces that can be cut, we divide $6\frac{3}{4}$ in. by the length of one piece. Our problem becomes:

$$6\frac{3}{4} \div \frac{9}{16}$$

Step 1:

Changing $6\frac{3}{4}$ to an improper fraction, our problem becomes:

$$\frac{27}{4} \div \frac{9}{16}$$

And we now proceed as in the division of fractions.

Step 2:

$$\overset{3}{\underset{1}{\cancel{27}}} \times \overset{4}{\underset{1}{\cancel{16}}} = 12$$

■ EXAMPLE 3:

Divide 15 by $11\frac{2}{3}$.

Solution and Explanation:

The first step is to change $11\frac{2}{3}$ to the improper fraction $\frac{35}{3}$. We then have $15 \div 11\frac{2}{3} = \frac{15}{1} \div \frac{35}{3}$.

Inverting the divisor, $\frac{35}{3}$, and changing the division sign to multiplication, we have $\frac{15}{1} \times \frac{3}{35}$ which reduces to $\overset{3}{\underset{1}{\cancel{15}}} \times \underset{7}{\frac{3}{\cancel{35}}} = \frac{9}{7}$ or $1\frac{2}{7}$. Hence, $15 \div 11\frac{2}{3}$ equals $\frac{9}{7}$ or $1\frac{2}{7}$.

If the divisor is a *whole number,* then this whole number can be considered as a fraction which has 1 as its denominator and the whole number as its numerator. The division is then carried out in the same way as the division of ordinary fractions.

■ EXAMPLE 4:

A thin strip of metal $1\frac{7}{8}$ in. wide is cut into two equal strips. What is the width of each part, assuming no loss in cutting?

Solution and Explanation:

To solve this problem, we must divide $1\frac{7}{8}$ by 2. First, $1\frac{7}{8}$ is changed to the improper fraction $\frac{15}{8}$.

$1\frac{7}{8} \div 2$ then becomes $\frac{15}{8} \div \frac{2}{1}$, or $\frac{15}{8} \times \frac{1}{2}$ which equals $\frac{15}{16}$.

Therefore, each part is $\frac{15}{16}$ in. wide.

4.7 Problems Involving the Division of Fractions

1. Divide: $10\frac{3}{4}$ by $7\frac{5}{8}$; $8\frac{2}{3}$ by $\frac{7}{12}$; $9\frac{1}{7}$ into four equal parts.

2. What is the weight of a coil of wire 2000 ft. long if 160 ft. of the wire weigh 1 lb.?

3. A special-size bolt weighs $\frac{1}{4}$ lb. How many such bolts are there in a box which weighs $80\frac{1}{4}$ lb., if the box when empty weighs $3\frac{1}{4}$ lb.?

4. A fuel oil tank for a large building has a capacity of 8000 gal.

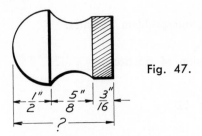

Fig. 47.

What is its capacity in cubic feet if there are $7\frac{1}{2}$ gal. per cubic foot?

5. Allowing $\frac{3}{16}$ in. for finishing up each piece, how many knobs like the one in Figure 47 can be cut from a bar $19\frac{1}{2}$ in. long?

6. The weights of a cubic foot of platinum and a cubic foot of water are listed as 1342 lb. and $62\frac{1}{2}$ lb. respectively. How many times heavier is a cubic foot of platinum than a cubic foot of water?

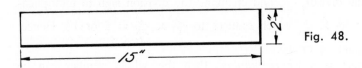

Fig. 48.

7. Redraw the sketch in Figure 48 (to one half actual size) and then draw lines across it showing the length of the piece divided into six equal parts. What will be the distance between these lines?

CHAPTER 5

Decimal Fractions

5.1 Introduction

In this, and succeeding chapters, you will become acquainted with another and very important way of writing numbers. This is the decimal notation.

Most of our computational work is done in terms of decimals. Many of the dimensions used in design, manufacturing, and production processes are in decimal form. It will consequently pay you well to master the operations with decimal numbers that will be taken up in this and the following chapters.

5.2 Decimal Notation

Decimal fractions are fractions whose denominators are 10, 100, 1000, or some other power of 10. These denominators, however, are only expressed when the decimal fraction is being read. When a decimal fraction is written, the denominator is omitted and replaced by a dot (.), called a decimal point, which is placed in the numerator so that there will be as many digits to the right of the point as there were zeros in the denominator of the fraction.

Thus, instead of writing $\frac{3}{10}$, we write 0.3. Thus $\frac{28}{100}$, $\frac{365}{1000}$, $\frac{5946}{10000}$, and $\frac{27153}{100000}$ becomes 0.28, 0.365, 0.5946, and 0.27153, respectively. Notice that we write a zero *in front* of the decimal point in writing any decimal fraction. This is considered the *best* practice. When we examine the above fractions and their decimal form, we see that there are as many figures *to the right* of the decimal point as *there are zeros* in the *denominator* of the particular fraction.

The micrometer is one of the basic measuring tools of the machinist.

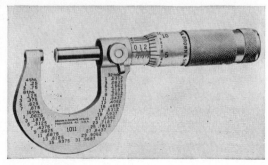

Brown & Sharpe Mfg. Co.

Frequently we have fewer figures in the numerator than there are zeros in the denominator, as, for example, in $\frac{36}{1000}$. Here we write a *zero to the left* of the figures 36, and then we put in the decimal point. Thus $\frac{36}{1000}$ becomes 0.036. Similarly $\frac{25}{1000}$ becomes 0.025, $\frac{4}{100}$ becomes 0.04, $\frac{15}{10000}$ becomes 0.0015. In *every case* we must have as many figures to the *right of the decimal point* as there would be zeros in the denominator of the fraction if it were written.

From a study of the above illustrations it is seen that the *first* digit to the *right* of the decimal point is in the *tenths* place and indicates the number of tenths; the second digit to the right of the decimal point is in the *hundredths* place and indicates the number of hundredths; the third digit to the right of the decimal point is in the *thousandths* place and indicates the number of thousandths, and so on.

A number which consists partly of a whole number and partly of a decimal fraction is indicated by writing the whole number, then the decimal point and then the decimal part of the number. Thus we would write 2 and $\frac{350}{1000}$ as 2.350; 47 and $\frac{8}{100}$ as 47.08; 175 and $\frac{67}{10000}$ as 175.0067. We would also write $\frac{887}{100}$ as 8.87; $\frac{7075}{100}$ as 70.75. Thus the *whole* numbers are written to the *left* of the decimal point, the numbers less than 1 (the decimal fractions) are written to the *right* of the decimal point.

Reference to Figure 51 will make this quite evident. The chart shows the relative positions of the various places with regard to the decimal point. Numbers to the *left* of the decimal point are whole numbers, whose value is *larger* than 1; numbers to the right of the decimal point are numbers whose value is *less* than 1. We should remember that when we write a number which has *no* decimal part, the decimal point is not written after the units digit.

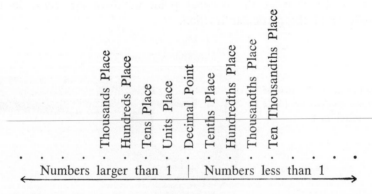

Fig. 51.

Thus, when we write the number nineteen, we simply write 19 without a decimal point after the 9. When we wish to write the number two thousand, we write 2000 and no decimal point is necessary.

Referring to Figure 51, we see that it will enable us to read the following decimal fractions and decimal numbers.

0.4	is read "four tenths"
0.04	is read "four hundredths"
0.004	is read "four thousandths"
0.251	is read "two hundred fifty-one thousandths"
200.0162	is read "two hundred *and* one hundred sixty-two ten thousandths"
36.65	is read "thirty-six *and* sixty-five hundredths"
1.250 in.	is read "one *and* two hundred fifty thousandths inches"
0.0125 in.	is read "one hundred twenty-five ten-thousandths inches"

In business and technical work, however, and especially when one is checking a set of numbers and reading them to someone else, it is the practice to use the word *point* instead of the word *and,* and to call out each digit individually.

Thus, in the examples above, we would read 36.65 as

a) "three, six, *point,* six, five" or as

b) "thirty-six, *point,* sixty-five."

Method *a*) is to be preferred.

It should be clear now how valuable this method of number representation is and why it is considered one of man's greatest accomplishments.

Let us now consider the decimal fractions 0.4, 0.04, and 0.004. Although the figure 4 is used, the value of the decimal fractions is different because of the position the 4 occupies with respect to the decimal point. Thus 0.4 is 10 times 0.04 and 100 times 0.004. Also 0.04 is 10 times 0.004. Likewise, 0.004 is one tenth of 0.04 and one hundredth of 0.4. Moving the decimal point *one* place to the *left* divides the number by 10, *two* places to the *left* divides the number by 100, *three* places to the *left* divides the number by 1000, etc. Moving the decimal point *one* place to the *right* multiplies the number by 10; *two* places to the *right* multiplies the number by 100; *three* places to the *right* multiplies the number by 1000, and so on.

Because this type of notation expresses numbers by means of powers of ten, it is called a *decimal* notation, from the Latin words *decimus* meaning "tenth," or *decem* meaning "ten."

This important idea is further illustrated in the following arrangement of the number 2.041. Let us move the decimal point *to the right, one place at a time.* We would obtain, starting with 2.041,

     20.41, which is ten times 2.041
     204.1, which is ten times 20.41
     2041, which is ten times 204.1.

If we moved the decimal point *to the left, one place at a time,* we would obtain:

     0.2041, which is one tenth of 2.041
     0.02041, which is one tenth of 0.2041
     0.002041, which is one tenth of 0.02041.

Although the *value* of a decimal number is not changed when zeros are written to the right of it, it should be mentioned that what may be called the "degree of precision" of the number *is* affected. Thus, if we are given the decimal number 0.25, we say this is known to an accuracy of two significant digits. If we now write it as 0.250, we are saying it is accurate to three significant digits. This should be avoided in computations since we have no authority to change a number of a given accuracy into a number of greater accuracy by writing zeros after it.

5.3 Problems Involving the Expression of Decimals

  1. Express in figures:
    a) Five hundred and nine thousandths,
    b) Five hundred nine thousandths,
    c) Five hundred nine and nine hundredths,
    d) Two thousand and fifteen ten-thousandths,
    e) Two thousand fifteen ten-thousandths,
    f) Two thousand fifteen and one thousandth,
    g) Two and fifteen thousandths.

  2. In the drawing of a template in Figure 52, write the value of each dimension in words.

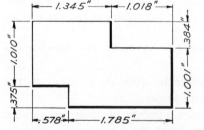

Fig. 52.

  3. A shop drawing calls for a round brass disk four and eight hundred forty-five thousandths inches in diameter, with a circular hole

five hundred thousandths of an inch in diameter through its center. Make a sketch of this disk, showing these dimensions.

4. A checker found that a dimension, which should have read twenty-nine thousandths inches, was shown as 0.290 in. How should it have been indicated?

5. Read the following aloud:

"Aluminum weighs 0.098 lb. per cubic inch."

"Gold weighs 0.697 lb. per cubic inch."

"The area of a circle equals 0.7854 times the square of its diameter."

"A cubic foot of water weighs 62.425 lb."

"At what are called 'standard conditions' a cubic foot of air weighs 0.0807 lb."

6. Gasoline is only 0.66 times as heavy as water. Express this decimal in words.

7. Sea water is about one and three hundredths times heavier than pure water.

8. Express the following as decimal fractions or decimal numbers:

$$\frac{43}{1000}, \quad \frac{25}{10000}, \quad \frac{498}{100}, \quad 1\frac{525}{1000}, \quad 5\frac{790}{100},$$
$$3\frac{85}{1000}, \quad \frac{164}{1000}, \quad \frac{8}{100}, \quad \frac{5}{10}, \quad 8\frac{5}{10}$$

9. Write the following in decimal form:

 a) One and one hundred thirty thousandths,

 b) Four hundred six thousandths,

 c) Six thousand and six ten-thousandths,

 d) Six thousand six ten-thousandths.

10. Write in words the dimensions that are shown in Figure 53.

Fig. 53.

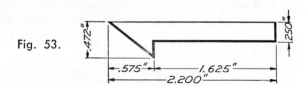

5.4 Addition of Decimals

The addition of decimals is performed in the same manner as the addition of whole numbers. The numbers to be added, which are the addends, are so arranged that (1) *all* the decimal points are in the same column and (2) the tenths are under tenths, hundredths under hundredths, thousandths under thousandths, and so on.

The whole number parts should also be arranged so that units are under units, tens under tens, hundreds under hundreds, thousands under

Precision measurement is
a requirement of modern
industry.

Clausing

thousands, and so on. The addition is then carried out column by
column, starting at the right, as in the case of whole numbers.

The procedure is illustrated by the following examples.

■ EXAMPLE 1:

Find the sum of 15.068, 0.064, 0.0037, 263.2, and 8.71.

Solution and Explanation:

Following the directions given above, we arrange each of the addends
so the decimal points are in the same column. We get:

$$
\begin{array}{r}
15.068 \\
0.064 \\
0.0037 \\
263.2 \\
+\quad 8.71 \\
\hline
\text{Sum} = \overline{287.0457}
\end{array}
$$

The addition is then performed as in the case of whole numbers.
The sum of 15.068, 0.064, 0.0037, 263.2, and 8.71 is 287.0457. A
check on the correctness of the addition is to add in a direction opposite
to the way we added to get the sum 287.0457. Normally we add going
down; that means in doing the check, we add going *up.* If we get the
same sum, we will feel quite sure that the answer is correct.

■ **EXAMPLE 2:**

Figure 54 represents a steel pin. The dimension giving the total length of this pin has been omitted from the drawing. Redraw the pin, showing the *total* length of the pin.

Fig. 54.

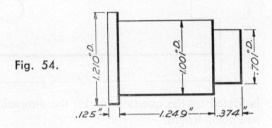

Solution and Explanation:

The total length of this pin is equal to the sum of the three dimensions: 0.125 in., 1.249 in., and 0.374 in., which indicate the length of the different portions making up the *total* length. The sum is found by arranging these decimals as previously explained and adding them as shown below:

$$\begin{array}{r} 0.125 \\ 1.249 \\ + \ 0.374 \\ \hline 1.748 \end{array}$$

The total length is consequently 1.748 in. The dimensions marked with a *D,* like 1.210″D, 1.001″D, indicate that the pin is cylindrical in shape, the dimensions giving the diameters of the respective portions. This notation is used in single-view drawings.

5.5 Problems Involving Addition of Decimals

1. Find the sum of each of the following:
    a) 5.9, 0.039, 2.18, 3.15;
    b) 9.755, 0.0375, 5.015, 3.2365;
    c) 14.0625, 98.4375, 0.0625, 0.5;
    d) 9.063, 0.845, 1.0355, 34.3467.

2. Find the sum of: two and seventy-three ten-thousandths; four and one hundred five thousandths; sixty-three hundredths; fifty-two thousandths; eight; fourteen; seven and two hundredths; sixteen ten-thousandths.

3. Redraw the measuring gauge (Fig. 55), writing in the positions

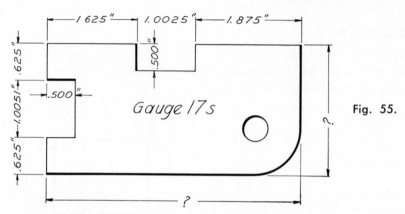

Fig. 55.

Gauge 17s

indicated by the question marks, the dimensions that give the total width and total length.

4. In grinding a steel plate, the grinding wheel reduces the thickness of the plate 0.015 in. during the first minute of grinding, 0.0215 in. the second minute, and 0.0195 in. the third minute of grinding. What is the total amount removed in these three minutes?

5. The drawing of the special steel tube (Fig. 56) does not have the outside diameter given. From the sketch shown, determine what this diameter should be.

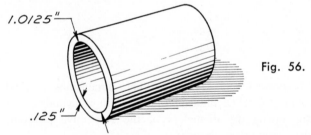

Fig. 56.

6. The milling-machine cutter in Figure 57 has its dimensions indicated in a separate detail drawing. From these dimensions determine the total width of this cutter.

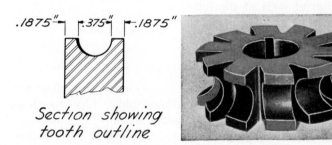

Section showing tooth outline

Fig. 57.

7. The inside diameter of an insulating plug is 0.192 in., and its wall thickness is 0.152 in. What is its outside diameter?

8. Determine the total length of the template illustrated in Figure 58.

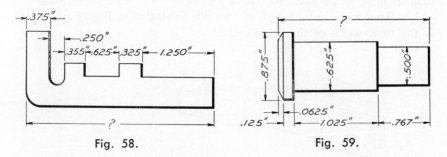

Fig. 58.   Fig. 59.

9. From the drawing (Fig. 59) of a crankpin, calculate its total length. Make a sketch of this pin, placing in position all dimensions, including the one giving the total length.

10. What is the total length and the total width of the steel punching shown in Figure 60? Redraw the piece putting in all dimensions.

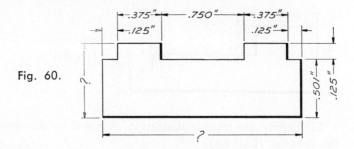

Fig. 60.

11. Two important dimensions as noted by the question marks are missing from Figure 61. What are they?

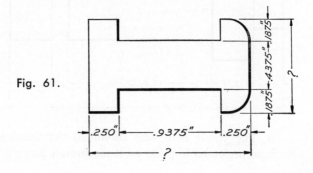

Fig. 61.

12. Three strips of sheet brass measuring in thickness 0.032 in., 0.035 in., 0.025 in. are bound together in one piece by placing the strips on top of each other and clamping them together. What is the combined thickness of these strips when so bound together?

13. What is the total length of the link illustrated in Figure 62? What is the total width of the open end?

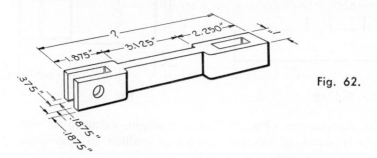

Fig. 62.

14. Redraw the piece in Figure 63 placing on it all the dimensions, including the dimension that gives the total length.

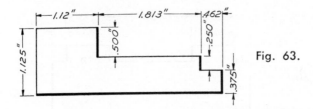

Fig. 63.

15. Supply the missing dimension as noted by the question mark on the drawing (Fig. 64).

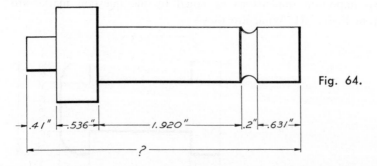

Fig. 64.

16. The young man who submitted the drawing in Figure 65 to his foreman neglected to place on it the overall dimension. What should it be?

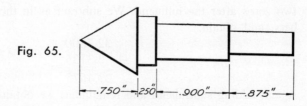

Fig. 65.

.750" .250" .900" .875"

5.6 Subtraction of Decimals

Subtraction of decimal fractions is performed in a manner similar to the subtraction of whole numbers. We write the minuend (the number from which we are to subtract); under this we put the subtrahend (the number to be subtracted) so that decimal points are directly under each other. This will result in tenths being under tenths, hundredths under hundredths, thousandths under thousandths, and so on. Likewise, units will be under units, tens under tens, hundreds under hundreds, thousands under thousands, and so on.

The subtraction is now performed as for whole numbers, the decimal point in the remainder being placed directly under the other decimal points.

The following examples will illustrate the application of this rule.

■ **EXAMPLE 1:**

Subtract 2.3105 from 9.7738.

Solution and Explanation:

Arranging the minuend and the subtrahend so the decimal points are directly under each other and subtracting, we obtain:

$$
\begin{array}{ll}
9.7738 & \text{Minuend} \\
-\ 2.3105 & \text{Subtrahend} \\
\hline
7.4633 & \text{Difference or remainder}
\end{array}
$$

Hence, 2.3105 subtracted from 9.7738 equals 7.4633. To check our work, we mentally add the subtrahend and remainder, getting 9.7738, the minuend. We are quite sure we have not made a blunder.

■ **EXAMPLE 2:**

From 32.78 subtract 3.3125.

Solution and Explanation:

We arrange the minuend and subtrahend in proper order and write two zeros after the minuend. We subtract as in the case of whole numbers, and obtain:

$$
\begin{array}{r}
32.7800 \\
- \quad 3.3125 \\
\hline
29.4675
\end{array}
$$

Again, adding subtrahend and remainder, we obtain 32.78, the minuend. We conclude that the remainder we obtained is correct.

■ **EXAMPLE 3:**

Subtract 0.7854 from **5.**

Solution and Explanation:

In order to carry out this subtraction four zeros are added after the decimal point, which follows the number 5. The subtraction then takes place in the usual manner.

$$
\begin{array}{r}
5.0000 \\
- \, 0.7854 \\
\hline
4.2146
\end{array} = \text{Difference}
$$

Therefore 0.7854 subtracted from 5 equals 4.2146.

■ **EXAMPLE 4:**

Subtract 1.7321 from **7.**

Solution and Explanation:

To perform the subtraction, we write the 7, place a decimal point after it and add four zeros to the right of it. Under this we write 1.7321 and subtract. Our work appears as follows:

$$
\begin{array}{r}
7.0000 \\
- \, 1.7321 \\
\hline
5.2679
\end{array}
$$

Therefore, 1.7321 subtracted from 7 equals 5.2679.

5.7   Problems Involving Subtraction of Decimals

1. Solve the following:
    a) $6.837 - 3.770 = ?$
    b) $33.725 - 19.838 = ?$
    c) $2.449 + 1.732 - 1.414 = ?$
    d) $12 - 0.7854 = ?$

2. In a certain city a skilled building worker was receiving $3.40 per hour, while an unskilled building laborer was receiving $2.20 per hour. How much more per hour did the skilled worker receive?

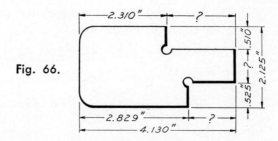

Fig. 66.

3. The drawing in Figure 66 was given to a toolmaker to be used in making a special gauge for measuring parts of a machine that is to be made in a small manufacturing plant. The foreman finds that three important measurements are missing. Draw a new sketch of this gauge placing on it all measurements.

4. Find the inside diameter of the piece of tubing in Figure 67.

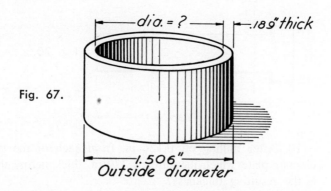

Fig. 67.

5. To reduce a measuring gauge to its proper thickness, 0.0025 in. must be ground off one flat side. Before this grinding takes place, however, the gauge measures 0.375 in. thick. What should be the measurement when the above grinding is done?

6. The drawing of a special machine key (Fig. 68) was returned to the drafting room with question marks regarding three missing dimensions. Redraw this sketch putting in all dimensions.

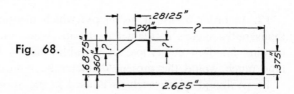

Fig. 68.

7. Determine the distance between the centers of the holes in the drill jig illustrated in Figure 69.

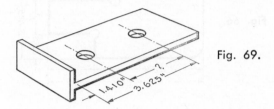

Fig. 69.

8. A steel bar $1\frac{1}{8}$ in. in diameter and 1 ft. long weighs 3.381 lb. An aluminum bar of the same dimensions weighs 1.208 lb. What is the difference in weight of these two bars?

9. Redraw the sketch in Figure 70 and put in all missing dimensions.

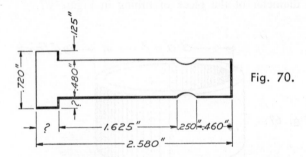

Fig. 70.

10. After milling off 0.126 in. from each of the two flat sides of a circular plate which measured 1.370 in. thick before the operation, what is the resulting thickness?

11. The draftsman who made the drawing in Figure 71 omitted an important dimension. Redraw the piece and place in position all of the dimensions.

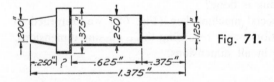

Fig. 71.

12. In order to use a piston pin which measures one and twenty-one thousandths inches in diameter, the mechanic must reduce the diameter to nine hundred eighty-five thousandths inches. In performing this task how much would the present diameter be reduced?

13. A liquid quart, such as is used in measuring milk, contains 57.75

cu. in. A dry quart, used in measuring vegetables contains 67.2 cu. in. How many cubic-inches difference is there between these two measures?

14. A copper rod 2 in. in diameter and 3 ft. long weighs 36.46 lb., while a brass rod of the same dimensions weighs 34.75 lb. Find the difference in the weight of these two rods.

15. When a high-quality insulating bushing was first cut, its outside diameter was 3.080 in. After finishing, the outside diameter was 3.015 in. By how much was the diameter reduced?

16. The actual diameter of a given shaft is 3.2478 in. The measurement of the inside diameter of the bearing in which this shaft runs is 3.249 in. Find the clearance.

5.8 Review Problems in Addition and Subtraction of Fractions

1. Write the following as decimals:
   a) Eleven and nine hundred eighty-four thousandths.
   b) Two and six-thousand sixty ten-thousandths.
   c) Thirty-eight thousandths inches.
   d) Seven hundred six thousandths.
   e) Nine hundred eight ten-thousandths.

2. Write the following in numerical form and find their sum: five and thirty-two hundredths; twelve and eighty-five hundredths; thirty-seven and one thousandth; eighteen; sixty-two thousandths.

3. a) From fifty-five and eight ten-thousandths subtract seven and seventeen hundredths.
   b) From forty-six subtract sixty-five thousandths.

4. A cubic inch of iron weighs 0.283 lb. A cubic inch of platinum weighs 0.774 lb. What is the difference in the weights of these metals per cubic inch?

5. In trying to fit a gear on a spindle, an auto mechanic finds that the hole in the gear measures 0.738 in. in diameter while the spindle diameter measures 0.752 in. How much will the diameter of the spindle have to be reduced in order to just fit into the hole in the gear?

6. What amount added to 2.718 will equal 19.32?

7. The wall thickness of a length of steel tubing is 0.185 in. The inside diameter of this tubing is 1.125 in. What is the outside diameter?

8. Four gauge blocks used by a toolmaker for accurate measuring are 0.285 in.; 0.750 in.; 0.1875 in.; and 0.365 in. respectively. What is their combined thickness?

9. A note on the drawing of a steel block 3.200 in. thick states "grind and polish to 3.102 in." What thickness of material is to be removed in these operations?

10. A piece of flat steel, measuring 1.016 in. thick, is placed on a

surface grinder in order to reduce the thickness to 0.987 in. During this operation how much is the thickness reduced?

11. Determine the length of the gauge in Figure 72.

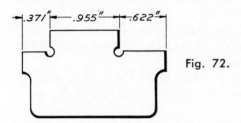

Fig. 72.

12. The draftsman overlooked giving the total length of the gear spindle in the drawing in Figure 73. What should it be?

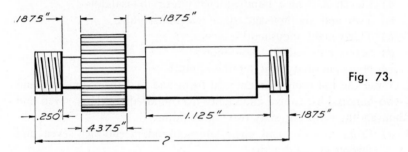

Fig. 73.

CHAPTER 6

Multiplication and Division of Decimals

6.1 Introduction

In this chapter you will learn how to multiply and divide decimal numbers, and how to solve practical shop problems involving these operations. If you learn how to add, subtract, multiply, and divide whole numbers, fractions, decimal fractions and decimal numbers correctly you will have a great advantage over other workers in the shop, drafting room, or engineering office. In spite of the increasing use of electronic computers, desk calculators, slide rules, tables, and other mathematical aids, it is still necessary for many technical workers to be able to perform these four fundamental operations, and be confident of their correctness.

This ability, along with the ability to estimate answers and use common sense is an ability which should pay you handsome dividends during your lifetime of work.

6.2 Multiplications of Decimals

When decimals are to be multiplied, we proceed in the same way as in the multiplication of whole numbers. When we have completed the multiplication, we must locate the decimal point in the product. We do this in two steps:

1. We add the number of decimal places in *both* the multiplier and multiplicand.

2. We locate the decimal point in the product so there are as many places to the *right* of it as the total number of places we counted in both multiplier and multiplicand.

The following example shows the application of this rule.

■ **EXAMPLE 1:**

Multiply 5.62 by 0.078.

Solution and Explanation:

We write the multiplicand and then the multiplier under it, and perform the multiplication as for whole numbers:

$$
\begin{array}{rl}
5.62 & \leftarrow \text{Multiplicand} \\
\times\,0.078 & \leftarrow \text{Multiplier} \\
\hline
4496 & \\
3934 & \hspace{-0.5em}\Big\} \leftarrow \text{Partial products} \\
\hline
0.43836 & \leftarrow \text{Product}
\end{array}
$$

The construction of modern buildings has been made possible not only by the development of structural steel, but also by the application of mathematics.

Bethlehem Steel Co.

In locating the decimal point in the product, we:

1. Add the number of decimal places in the multiplier (3) and multiplicand (2), getting 5.

2. We locate the decimal point in the product so that there are five decimal places to the right of it. (We do this by starting from the rightmost figure of the product and counting to the left five places.)

The product is consequently 0.43836.

It frequently happens that the total number of decimal places in both multiplicand and multiplier is greater than the number of figures in the product. In such cases, enough *zeros* are added *in front* of the product to make up the number of decimal places needed. The following example illustrates this procedure.

■ **EXAMPLE 2:**

Find the product of 3.14 and 0.0026.

Solution and Explanation:

Writing the multiplicand and multiplier, and carrying out the multiplication, we obtain:

$$
\begin{array}{rl}
3.14 & \leftarrow \text{Multiplicand} \\
\times\, 0.0026 & \leftarrow \text{Multiplier} \\
\hline
1884 & \\
628 & \\
\hline
0.008164 &
\end{array}
$$

Two zeros
written in front
of product ⟵

Digits in original product

A practical shop application of these processes occurs in calculations relating to circles. A circle is a closed plane curve every point of which is the same distance from a point inside it called the center.

Referring to Figure 74, we see that the circumference of a circle is

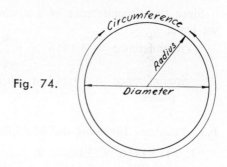

Fig. 74.

the *total* distance around it. The *radius* of a circle is the distance from any point of the circle to the center. A straight line passing through the center of a circle and joining any two of its points is called a diameter. A diameter of any circle is twice as long as its radius.

The circumference of a circle is equal to π (pronounced "pie") times its diameter, or to 2 times π times its radius. The numerical value of π can be taken as $\frac{22}{7}$, $3\frac{1}{7}$, or 3.14; but for very accurate work, 3.1416 is used for the value of π.

The use of these various terms is shown in the following problems.

■ **EXAMPLE 3:**

A circular steel disk has a radius of 1.37 in. What is its circumference?

Solution and Explanation:

Since the circumference of a circle equals 3.1416 times its diameter, the first step is to determine the diameter of the disk. The diameter of a circle equals twice its radius. Hence, the diameter is 2 × 1.37 or 2.74 in.

Since the circumference of a circle equals 3.1416 times its diameter, we have:

$$\text{circumference} = 3.1416 \times 2.74$$

or

$$\text{circumference} = 8.607984 \text{ in.}$$

If we round this off to three decimal places we can say that the circumference of this disk is 8.608 in.

■ EXAMPLE 4:

The outside diameter of a UHF-TV transmission line is 6.125 in. What is its circumference?

Solution and Explanation:

Since the circumference of a circle equals 3.1416 times its diameter, we have:

$$\text{circumference} = 3.1416 \times 6.125$$

or

$$\text{circumference} = 19.242 \text{ in.}$$ when rounded off to three decimal places.

6.3 Problems Involving the Multiplication of Decimals

1. *a*) 3.1416 × 3.02 = ?
   b) 0.7854 × 1.311 = ?
   c) 2.435 × 2.5 × 2.5 = ?
   d) 0.762 × 1.125 = ?
   e) 1.575 × 0.591 = ?
   f) 0.242 × 57.29 = ?

2. Mercury is 13.6 times heavier than water. If a cubic foot of water weighs 62.4 lb., how much does a cubic foot of mercury weigh?

3. In the square (Fig. 75) the distance *AC* (or *BD*) is called the diagonal. From geometry we know that this distance is equal to 1.414

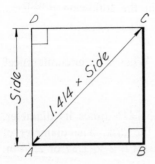

Fig. 75.

times the length of one side of the square. If the side of a square is 3.25 in., what is the diameter of the circle that will just touch the corners of this square? It is also known that the side $= \frac{\text{diagonal}}{1.414}$.

4. How large in diameter must the hole be drilled to just receive a square plug gauge which measures 0.75 in. on the edge as shown in Figure 76.

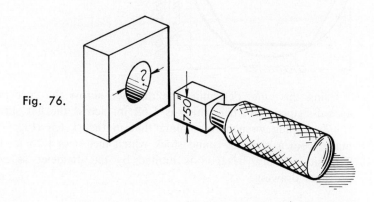

Fig. 76.

5. The largest square that can be drawn inside of a circle has a side whose length equals .707 times the diameter of that circle. This is shown in the illustration below. According to this rule, what is the largest square that can be machined on the end of a shaft which measures 2.500 in. in diameter? How this might look is illustrated in Figure 77. The size of the square is carried out to the third decimal place only.

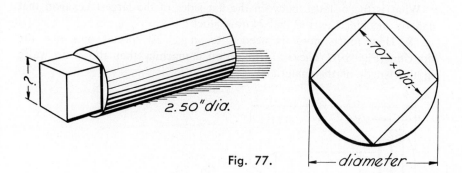

Fig. 77.

6. The distance across the corners of a hexagon equals 1.155 times the distance across the flat sides. This is also equal to the diameter of the circle which passes through the corners of the hexagon (Fig. 78).

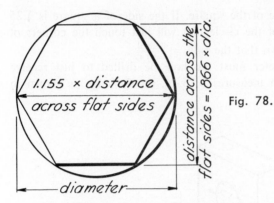

Fig. 78.

Using this rule, determine the distance across the corners of a hexagonal-shaped steel bar which is 1.62 in. across the flat sides.

7. A plug wrench resembling that in the sketch (Fig. 79) is to be made from a piece of round stock which measures 1.25 in. in diameter. The side of this hexagon is limited by the diameter as noted in the previous drawing.

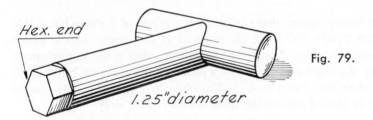

Fig. 79.

What is the distance between the flat sides of the largest hexagon that can be machined as the end of this stock?

8. How much stock is needed to make 20 special pins like the drawing (Fig. 80)? These are made on a machine that allows no waste in the length of the material.

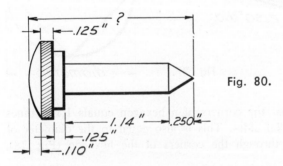

Fig. 80.

9. Using the following rule for round-headed rivet proportions, determine the values of dimensions A and B in rivets that have a diameter (D) of .375 and .500 in. D = diameter of rivet; A = diameter of rivet head; B = thickness of rivet head; $A = 1.75 \times D$; $B = 0.75 \times D$.

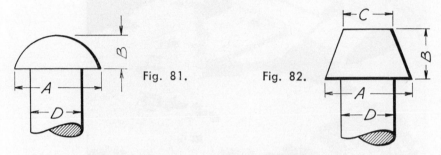

Fig. 81.   Fig. 82.

10. Determine the proportions of a .500-in. rivet, using the following rules for a rivet with a cone-shaped head. D = diameter of rivet; A = bottom diameter of head; B = thickness of head; $A = 1.75 \times D$; $B = 0.9375 \times D$; $C = 0.875 \times D$.

11. The drawing below shows an equilateral triangle (a triangle having three equal sides) inscribed in a circle of radius R. From geometry, we know that the length of each side is equal to $1.732 \times R$ (Fig. 83). How long is the side of an equilateral triangle inscribed in a circle of radius 3.75 in.?

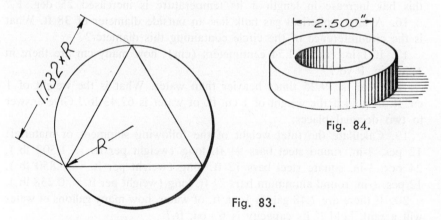

Fig. 84.

Fig. 83.

12. A tank built for use in a sewage treatment plant has a diameter of 125 ft. What is the circumference of this tank?

13. What are the dimensions of a square block of metal that will just fit into the hole in the steel ring shown in Figure 84? Make a drawing of a 2.500-in. circle and lay out such a square.

Copyright D. S. Kennedy & Co.

An 84 ft. elevation and azimuth reflector. Radio and radar technology have added much to man's understanding of his own world and those far out in space.

14. A water tank holds 15,000 gal. If 1 gal. of water weighs 8.33 lb., what is the weight of the water in this tank?

15. A bronze bar 1 ft. long will increase in length by 0.000116 in. for each degree (Fahrenheit) increase in its temperature. How much will this bar increase in length if its temperature is increased 25 deg. F.?

16. A large spherical gas tank has an outside diameter of 38 ft. What is the circumference of the circle containing this diameter?

17. If 1 in. equals 2.54 centimeters (cm), how many cm are there in 1 ft.? in 1 yd.?

18. Gold is 19.25 times heavier than water. What is the weight of 1 cu. ft. of gold if the weight of 1 cu. ft. of water is 62.43 lb.? Give answer to two decimal places.

19. Calculate the total weight of the following shipment of material: 12 pcs. $\frac{3}{4}$-in. round steel bars $9\frac{1}{2}$ ft. long (weight per ft. = 1.502 lb.), 24 pcs. $\frac{1}{2}$-in. square steel bars 12 ft. long (weight per ft. = 0.850 lb.), 12 pcs. $\frac{1}{2}$-in. round aluminum bars $2\frac{1}{2}$ ft. long (weight per ft. = 0.238 lb.).

20. If there are 7.48 gal. in 1 cu. ft. of water, how many gallons of water will a tank hold if its capacity is 67 cu. ft.?

21. A high-frequency transmitting antenna has four stainless-steel ground rods each 3 ft. long. If each rod is $\frac{1}{2}$ in. in diameter and weighs 0.668 lb. per foot, what is the weight of the four rods?

22. A certain thickness of brass stock 12 in. wide weighs 0.352 lb. per foot of length. How much would a 55-ft. roll of this stock weigh?

23. After slitting three pieces each 1.875 in. wide from a metal strip 6 in. wide, what is the width of the piece remaining?

6.4 Division of Decimals

Division of decimal numbers is performed in a manner similar to the division of whole numbers. It is considered best, for purposes of clearness, to illustrate by means of examples the most common cases that arise in this type of division.

■ **EXAMPLE 1:**

The divisor is a whole number.
Divide 7.854 by 60.

Solution and Explanation:

Step 1:
We arrange the work in the same way as for division of whole numbers, and place the decimal point in the quotient, *directly* above the decimal point in the dividend:

$$60 \overline{\smash{)}\, 7.854}$$

Step 2:
Now 60 does not go into 7, but goes into 78 once. We put the one above the 8, the second digit of the dividend. We multiply 60 by 1, write the 60 under the 78 in the dividend and subtract. Our work appears thus:

$$
\begin{array}{r}
.1 \\
60 \overline{\smash{)}\, 7.854} \\
\underline{6\,0} \\
1\,8
\end{array}
$$

Step 3:
Since 18 is less than 60, we bring down the 5 from the dividend. Our *new dividend* is 185. Now 60 goes into 185 3 times, thus 3 is the second digit of the quotient. We write this after the 1 in the quotient and *directly above* the 5 of the original dividend. We multiply 60 by 3, write the product 180 under 185 and subtract. Our work appears thus:

$$
\begin{array}{r}
.13 \\
60 \overline{\smash{)}\, 7.854} \\
\underline{6\,0} \\
1\,85 \\
\underline{1\,80} \\
5
\end{array}
$$

Step 4:

We now bring down the 4 from the original dividend, getting a new dividend, 54. But since 60 will *not* go into 54, we put a zero to the right of the 4 in the original dividend and carry it down to the new dividend, making it 540. We also put a zero to the right of the 3 in the quotient. We see that 60 will go into 540 nine times. We put the 9 after the zero in the quotient. Multiplying 60 by 9, we get 540. We write this 540 under the 540 of the last new dividend and subtract. The division is finished. The quotient is .1309, and the work appears thus in complete form:

$$
\begin{array}{r}
.1309 \\
60\overline{\smash{\big)}\,7.8540} \\
\underline{6\,0} \\
1\,85 \\
\underline{1\,80} \\
540 \\
\underline{540}
\end{array}
$$

To check our work, we multiply the quotient by the divisor. We have:

$$
\begin{array}{r}
.1309 \\
\underline{60} \\
7.8540
\end{array}
$$

We conclude that our division was correct.

■ **EXAMPLE 2:**

The divisor is a decimal number.
Divide 58.732 by 3.14.

Solution and Explanation:

Step 1:

We arrange the work in the same way as for the division of whole numbers:

$$
3.14\,\overline{\smash{\big)}\,58.732}
$$

Step 2:

We now move the decimal point in the *divisor two* places to the *right,* changing it from 3.14 to 314. We show this by means of a mark ʌ called a *caret.* We also move the decimal point *two* places to the *right* in the *dividend,* making it 5873.2 instead of 58.732. We also show this by means of a caret. We can do this because, in problems in division, if the dividend and divisor are multiplied by the same number except zero (here the number was 100) the value of the *quotient* will remain unchanged. The decimal point in the quotient is now placed directly above the caret in the dividend. We are now ready to determine the quotient. Our work appears thus:

Step 3:

$$\begin{array}{r} 1. \\ 314_\wedge\overline{)5873_\wedge2} \\ 314 \\ \hline 2733 \end{array}$$

Dividing, we find that 314 goes into 587 once. We put the 1 over the 7 in the dividend. Multiplying 314 by 1, we get 314, which is placed under 587. Subtracting, we get 273. Since 273 is less than 314, we bring down the next number in the dividend, which is 3. Our *new partial dividend* is 2733.

Step 4:

The number 314 now goes into the new dividend 8 times. This is the *second* digit of the quotient. We put this 8 above the 3 in the dividend and next to the 1 in the quotient. Multiplying 314 by 8, we get 2512, which we put under 2733 and subtract, getting 221. The work appears thus up to this point:

$$\begin{array}{r} 18. \\ 314_\wedge\overline{)5873_\wedge2} \\ 314 \\ \hline 2733 \\ 2512 \\ \hline 221 \end{array}$$

Step 5:

We now bring down the 2 in the dividend making the *new partial dividend* 2212. Three hundred and fourteen goes into 2212 seven times. We place the 7 to the right of the decimal point and *directly* above the 2 in the original dividend. Multiplying 314 by 7 we get 2198. Putting this under 2212 and subtracting, we get 14. The work appears thus to this point:

$$\begin{array}{r} 18.7 \\ 314_\wedge\overline{)5873_\wedge2} \\ 314 \\ \hline 2733 \\ 2512 \\ \hline 2212 \\ 2198 \\ \hline 14 \end{array}$$

If we wish to carry the division further, we annex zeros to the *right* of the 2 in the original dividend. Thus, annexing one more zero, and bringing it down to the new partial dividend, we get 140 for the new partial dividend. But 314 will not go into 140. Hence we annex a *second* zero in the original dividend, and bring it down to the new partial dividend, making it 1400 and putting a *zero* after the 7 in the quotient. The work appears thus:

$$
\begin{array}{r}
18.704 \\
314_\wedge \overline{\smash{)}5873_\wedge 200} \\
314 \\
\hline
2733 \\
2512 \\
\hline
2212 \\
2198 \\
\hline
1400
\end{array}
$$

and we are ready to begin another "cycle" of division, that is, we are ready to find the next digit of the quotient.

Step 6:

We find that 314 goes into 1400 four times. We write the 4 in the quotient after the 0. Multiplying 314 by 4, we get 1256. We write this under 1400 and subtract. The remainder is 144. The quotient at this stage is 18.704, and the work appears thus:

$$
\begin{array}{r}
18.704 \\
314_\wedge \overline{\smash{)}5873_\wedge 200} \\
314 \\
\hline
2733 \\
2512 \\
\hline
2212 \\
2198 \\
\hline
1400 \\
1256 \\
\hline
144
\end{array}
$$

If we are asked to give the quotient to *two* decimal places, it is unnecessary to carry the work out any further. The quotient can be "rounded off" and given as 18.70. If we are asked to give the quotient to *three* decimal places we would have to carry the division to four decimal places and then round the answer to three decimal places. If we were asked to give the quotient to *one* decimal place we would give it as 18.7. We again would check our work by multiplying the quotient by the original divisor and adding the remainder to this product.

Check

18.704	← Quotient
3.14	← Original divisor

$$\overline{}$$

74816
18704
56112

$$\overline{}$$

58.73056	← Product of quotient and original divisor
144	← Remainder

$$\overline{}$$

58.73200	← Original dividend (with two zeros annexed)

■ **EXAMPLE 3:**

Divide 2.867 by 73.4.

Solution and Explanation:

Step 1:

As in the other examples, we arrange the work in the same way as for division of whole numbers:

$$73.4 \overline{\smash{\big)}\ 2.867}$$

Step 2:

The divisor is now made a whole number by moving its decimal point *one* place to the right and marking its *new position* with a caret. The decimal point in the dividend is also moved one place to the right, and its new position is marked with a caret also.

The work appears thus at this stage:

$$734_{\wedge} \overline{\smash{\big)}\ 28_{\wedge}67}$$

The decimal point in the quotient is placed directly above the decimal point in the dividend. We are now ready for the next step.

Step 3:

The number 734 divides 2867 in the dividend three times. We place a zero above the 6 in the dividend, to the right of the decimal point, and the 3 to the right of the zero (directly above the 7 in the dividend). The work now looks like this:

$$0.03$$
$$734_{\wedge} \overline{\smash{\big)}\ 28_{\wedge}67}$$

Multiplying 734 by 3, we put the product (2202) under 2867 of the dividend and subtract. The work appears thus:

$$0.03$$
$$734_{\wedge} \overline{\smash{\big)}\ 28_{\wedge}67}$$
$$\underline{22\ 02}$$
$$6\ 65$$

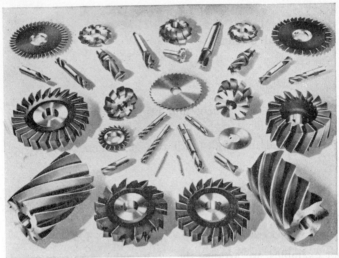

Brown & Sharpe Mfg. Co.

A variety of cutters available for shaping metal. Decimals
are the language of the machinist.

Step 4:

To carry out the division further, we place a zero after the 7 in the
dividend and carry it down to the new "partial dividend," making it 6650:

$$0.03$$
$$734_\wedge \overline{)\ 28_\wedge 670}$$
$$22\ 02$$
$$\overline{\ 6\ 650}$$

We see that 734 goes nine times into 6650. This 9 is the third digit of
the quotient and is placed to the *right* of the 3 in the quotient and
directly above the 0 of the dividend. The product 734 by 9, which is 6606,
is written under the 6650 as shown, and subtracted from it.

The work appears thus at this stage:

$$0.039$$
$$734_\wedge \overline{)\ 28_\wedge 670}$$
$$22\ 02$$
$$\overline{\ 6\ 650}$$
$$6\ 606$$
$$\overline{\ 44}$$

We are now ready for another cycle of division.

Step 5:

We now place another zero to the right of the one already in the dividend, and carry it down to the new partial dividend, making it 440. But 734 does not go into 440. Hence *one more* zero is placed in the dividend and a zero is placed in the quotient next to the 9.

The work appears thus to this point:

```
            0.0390
    734 ⌐ 28 67000
            22 02
            ─────
             6 650
             6 606
            ─────
              4400
```

Step 6:

We see now that 734 goes five times into 4400. (734 × 5 = 3670) We place this 5 (which is the fifth digit of the quotient) in the fifth place to the right of the decimal point in the quotient (making the quotient .03905), and write 3670 under 4400 and subtract. At this stage the work appears thus:

```
            0.03905
    734 ⌐ 28 67000
            22 02
            ─────
             6 650
             6 606
            ─────
              4400
              3670
             ─────
               730
```

We have thus carried out the division to five decimal places, and have a remainder of 730.

Checking our work at this stage gives:

```
        0.03905
          73.4
        ───────
         15620
         11715
        2 7335
        ───────
        2.866270
            730   Remainder
        ───────
        2.867000   Check
```

We can now say that the quotient is

  0.0391 to four decimal places, or
  0.039 to three decimal places, or
  0.04   to two decimal places.

6.5   Problems Involving Division of Decimals

1. Solve the following, carrying the results to four decimal places:
   a) Divide seven tenths by nine and four tenths.
   b) Divide two and eighty-five hundredths by thirty-five thousandths.
   c) 78.54 ÷ 3.25 = ?
   d) 0.0625 ÷ 4.22 = ?
   e) 5.5 ÷ 0.0034 = ?

2. A length of aluminum pipe weighs 160 lb. If each foot of this pipe weighs 14.00 lb., what is the length of the pipe?

3. A radio amateur uses the following rule to compute the length of an antenna. "The length of a half-wave antenna in feet is found by dividing 468 by the frequency in megacycles." What is the half-wave length of an antenna if the frequency is 21.25 megacycles?

4. The weight of a steel beam is 230 lb. Find the length of this beam if it weighs 18.4 lb. per foot of length.

5. One hundred feet of No. 4 copper wire weigh 12.64 lb. If 850 ft. of this wire are needed in an electrical power installation, what is the weight of this length of wire? Give the answer to two decimal places.

6. The pressure exerted by the air on each square foot of area at sea level is 2117 lb. What is the pressure of the air per square inch at sea level?

7. A high-efficiency air-dielectric coaxial cable weighs 0.16 lb. per foot. How many feet of this cable are there in a roll weighing 200 lb.?

8. A steel water tank has a circumference of 47 ft. Find its diameter to two decimal places.

9. If 1000 ft. of wire weigh 1.89 lb., how many feet of this wire weigh 1 lb.?

10. If the distance that the U. S. satellite Courier I travels in one revolution in its orbit is 28,900 miles, and the time is 1.73 hr., what is its orbital speed in miles per hour?

11. Brass rod 1 in. in diameter weighs 2.89 lb. per foot. How many feet of this rod are there in a shipment weighing 130 lb.? Carry the answer to one decimal place.

12. Steel measuring ¼ in. thick by 2 in. wide weighs 1.70 lb. per foot. A rack made from this kind of stock weighs 80 lb. How many feet of this material were used in making this rack? (Give answer to nearest foot.)

13. No. 12 copper wire weighs 19.77 lb. per 1000 ft. How many feet are there in a 50-lb. roll of this wire? *Hint:* Divide the weight of the roll by 19.77 to three decimals. Multiply this quotient by 1000.

14. A steel floor plate has an area of 36 sq. ft. and weighs 313.2 lb. What is its weight per square foot?

Machining on a lathe is
done to .001 of an inch.

Clausing

15. A steel ball 3 in. in diameter has a volume of 14.14 cu. in. and weighs 4.00 lb. What is its weight per cubic inch? Give answer to three decimal places.

16. A 50-ft. length of seamless steel tubing has an outside diameter of 2 in., a wall thickness of $\frac{3}{8}$ in., and weighs 325.4 lb. What is its weight per foot of length?

6.6 Changing Fractions to Decimals

In performing certain calculations it frequently becomes necessary to change common (proper) fractions to their equivalent decimal form. Now fractions of this kind can be considered as the quotient of two whole numbers. If we divide the numerator of a fraction by its denominator, we can change or *reduce* it to its decimal form.

In performing the division, we set the problem up as for long division of whole numbers. We next place a decimal point after the dividend (which is the numerator of the fraction) and place another decimal point directly above it in the place where the quotient is to be written. We are now ready to begin the actual division. Zeros may be added to the right of the decimal point as needed to complete the division. The procedure is illustrated by the following examples.

■ EXAMPLE 1:

Change $\frac{5}{16}$ to its equivalent decimal form.

Solution and Explanation:

Setting up the division as for whole numbers and locating the decimal points, we have:

Step 1:

$$16 \overline{\smash)\stackrel{\textstyle .}{5.}}$$

In completing the division, we annex four zeros to the right of the decimal point in the dividend. The division stops with the fourth decimal place. Our completed work appears as in:

Step 2:

$$
\begin{array}{r}
0.3125 \\
16 \overline{\smash)5.0000} \\
4\,8 \\
\hline
20 \\
16 \\
\hline
40 \\
32 \\
\hline
80 \\
80 \\
\hline
\end{array}
$$

Thus, $\frac{5}{16}$ changed to a decimal becomes 0.3125.

■ **EXAMPLE 2:**

Change $\frac{8}{11}$ to its decimal equivalent.

Solution and Explanation:

Arranging the division as in the case of whole numbers and locating the decimal points as in the previous example, we have:

Step 1:

$$11 \overline{\smash)\stackrel{\textstyle .}{8.}}$$

We then proceed with the division, and find that the digits of the quotient begin repeating in groups of two digits:

Step 2:

$$
\begin{array}{r}
0.7272 \\
11 \overline{\smash)8.0000} \\
7\,7 \\
\hline
30 \\
22 \\
\hline
80 \\
77 \\
\hline
30 \\
22 \\
\hline
\end{array}
$$

If the denominator of a fraction can be factored (separated) into the product of any number of two's or five's, or both, its decimal equivalent will be found to terminate or end.

Fractions whose denominators do not fulfill these requirements will not terminate or end when converted to decimal form. Consequently, the division must be stopped when the number of decimal places in the quotient reaches the degree of precision that we need.

It is interesting to note that the commonly used divisions of an inch, such as the $\frac{1}{2}$ in., $\frac{1}{4}$ in., $\frac{1}{8}$ in., etc., all terminate when converted to decimal form.

Thus we have:

$$\frac{1}{2} = 0.500000 \text{ (terminated at 1st decimal place)}$$
$$\frac{1}{4} = 0.250000 \text{ (terminated at 2nd decimal place)}$$
$$\frac{1}{8} = 0.125000 \text{ (terminated at 3rd decimal place)}$$
$$\frac{1}{16} = 0.062500 \text{ (terminated at 4th decimal place)}$$
$$\frac{1}{32} = 0.031250 \text{ (terminated at 5th decimal place)}$$
$$\frac{1}{64} = 0.015625 \text{ (terminated at 6th decimal place)}$$

The first five of these have had zeros annexed to fill six decimal places so that all of the decimal forms will have the same number of places. Since *all* of these commonly used fractions of an inch terminate when expressed in decimal form, any multiple of them will also terminate. Thus, $\frac{7}{8} = 7 \times \frac{1}{8} = 7 \times 0.125000 = 0.875000$ to six places.

6.7 Changing Decimal Fractions to Common Fractions

Decimals (decimal fractions) which terminate can always be changed to common fractions. By a common fraction we mean a fraction whose numerator and denominator are both whole numbers. Every such decimal fraction can be written as a fraction with a denominator which is 10 or some power of 10, like 100, 1000, or 10,000. Hence, the first step in changing decimal fractions of this type to common fractions is to write them as common fractions with the denominator 10, 100, 1000, and so on, as the case may be. The next step is to divide the numerator and denominator by the factors common to both until the resulting fraction is in its lowest terms.

The following example will illustrate the procedure.

■ **EXAMPLE 1:**

Find the common fraction equivalent to 0.375.

Solution and Explanation:

We first write 0.375 in its common fraction form:

$$0.375 = \frac{375}{1000}$$

Dividing numerator and denominator by the factors common to both, we have:

$$0.375 = \frac{\overset{\overset{3}{\cancel{15}}}{\cancel{75}}\cancel{375}}{\underset{\underset{8}{\cancel{10}}}{\underset{200}{\cancel{1000}}}} = \frac{3}{8}$$

Thus 0.375 is equivalent to the common fraction $\frac{3}{8}$.

The conversion of the decimal fraction 0.375 to its common fraction equivalent was possible because of the fact that, when it was written as $\frac{375}{1000}$, it was possible to divide 375 and 1000 by the factors common to both.

The reduction (or the changing) of a decimal fraction to a common fraction in lowest terms is possible only *if* there are common factors in both the numerator and the denominator. If there are no such factors, the decimal fraction can still be written as a common fraction, but it cannot be reduced.

■ **EXAMPLE 2:**

Change 0.063 to its equivalent common fraction form.

Solution and Explanation:

We write $0.063 = \frac{63}{1000}$.

We now find it impossible to divide 63 and 1000 by any common factor. In fact, $63 = 3 \times 3 \times 7$. $1000 = 2 \times 2 \times 2 \times 5 \times 5 \times 5$. There is no factor common to 63 and 1000. Hence the common fraction cannot be reduced, and all we can do is to write $0.063 = \frac{63}{1000}$.

An easy way to tell if the decimal fraction can be reduced to lower terms is to see if its numerator contains the factors 2 or 5 or both. If it does, the decimal fraction can be reduced; if it does not, the decimal fraction cannot be reduced.

If decimal numbers have values larger than 1, as, for example, 3.75 and 1.125, they are called mixed decimal numbers or mixed decimals. Decimal numbers such as 0.975 and 0.0625 whose value is less than one are called pure decimals.

A mixed decimal can be changed to a mixed number. In doing this, the decimal part (the part to the right of the decimal point) is first changed to a common fraction in lowest terms. This fraction is then combined with the whole number part of the mixed decimal to give the desired mixed number.

The costs involved in America's space exploration demand the greatest care in planning and execution of these programs.

National Aeronautics and Space Administration

■ **EXAMPLE 3:**

Reduce 3.875 to a mixed number.

Solution and Explanation:

First we change 0.875 to a common fraction in lowest terms. We have:

$$0.875 = \frac{875}{1000} = \frac{7}{8}$$

Combining this with 3, the whole number part of the mixed decimal, we get the mixed number $3\frac{7}{8}$. Thus:

$$3.875 = 3\frac{7}{8}$$

6.8 Problems Involving Changing Decimal and Fractional Forms

1. Change to their equivalent fractional form: 0.125; 0.3125; 0.9375; 0.79; 5.1875; 9.5625; 0.930.

2. Change 0.375 to a common fraction in its lowest terms. Then change this fraction to an equivalent fraction whose denominator is 72.

3. How many 32nds of an inch are there in 0.4375 in.? How many 16ths of an inch are there in 4.4375? How many 64ths of an inch are there in 0.625 in.?

4. Change the following to fractional form or to mixed number form: 0.1875; 8.450; 12.250; 4.5025; 11.0625; 7.49.

5. Change 0.125 to 72nds; 0.875 to 64ths; 0.750 to 60ths; 0.44 to 75ths; 0.9 to 30ths; 0.43750 to 80ths.

6. Redraw Figure 85 changing all dimensions, including the total length, to fractional form.

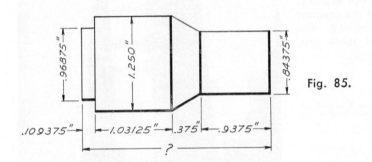

Fig. 85.

7. In the drawing (Fig. 86) change all decimal dimensions, including the total length, to equivalent fractional form.

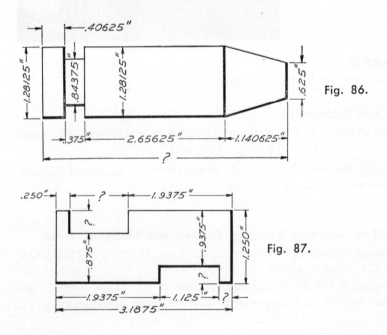

Fig. 86.

Fig. 87.

8. Redraw the template (Fig. 87) giving all dimensions, including those indicated by question marks, in lowest fractional form.

9. The thickness of a gear blank is marked as 0.625 in. Express this dimension as a common fraction.

10. Redraw the pattern drawing (Fig. 88) and change the dimensions to their decimal equivalents.

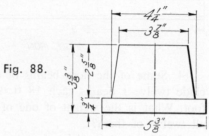

Fig. 88.

11. A steel bar $1\frac{1}{4}$ in. in diameter weighs 6.01 lb. per foot of length. What is the weight of a bar of such material $8\frac{3}{4}$ ft. long?

12. A machinist's apprentice was given a piece of stock $\frac{7}{8}$ in. in diameter to turn down to $\frac{3}{4}$ in. in diameter. His first cut across the piece reduced the diameter by 0.08 in. Is the piece now of the desired diameter? Why or why not?

13. A shaft was turned down to a diameter of $2\frac{13}{16}$ in. It was then ground to 2.017 in. By what amount was the diameter reduced?

14. Add $1\frac{5}{8}$, $8\frac{3}{4}$, 2.849, 4.6275, 9.0625, $12\frac{7}{16}$.

15. A wide-flange steel beam weighs 15.5 lb. per foot of length. What is the weight of such a beam if its length is 12 ft. 9 in.?

16. Change the following decimal dimensions to the nearest 32nd of an inch: 0.344; 0.837; 0.595; 0.279; 0.964.

6.9 Review Problems in Multiplication and Division of Decimals

1. Perform the following multiplications or divisions as indicated:
    a) 0.625 × 1.25 × 0.25
    b) 3.14 × 3.75 × 3.75
    c) 3.675 × 37.75
    d) 0.7854 × 0.75 × 0.375
    e) Divide 13.50 by 0.884
    f) Divide 122.4 by 10.2
    g) Divide 71.76 by 2.99
    h) Divide 17.6 by 0.095
    i) Find the quotient if 16 is divided by 7.05.

2. The radio telescope at Jodrell Bank, England, has a diameter of 250 ft. What is its circumference?

3. An angle iron whose dimensions are 3 × 3 × ¼ has a weight of 4.9 lb. per foot of length (Fig. 89). What is the weight of 20 such angle irons, each 20 ft. 9 in. long?

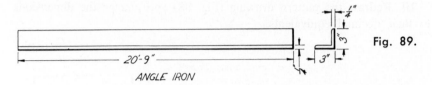

Fig. 89.

ANGLE IRON

4. Some of the floor beams of a typical floor of a steel structure include twelve I beams each 18 ft. 9 in. long and weighing 42.9 lb. per foot. What is the weight of one of these beams? What is the weight of all twelve of them?

5. What is the weight of twelve reinforcing bars each 15 ft. 4 in. long and weighing 0.668 lb. per foot of length?

6. It is estimated that about 1.11 cu. yd. of plaster will cover 100 sq. yd. of surface area to a thickness of ⅜ in. How many cubic yards will be needed to cover an area of 240 sq. yd. to this thickness?

7. An order of sheet-steel strips weighs 150 lb. If this material weighs 1.28 lb. per foot, how many feet of this material are there in this order?

8. On April 23, 1961, hailstones 6 in. in diameter fell during a tornado. The volume of such stones was about 113.1 cu. in. If a cubic inch of ice weighs 0.033 lb., what was the weight of one of these hailstones?

CHAPTER 7

Money

7.1 Introduction — U. S. Money System

Calculations involving the use of money enter into the daily lives of practically every one of us as we go about our affairs, whether we are students, workmen, householders, or businessmen.

Because of this it is very important that one have at least a working knowledge of those elementary calculations commonly used in buying, selling, business transactions, and employment.

The unit of the money system in the United States is the dollar. This is subdivided into the following smaller units, each amount being represented by its own coin:

The 1-cent piece, or penny, which equals $\frac{1}{100}$ of a dollar.

The 5-cent piece, or nickel, which equals $\frac{5}{100}$ of a dollar.

The 10-cent piece, or dime, which equals $\frac{10}{100}$ of a dollar.

The 25-cent piece, or quarter, which equals $\frac{25}{100}$ of a dollar.

The 50-cent piece, or half dollar, which equals $\frac{50}{100}$ of a dollar.

There are also larger multiples of the dollar, as two dollars, five dollars, ten dollars, twenty dollars, and so on. These larger divisions make for convenience in handling large sums. They are usually issued in the note or bill form.

The symbol used in writing amounts of money is the $, known as the dollar sign. It is placed just in front of the figure, or figures, representing the number of dollars, as $25, which is read "twenty-five dollars."

The writing of amounts of money resembles the writing of decimals. The decimal point is used to separate dollars from cents, and is placed directly after the number representing dollars, as in $5.15.

If the amount is less than one dollar, the decimal point is placed in front of the "cents" only when the dollar sign is expressed, as in the amount forty-eight cents, expressed $0.48; or the amount six cents, expressed $0.06. The use of the zero before the decimal point is to indicate that there are "no dollars" expressed.

As seen, the first figure to the right of the decimal point represents tenths of a dollar, or dimes. The second figure to the right of the point represents hundredths of a dollar, or cents.

The correct manner of expressing amounts of money is illustrated below:

Two hundred four dollars and seven cents is written: $204.07.

Twenty-one dollars and twelve cents is written: $21.12.

Four dollars and thirty-two cents is written: $4.32.

Five dollars is written: $5.00, or $5.

Fifty-six cents is written: $0.56, or 56¢.

Nine cents is written: $0.09, or 9¢.

Twelve and one-half cents is written: 0.12\frac{1}{2}$, or 12$\frac{1}{2}$¢.

The sign ¢ indicates cents, and is quite often used in amounts less than one dollar where it is desired not to express the dollar sign. However, when the sign ¢ is used, neither the dollar sign, $, nor the decimal point should be used.

It is not correct to express seventy-two cents as $0.72¢ because the cent sign (¢) when used, takes the place of the dollar sign, the decimal point, and the zero before the decimal point.

Correctly expressed the above amount should be written either $0.72 or 72¢.

For the same reason amounts like six and one-half cents would not be expressed as 0.06\frac{1}{2}$¢, but rather 0.06\frac{1}{2}$ or 6$\frac{1}{2}$¢, the latter being preferred.

7.2 Problems Involving Expression of Money

1. Write in words the following amounts:

$5.32; $0.19; $359.45; $0.08; 23¢; 59¢; 2.12\frac{1}{2}$

2. Examine the following amounts and write correctly those that are not properly expressed:

$0.85; $0.23¢; $10.25; $0.65¢; 3¢; 0.05\frac{1}{2}$¢

3. An electrician's apprentice is sent by his employer to buy an adjustable wrench and a light-duty utility drill. He asks the boy to write down the cost of each item on a sheet of paper and place it on his desk when he returns with the items. The adjustable wrench costs three dollars and twenty-three cents and the drill costs nine dollars and eighty cents. Write out a statement similar to what the apprentice should give his employer, using figures to express the cost of each item he purchased.

4. A young man, accepting a job as a helper in a garage, was told that his daily pay would be ten dollars and twenty cents. Express this amount in figures.

5. Express in figures:

a) Five hundred dollars and seventy-two cents;

b) Eight dollars and twelve cents;

c) Forty-two and one-half cents;

d) Thirty-seven and one-half cents;

e) Eight cents;

f) Nineteen dollars and sixty cents.

6. A boy, who works in a store after school hours, is paid ten dollars and forty-five cents for working three afternoons. Express this amount in figures.

7. After working one week, an apprentice in one of the building trades received ninety-nine dollars and twenty cents, before deductions. Express this amount in figures.

8. A hardware catalogue lists the following items:

> one toolbox, ninety-five cents;
> one blowtorch, six dollars and twenty-five cents;
> one pipe vise, seven dollars and ninety-five cents;
> one door lock, nine dollars and seventy-five cents;
> one pair of butt hinges, forty-seven cents.

List these prices in figures.

9. A part-time draftsman received the following pay during the days he worked:

$$\$3.90, \ \$15.60, \ \$13.65, \ \text{and} \ \$11.70$$

Write each of these amounts in words.

7.3 Addition, Subtraction, Multiplication and Division Involving Money

Numbers representing amounts of money are added, subtracted, multiplied, and divided the same as decimal numbers.

In adding and subtracting, care must be taken to see that the decimal points and figures line up properly. The decimal points should be in a vertical line, thus placing dollars under dollars, and cents under cents, as shown in the examples below.

Example Illustrating Addition and Subtraction Involving Money:

To equip his tool chest a young man paid $10.60 for two planes, $11.85 for two saws, and $2.09 for a hammer. If he had two ten-dollar bills and one five-dollar bill, how much did he receive in change after his purchases? (Sales tax not included.)

Solution and Explanation:

Cost of planes	$10.60
Cost of saws	11.85
Cost of hammer	2.09
	$24.54 = total cost

The amount of change he received would be equal to the difference between $25 and the total cost, $24.54. This works out as follows:

$25.00 = amount given in payment
24.54 = cost of tools
$ 0.46 = change to be received after
paying for the above tools.

Example Illustrating Multiplication Involving Money:

A plumber bought six bars of plumber's solder at 83¢ a bar. How much change did he receive if he paid for this with a five-dollar bill?

Solution and Explanation:

Since one bar of solder costs 83¢, then six bars cost 6 times this amount. Hence:

$$\begin{array}{r} \$0.83 \\ \times\ 6 \\ \hline \$4.98 \end{array} = \text{cost of the solder}$$

The amount of change he receives is equal to the difference between this amount and the five dollars:

$$\begin{array}{r} \$5.00 \\ 4.98 \\ \hline \$0.02 \end{array}$$

Hence he receives two cents in change.

Example Illustrating Division Involving Money:

A radio amateur wishes to buy a length of "twin-line" antenna transmission line, selling at 6¢ per foot. If he has $4.50 to spend, how many feet of line can he buy?

Solution and Explanation:

Since each foot of line costs 6¢, he can buy as many feet as 6¢ is contained in $4.50:

$$\begin{array}{r} 75. \\ 0.06_{\wedge}\ \overline{\smash{\big)}\ 4.50_{\wedge}} \\ \underline{4\,2} \\ 30 \\ \underline{30} \end{array}$$

He can buy 75 ft. of transmission line. This could also have been worked out by changing the 4.50 to 450¢ and dividing 450¢ by 6¢:

$$\begin{array}{r} 75 \\ 6\ \overline{\smash{\big)}\ 450} \\ \underline{42} \\ 30 \\ \underline{30} \end{array}$$

7.4 General Problems Involving Money

1. A worker in a machine shop is paid at the rate of $2.56 an hour. In one week he worked 40 hr. regular time and 6 hr. overtime. If he got time and a half for overtime, what did he earn that week?

2. Copper ground wire, number 4, sells for $9\frac{1}{2}$ cents per foot of length. What is the cost of 90 ft. of this wire?

3. A boy working in a store receives $44.00 per week for eight weeks of his summer vacation. He spends the following amounts before returning to school:

1 pair of shoes	$13.95
1 sport coat and slacks combination	$39.75
1 pair basketball shoes	$ 6.89
School supplies	$24.75

Find:

a) The total amount he earned.

b) The total amount he spent.

c) If he put the rest in the bank, how much did he deposit?

4. In a major steel construction job 24,650,000 lb. of structural steel were used. The average cost per pound was estimated at 26 cents. What was the total cost of this amount of steel?

5. In 1955 an instrument man on a surveying party was paid $2.75 per hour. In 1956 he received $3.00 per hour. If he worked 40 hr. per week how much were his weekly earnings in 1955? in 1956? How much more did he earn per week in 1956?

6. A special job of printing requires $5\frac{1}{2}$ reams of paper. This paper is sold at $2.50 per ream, but an extra charge of 25 cents is made for breaking up a ream in order to get the extra $\frac{1}{2}$ ream required. What is the total cost of this material?

7. On a certain repair job nine bars of plumber's solder were used. If each bar sold for 83 cents, what was the cost of the solder?

8. A man buys five 5-gal. cans of aluminum paint which costs $3.65 for each 5-gal. can. What did he pay for the entire amount of paint?

9. A radio amateur bought the following parts:

2 capacitors at 41 cents each

2 capacitors at 21 cents each

4 resistors at 10 cents each

1 potentiometer at $1.76

How much change will he receive from a $5.00 bill?

10. A workman in a small plant worked 38 hr. at $1.94 per hour. His pay envelope contained $75.66. Assuming no deductions, did he receive the correct amount?

11. An electronics experimenter bought the following components:

2 transistors at 90¢ each
1 potentiometer at 91¢
6 resistors at 24¢ each
1 capacitor at 74¢
1 battery at $1.50

What was the total cost of the components? (Sales tax neglected.) What change would he receive if he gave the salesman a ten-dollar bill?

12. To paper three rooms in a house requires 26 rolls of wallpaper. Eight of these rolls costs $2.65 each, 10 cost $2.35 each, and the balance cost $1.95 each. What is the total cost of the paper used on this job?

13. On an automobile trip, 8 gal. of gasoline were used up to the time of making the first stop. At this stop 12 gal. more were bought. The 8 gal. cost 31¢ per gallon, and the 12 gal. cost 29.5 cents per gallon. What was the total cost of the gasoline purchased?

14. A carpenter takes 5 hr. to build a cabinet for use in a kitchen. He charged for his work at the rate of $3.80 per hour. The materials used in building the cabinet cost $18.50. What is the total cost of the cabinet as completed?

15. A carpenter bought a try square for $1.50, a folding rule for $1.60, and a set of wood chisels at 85¢ each. If, in addition to the cost of these items, he paid a sales tax of 13¢, how much change did he receive from a $10 bill?

16. On a certain construction job 14 laborers were used in connection with the handling and pouring of concrete. If each worked 40 hr. at $2.35 per hour, what did each man earn in one week? What were the total earnings of the 14 men?

17. An elevator construction helper is paid at the rate of $2.87 per hour. During one week he works 40 hr. at straight time and also puts in 6 hr. of overtime, for which he receives time and one half. What did he earn for this particular week?

18. A journeyman carpenter is paid at the rate of $4.10 per hour. What does he earn if he works 40 hr. a week?

19. A workman earns $96.80 for a 40-hr. week. What is his hourly rate of pay?

20. On an automobile trip from Chicago to Milwaukee, the driver bought 12 gal. of gasoline at 29.5¢ per gallon and paid $2.40 for a change of oil. What was the total cost of the gas and oil?

21. On a certain tunnel construction project 5800 lb. of steel castings were used. The cost of these castings was $2,030. What was the cost per pound?

7.5 Review Problems Involving Money Calculations

1. How would you express the following in figures:
   a) Sixty-four dollars and nine cents; forty and one-half cents; one hundred five dollars and seven cents; seven dollars and four and one-half cents; eight cents
   b) How would you express in writing the following amounts: 62¢; $0.08; ½¢; $1.01; $210.73; $35.43

2. How much change should a boy get in presenting a $10 bill in payment for a pair of overalls at $3.69 and a work shirt for $1.34 if a sales tax of 10¢ must also be paid?

3. A boy's uncle gave him $5 and told him to divide it equally among his three younger brothers after taking out $1.70 for himself. How much did each of the younger brothers get?

4. An electrical worker, paid at the rate of $4.75 per hour, works 8 hr. per day. The job he is assigned to runs 24 working days. What did he earn on this job?

5. A certain kind of flathead nail sells for 24¢ per pound. How many pounds may be bought for $1.20?

6. A boy working after school hours keeps the following record for one week's work. What are his net earnings for the week?
   Monday — Runs four errands at 25 cents each
   Tuesday — Works in grocery store for 3 hr. at $1.10 per hour
   Wednesday — Helps neighbor in yard for $1.00
   Thursday — Works in grocery store for 3 hr. at $1.10 per hour
   Friday — Helps in delivering groceries: $1.50
   Saturday — Works 4 hr. in grocery store at $1.10 per hour

7. A boy buys the following airplane parts and equipment:

1 airplane kit	at $ 5.95
1 airplane engine	at $14.95
1 gas tank	at $ 0.95
1 fuel line	at $ 0.25
1 pint of fuel	at $ 0.85
2 propellers	at $ 0.25 each
2 wheels	at $ 1.40 a pair

The other material needed to assemble and fly the kit he has already bought. How much did he spend for the above parts and equipment?

8. A radio repairman buys a soldering iron for $2.94, five boxes of servicing hardware at 29¢ each, one set of high-voltage test leads at $3.28 and one dry-disk-type rectifier at $1.57. He pays, in addition to these costs, 18¢ sales tax. If he gives the salesman a ten-dollar bill, what change does he receive?

9. A factory worker turned in the following time ticket for one week:

Monday — 8 hr. at $2.74 per hour

Tuesday — 8 hr. at $2.74 per hour, and 1 hr. at time and one half per hour

Wednesday — 8 hr. at $2.74 per hour and 2 hr. at time and one half per hour

Thursday — Same as Tuesday

Friday — Same as Wednesday

Saturday — 4 hr. at time and one half per hour.

What did he earn for this week?

10. An ironworker receives $4.55 per hour. What does he earn in a week of 40 hr. regular time and 4 hr. of overtime at time and one half per hour?

CHAPTER 8

Percentage

8.1 Introduction

In this chapter you will learn how percentage is used. Problems relating to purchasing, discounts, profits, losses, and so on, will be discussed and their solutions will be explained. Understanding problems of this kind will be of help to you in your daily living. It may also be of help to you in your place of business because you will have some idea of how purchases are made and how money is saved by obtaining discounts when materials and supplies are bought. Often the saving of a very small amount on the cost of a much-used item or a small increase in production may mean the difference between making a profit in a business or losing one's investment in it.

8.2 Calculating Percentages

Calculations involving percentage are used in determining amounts of increases, decreases, gains, losses, discounts, averages, efficiencies, and the like. These increases, decreases, and so on, are expressed in parts per hundred. A part per hundred is called a *percent,* which comes from the Latin words *per centum,* meaning "by the hundred." The symbol for the word "percent" is %. Another way of thinking of a percent is that it stands for so many hundredths.

To illustrate:

Thirty-two percent is written as 32%.

Four and one-half percent is written as $4\frac{1}{2}\%$.

When used in calculations, the number representing the percent should be changed to decimal form. This is done by replacing the percent sign % by the word "hundredths."

Thus, 34% should be first changed to 34 hundredths. Expressed as a decimal, 34 hundredths is 0.34. In this manner 34% changed to decimal form becomes 0.34. In this final form it may be used in calculations.

Should there already be a decimal point in the given percent, the change to decimal form can be accomplished by moving the decimal point *two places* to *the left* of its position.

For example, in changing 57.4% to decimal form it may first be expressed at 57.4 hundredths (fifty-seven and four tenths hundredths). The decimal point being already located in front of the figure 4, is then moved two places to the *left,* as explained. This puts it in front of the figure 5. Consequently 57.4% changed to a decimal becomes .574.

In a similar manner when changed to decimal form 135% becomes 1.35, 5% becomes .05, 2% becomes .02, $\frac{1}{2}\%$ becomes .005, $3\frac{1}{2}\%$ becomes .035.

Another way of expressing this procedure is "to change a percent to decimal form, omit the percent sign (%), and divide the number by 100."

After a percent has been changed as described above, the decimal form can be used in computations in the same way as ordinary decimals. This is illustrated in the following examples:

■ EXAMPLE 1:

When the total cost of a factory building was analyzed, it was found that the cost of the foundation amounted to 6.7% of the total cost. If the total cost of the building was $860,000, what was the cost of the foundation?

Solution and Explanation:

Step 1:
We first convert 6.7% to decimal form. Omitting the percent sign and dividing 6.7 by 100 we get .067.
Step 2:
Multiplying $860,000 by .067 we get

$$
\begin{array}{r}
860000 \\
.067 \\
\hline
6020000 \\
5160000 \\
\hline
\$57620.000
\end{array}
$$

Therefore the cost of the foundation was $57,620.

■ EXAMPLE 2:

A carpenter wanting to buy a 6-ft. rule finds one listed at $1.69, with a discount of 15 percent. What is the net cost of the rule?

Solution and Explanation:

The discount of 15 percent means that the list price is to be reduced by 15 percent. To find the amount of this reduction, we take 15 percent of $1.69, which means that we multiply $1.69 by .15:

$$
\begin{array}{r}
\$1.69 \\
.15 \\
\hline
845 \\
169 \\
\hline
\$0.2535
\end{array}
$$
or 25¢ reduction in price

That is, the price of $1.69 is reduced by 25¢, making the net price $1.44.

■ **EXAMPLE 3:**

The purchasing agent of a large retail hardware store ordered $950.00 worth of tools and measuring instruments. The hardware store was allowed discounts of 30 percent, 25 percent, and 10 percent. What was the net price of this equipment?

Solution and Explanation:

Discounts of this type are called *trade discounts,* and when two or more such discounts are given they are called *series* or *chain discounts.* The net price is computed in steps, and the total discount is *not* 30 percent + 25 percent + 10 percent or 65 percent.

The computation of the net price is carried out in the following manner.

Step 1:

We multiply $950 by the first discount 30 percent, or 0.30.

$$\begin{array}{r} \$950 \\ .30 \\ \hline \$285.00 \end{array} \text{ amount of first discount}$$

Subtracting $285 from $950, we get:

$$\begin{array}{r} \$950 \\ 285 \\ \hline \$665 \end{array}$$

Step 2:

We now multiply $665 by the second discount, 25 percent, or 0.25.

$$\begin{array}{r} \$665 \\ .25 \\ \hline 3325 \\ 1330 \\ \hline \$166.25 \end{array} \text{ amount of second discount}$$

Subtracting $166.25 from $665, we obtain:

$$\begin{array}{r} \$665.00 \\ \$166.25 \\ \hline \$498.75 \end{array}$$

Step 3:

We now multiply $498.75 by the third discount, 10 percent or 0.10:

$$\begin{array}{r} \$498.75 \\ .10 \\ \hline \$49.8750 \end{array} \text{ amount of third discount}$$

Subtracting this amount from $498.75 we obtain:

$498.750
 49.875

$448.875 net price

The net price is consequently $448.88.

■ **EXAMPLE 4:**

A contractor estimates a construction job at $25,500 and adds 8 percent of this amount for his profit. How much does his profit amount to and what will be his bidding price?

Solution and Explanation:

Since the contractor's profit is 8 percent, we must find 8 percent of $25,500. This is:

$$\overset{255}{\cancel{25500}} \times \frac{8}{\cancel{100}} = \$2,040. \quad (\text{Or } \$25,500 \times .08 = \$2,040.00)$$

Therefore the amount of the contractor's profit is $2,040. He would consequently "bid" or ask $25,500 + $2,040 or $27,540 for the job.

8.3 Changing Percent to Fractional Form

In some calculations a percent may be expressed and handled as a fraction. This is done by changing the percent to a decimal number which in turn is changed to a decimal fraction.

The decimal fraction is then reduced to lowest terms, giving the simplest fraction which is the equivalent of the percent.

This is illustrated in the following examples:

■ **EXAMPLE 1:**

Express 45% as a fraction.

Solution and Explanation:

45% changed to a decimal equals .45.

The decimal .45 equals the fraction $\frac{45}{100}$.

$\frac{45}{100}$ reduced to lowest terms equals $\frac{9}{20}$. Consequently, 45% changed to fractional form equals $\frac{9}{20}$.

■ **EXAMPLE 2:**

Change $16\frac{2}{3}\%$ to fractional form.

Solution and Explanation:

$16\frac{2}{3}\%$ changed to a decimal equals $.16\frac{2}{3}$.

$$.16\frac{2}{3} = \frac{16\frac{2}{3}}{100} = \frac{\frac{50}{3}}{100}.$$

Now $\dfrac{\frac{50}{3}}{100} = \dfrac{\frac{50}{3}}{\frac{100}{1}} = \dfrac{50}{3} \times \dfrac{1}{100} = \dfrac{50}{300}.$

Then $\frac{50}{300}$ reduced to lowest terms equals $\frac{1}{6}$.

Therefore $16\frac{2}{3}\%$ changed to fractional form equals $\frac{1}{6}$.

■ **EXAMPLE 3:**

Express $12\frac{1}{2}\%$ as a fraction.

Solution and Explanation:

$12\frac{1}{2}\%$ changed to a decimal equals $.125$.

Then $.125 = \frac{125}{1000}.$

The fraction $\frac{125}{1000}$ reduced to lowest terms equals $\frac{1}{8}$.

Therefore, $12\frac{1}{2}\%$ changed to fractional form becomes $\frac{1}{8}$.

When such percents are changed to fractions they are more conveniently used in calculations. However, unless the fractional form can be handled to better advantage, it is more advisable to use the decimal equivalents.

Percents like $33\frac{1}{3}\%$; $66\frac{2}{3}\%$; $16\frac{2}{3}\%$; and $11\frac{1}{9}\%$ are of this type. When changed to fractional form they become:

$33\frac{1}{3}\%$ or $\frac{100}{300}$, which equals $\frac{1}{3}$

$66\frac{2}{3}\%$ or $\frac{200}{300}$, which equals $\frac{2}{3}$

$16\frac{2}{3}\%$ or $\frac{50}{300}$, which equals $\frac{1}{6}$

$11\frac{1}{9}\%$ or $\frac{100}{900}$, which equals $\frac{1}{9}$

In such fractional forms these percents are readily used in calculations.

8.4 Problems Involving Calculations in Percentage

1. Express in decimal form: $82\frac{1}{2}$ percent; 9 percent; .4 percent; 132 percent; $2\frac{1}{2}$ percent; 1.3 percent. Express in percent form .52; 4.2; 6; .001; 8.07; 37.5. What is 19 percent of $5.00; 3 percent of 11; $8\frac{1}{2}$ percent of 20; .6 percent of 43; 124 percent of 55; 1.2 percent of $150?

2. Reduce to fraction form: 140 percent; 2 percent; 62.5 percent; 22 percent; 20 percent; 225 percent; 110 percent; 85 percent; $\frac{1}{2}$ percent; $14\frac{2}{7}$ percent.

3. During a summer vacation a young man put his savings, which

amounted to $575, in the bank. Just before school opened he withdrew 25 percent of this to buy clothes. How much did he draw out of the bank? How much remains in the bank in his account?

4. If a dealer bought a stock of appliances listed at $675 at discounts of 30 percent and 10 percent what would the net cost to him be? If, in addition to these discounts, he received a 2 percent discount for paying cash in 10 days, what would he save by doing so?

5. An apprentice was receiving $2.17 per hour during a certain period of his training. He was then given a raise of 11.5 percent. What was his new hourly wage? How much would he earn in an 8-hr. day?

6. A carpenter contractor ordered $1,250 of lumber for porch repairs in an apartment building. He was given a 10 percent contractor's (trade) discount and an additional 2 percent for paying cash. How much did he save on the purchases?

7. Office equipment totaling $1,280 was bought with trade discounts of 25 percent, 20 percent, and 10 percent. What was the net price of this equipment?

8. A job lot of hardware items listed at $2,200. Discounts of 25 percent, 15 percent, and 5 percent were allowed. What was the net price for these items?

9. The machine shop of a manufacturing plant uses 20 percent of a 50-gal. drum of cutting compound each month. At this rate how long should 50 gal. of this compound last?

10. In a school with an enrollment of 2200, 3.5 percent of the pupils were reported absent on a certain day. How many were absent on that day?

11. A family with a net income of $8,000 spends 15 percent of this amount per year for rent. How much of the net income is this per year? per month?

12. A cubic foot of ice is 91.7 percent as heavy as a cubic foot of water. If water weighs 62.425 lb. per cubic foot, what is the weight of a cubic foot of ice?

13. A quantity of brass weighing 2500 lb. is composed of 61 percent copper, 36 percent zinc, and 3 percent lead. How many pounds of each of these metals were in this amount of brass?

14. During a special sale a young man bought a $55.00 bicycle at a 22 percent discount. How much money did he save? What was the cost of the bicycle to him?

15. To raise a heavy casting from the floor to a workbench, a set of hoisting pulleys was used. The pulleys, not having been previously used in some time, did not work well and required a pull of 45 lb. to raise the casting. After oiling the pulleys well, however, this pull was

reduced 20 percent. What was the final pull on the rope needed to raise the casting?

16. A time and motion study enabled a group of assemblers to increase their production by 8 percent. If they received an 8 percent increase in their day's wages, what will each earn if they were paid $2.63 per hour before?

17. A carpenter's apprentice was paid $2.00 per hour during a certain period of his training, and then was given a 15 percent hourly increase in his wages. How many cents an hour more does he earn now? What is his new hourly rate?

18. When John got his first job he immediately laid out a budget plan. He planned to give 60 percent to his mother; 30 percent was to be used for clothes and savings; 10 percent was to be put aside for emergency. If he received a check of $142 every two weeks, how much did he set aside for each item of his budget?

19. Fifty pounds of babbitt metal are required for rebabbitting machine bearings. If the babbitt metal consists of 4.5 percent tin, 10 percent antimony, 85 percent lead, and the rest copper, how much of each of these metals is used in this amount of babbitt metal?

20. An automobile which was originally purchased for $3,100 is offered for resale as a used car at 30 percent less than the original price. What is the resale price?

21. A certain camera lens priced originally at $65.00 was offered for sale at 40 percent less than that price. What would a person pay for it now?

22. In advising a class of prospective high school graduates about maintaining passing grades, the principal explained that out of the previous class of 350 students, 6 percent failed to graduate because of poor scholarship. How many graduated from last year's class?

23. The following notice appeared on a shop bulletin board: "Shop accidents for the six months' period ending June 30 dropped 15 percent below that of the previous six months' period."

If there were 80 accidents during the previous 6 months' period referred to, how many accidents were there during the six months' period ending June 30?

24. A manufacturer of radio communication equipment employs 350 workers. On being awarded a large order, he increases his force by 25 percent. How many workers will he now have?

25. A television serviceman buys 15 radio tubes to be used in making repairs. The list price of this lot of tubes was $42.45. If he is allowed discounts of 50 percent and 15 percent, what is the net price of these tubes to the repairman?

26. A radio amateur operating on the 10-meter band calculates the length of his transmitting antenna to be 16.35 ft. During the tune-up process, he finds it necessary to reduce this length by 5.5 percent. What will be the final length of his antenna?

27. A journeyman carpenter buys a high-speed drill set listing at $8.00. He is allowed discounts of 25 percent and 10 percent. What is the net price that he pays?

28. During a sale a car owner was able to buy an automobile tire normally selling for $42.90 at a discount of 35 percent by bringing in an old tire. What did he pay for the new tire?

29. During a sale, a television set regularly sold at $210 was offered at a reduction of $33\frac{1}{3}$ percent. What was the new sale price of this set?

30. In making a batch of concrete which weighed approximately 1200 lb., about $16\frac{2}{3}$ percent of the weight is cement, $33\frac{1}{3}$ percent is sand, and 50 percent is gravel. How many pounds of each material are used in making this batch of concrete?

8.5　Changing Fractions to Percent Form

Fractions may be readily changed to percent form by the same process as that used in changing a fraction to a decimal.

The first step in this process is to divide the numerator of the fraction by its denominator, thereby changing the fraction to its decimal equivalent. The second step is to move the decimal point two places to the right, and place the percent (%) sign after the resulting number. If the decimal equivalent of the given fraction contains only two digits, the decimal point is still moved two places to the right but is *not* shown. The various cases are illustrated in the following examples.

■ **EXAMPLE 1:**

Change the fraction $\frac{1}{4}$ to percent form.

Solution and Explanation:

The fraction $\frac{1}{4}$ is first changed to its decimal equivalent by dividing its numerator, 1, by its denominator, 4. Hence, $\frac{1}{4} = .25$. We now move the decimal point **two** places to the right, changing .25 to 25 and place a percent sign after 25. The final result is 25 percent. Thus we find that $\frac{1}{4}$, in percent form, is 25%. Notice that the decimal point, which came after the digit 5 in 25, is *not* shown.

■ **EXAMPLE 2:**

What is the percent equivalent of $\frac{5}{8}$?

The use of computers
greatly reduced the time
needed in calculating
and analyzing complex
problems.

Electronic Associates, Inc.

Solution and Explanation:

Proceeding as in Example 1, we convert $\frac{5}{8}$ to its decimal form by dividing its numerator, 5, by its denominator, 8.

$$
\begin{array}{r}
.625 \\
8\,\overline{)\,5.000} \\
4\,8 \\
\hline
20 \\
16 \\
\hline
40 \\
40 \\
\hline
\end{array}
$$

We find that $\frac{5}{8}$ is equivalent to .625. Moving the decimal point *two* places to the right and placing a percent sign after the number obtained, we have 62.5 percent. Therefore, the percent form of $\frac{5}{8}$ is 62.5%.

■ **EXAMPLE 3:**

Change $\frac{1}{6}$ to percent form.

Solution and Explanation:

Dividing 1 by 6, we obtain $.16\frac{4}{6}$ or $.16\frac{2}{3}$, the decimal form of the fraction $\frac{1}{6}$. Expressing $.16\frac{2}{3}$ as a percent, we obtain $16\frac{2}{3}$ percent. The fraction $\frac{1}{6}$, expressed in percent form, is $16\frac{2}{3}\%$.

$$
\begin{array}{r}
.16\tfrac{4}{6} \\
6\overline{\smash{\big)}\,1.00} \\
\underline{6} \\
40 \\
\underline{36} \\
4
\end{array}
$$

■ **EXAMPLE 4:**

Determine the percent form of the fraction $\frac{5}{4}$.

Solution and Explanation:

Proceeding as in the previous examples, we find that the decimal equivalent of $\frac{5}{4}$ is 1.25. Moving the decimal point two places to the right and writing a percent sign after the number obtained, we have 125%.

Thus, expressed as a decimal, $\frac{5}{4}$ equals 1.25. Expressed as a percent, 1.25 is 125%; consequently, the percent form of $\frac{5}{4}$ is 125%.

$$
\begin{array}{r}
1.25 \\
4\overline{\smash{\big)}\,5.00} \\
\underline{4} \\
1\,0 \\
\underline{8} \\
20 \\
20
\end{array}
$$

We see from these calculations that fractions less than 1, when changed to percent form, will be less than 100%. Fractions greater than 1, when changed to percent form, will be greater than 100%.

8.6 How to Determine Percent

Previous to this, consideration has been given principally to calculations involving the use of percentage, and to methods of changing fractional and percent forms. Sometimes it is necessary to know what percent one number is of another number, or how a percent may be determined when certain facts are given.

■ **EXAMPLE 1:**

What percent of 60 is 48?

Solution and Explanation:

In fraction form, 48 is $\frac{48}{60}$ of 60. However, $\frac{48}{60}$ is not in percent form. We can, however, reduce $\frac{48}{60}$ to $\frac{4}{5}$ Dividing 4 by 5, we obtain 0.8. Expressing this as a percent, we obtain 80%. Therefore, 48 is 80% of 60. As a check that this is correct, we compute 80% of 60. This is $\frac{80}{100} \times 60$ or $.80 \times 60$ or 48. This proves that 48 is 80% of 60.

$$
\begin{array}{r}
.8 \\
5\,\overline{\smash{)}\,4.0} \\
4\,0 \\
\hline
\end{array}
$$

8.7   Determining Efficiencies, Profits, and Ratings

The foregoing method is also used in determining efficiencies, profits, and ratings. Typical conditions involving these are illustrated in the following examples.

■ EXAMPLE 1:

It is estimated that on a certain job a journeyman printer can print 1000 folders on a printing press in 3 hr. To do the same work, however, will take an apprentice printer 4 hr. How efficient is the apprentice on this particular job?

Solution and Explanation:

The journeyman's time on the job is 3 hr.

The apprentice's time on the job is 4 hr.

The apprentice's rating would be found by dividing the journeyman's time, which is sometimes called the *estimated* time, by the *actual* time it took to do the job, 4 hr. This works out as

$$
3 \div 4 \text{ or } 4\,\overline{\smash{)}\,\begin{array}{r} .75 \\ 3.00 \\ 2\,8 \\ \hline 20 \\ 20 \\ \hline \end{array}}
$$

.75 expressed as a percent equals 75%.

That is, the apprentice is 75% efficient on this particular job when compared with the journeyman printer.

■ EXAMPLE 2:

A young man purchases a jackknife for 50¢. Later on he sells the same knife to a chum for 60¢. How much does he gain in the transaction?

What is his percent profit on this sale?

Solution and Explanation:

The profit in cash would be the difference between the selling price and the cost. This would be 60¢ — 50¢ or 10¢.

This 10¢ profit was gained on an investment of 50¢. Therefore, the fractional gain would be $\frac{10}{50}$ or $\frac{1}{5}$.

$\frac{1}{5}$ expressed as a decimal equals .20;

$$5 \overline{\smash{\big)}\,1.00} \quad .20$$
$$\underline{1\,0}$$
$$00$$

.20 expressed as a percent equals 20%.

That is, the boy made 20% profit on this sale.

■ EXAMPLE 3:

During the first day of his employment a young workman assembled 240 units, which he was told were to fit into mechanical toys that were being manufactured in that shop. However, the inspector on that work accepted but 228 of these units, and rejected the balance as not correctly assembled.

What percent of his work was acceptable this first day of employment?

Solution and Explanation:

An examination of the above figures show that out of 240 units 228 were acceptable. In other words, 228 of the 240, or $\frac{228}{240}$ were acceptable.

This fractional form $\frac{228}{240}$ is readily changed to percent form by dividing the numerator by the denominator as previously explained.

This works out as: 228 ÷ 240 or,

$$240 \overline{\smash{\big)}\,228.00} \quad .95$$
$$\underline{216\,0}$$
$$12\,00$$
$$\underline{12\,00}$$

.95 expressed in percent form becomes 95%.

That is, 95% of the young man's work was acceptable the first day of his employment.

The above problems illustrate that in order to determine an *efficiency*, a *profit*, or a *rating*, the process is really one of finding what percent one number is of another. This relation is expressed in fractional form and changed to a decimal, which in turn is changed to percent form as already explained.

8.8 Problems Involving Ratings, Profits, and Efficiencies

1. Change to percent form the following fractions and mixed numbers:
$$\tfrac{5}{32}; \ \tfrac{7}{9}; \ 1\tfrac{1}{8}; \ \tfrac{3}{16}; \ 2\tfrac{1}{4}; \ \tfrac{5}{8}; \ 4\tfrac{1}{6}; \ 10\tfrac{3}{5}$$
2. Determine what percent

   36 is of 48; 12 is of 50; 18 is of 15;

   $\tfrac{1}{2}$ is of 4; 5 is of 2; 132 is of 96

3. In its drive to reduce accidents, a shop safety committee recommended that certain guards be installed on several machines. The month following the installation of these guards there was a total of 12 accidents throughout the shop. The previous month's record showed there were 18 accidents. What was the percentage reduction?

4. Twenty-seven pounds of strip brass were needed to blank out an order of punchings on a foot press. The *scrap* remaining after this job was done weighed 3 lb. What percent of waste resulted from this operation?

5. By a slight change in the pattern a saving of $7\tfrac{1}{2}$ lb. is made in a casting that formerly weighed 60 lb. What percent of the former weight does this equal?

6. The calculated speed of a pulley on a printing press is 250 revolutions per minute. However, by actual check it is found that the pulley makes only 230 revolutions per minute. An investigation shows that this loss is due to belt slippage. What is the percent slippage in this particular case?

7. Because of a leaky faucet, $1\tfrac{1}{2}$ gal. of oil were lost from a can containing 25 gal. What is the percent loss?

8. In machining a brass casting weighing 36 lb. there is removed in the process $4\tfrac{1}{2}$ lb. of material. Determine the percent reduction in the weight of this casting as a result of this machining.

9. A shop that has been running on a 40-hr. week agrees to change to a 36-hr. week. The workmen are to receive the same weekly rate as formerly. What is the equivalent increase in the hourly rate of pay?

10. Out of 1080 pieces blanked on a foot press, the inspector rejects 27 pieces that were damaged in the operation. What percent spoilage does this equal?

11. Loose knots and checks in a 16-ft. board necessitate scrapping $1\tfrac{1}{2}$ ft. off one end and 2 ft. off the other end. What is the percent waste in this piece of lumber?

12. A learner on a spot-welding machine was able to weld 15 pieces per hour at the end of the first day of his employment. At the end of the second day he was able to weld 24 pieces per hour. At the end of the

next day this jumped to 33 pieces. Calculate the percent of hourly increase in production for each day over the first day.

13. As a result of a local safety campaign, the automobile accidents in an eastern city during a three-month period dropped from 32 to 20. What was the percent reduction in accidents during that period?

14. To lay out a drawing board and build it to specifications, it is estimated that it will take a cabinetmaker $2\frac{1}{2}$ hr. However, an apprentice does the job in $4\frac{1}{2}$ hr. What is the percent efficiency of the apprentice on this job?

15. A lathe hand engaged in turning a small pivot pin makes 75 pieces the first day on the job. The second day he increases the speed of his machine and makes 90 pieces. Determine his percent gain over the first day's output.

16. A young man employed in a woodworking shop finds that it takes him 3 hr. to turn up a wooden handle. After sharpening his wood turning tools he does the same job in $2\frac{1}{4}$ hr. Calculate the percent gain in time as a result of this precaution.

17. Because of improved business conditions a factory employing 120 men engages 15 extra men. What is the percent increase in employment?

18. To meet the demands for early delivery of orders for the Christmas trade, a toy factory employed 84 men. After the rush was over 36 of the workers were laid off. What percent of the working force remained?

19. An apprentice in the pressroom of a printshop spoils 60 sheets in a run of 1500 billheads. What percent spoilage does this equal?

20. In checking over a quantity of $\frac{1}{4}$-in. bolts the inspector found that out of a total of 160 bolts, 6 were undersize and 4 were oversize. What percent of the total number does each of these represent?

21. On his final examination in arithmetic a student has 42 problems correct out of 50. What is his percent rating?

22. During the first month of his employment a young man saved $8. The following month he saved $9.60. What does this increase equal when expressed in percent form?

23. The daily time card of a machine shop apprentice shows the following:

$2\frac{1}{2}$ hr. shaper work
$1\frac{1}{2}$ hr. milling-machine work
4 hr. benchwork

What percent of the day was given to each branch of work?

8.9 Review Problems Involving Percentage Calculations

1. Change to fractional form: twenty percent; one hundred thirty

percent; four percent; thirty-seven and one-half percent; seventy-five percent. Reduce to decimal form: $12\frac{1}{2}\%$; 2%; 140%; $.6\%$; 270%.

2. What percent of 64 is 16; 12 is 18; 125 is 10; $12\frac{1}{2}$ is $37\frac{1}{2}$; .36 is .009?

3. Determine the percent equivalent of:

$$\frac{15}{60}, \frac{3}{25}, \frac{7}{35}, \frac{1}{3}, \frac{9}{18}, \frac{6}{11}, \frac{49}{20}, \frac{1}{15}, \frac{17}{12}, \frac{72}{50}, \frac{13}{4}, \frac{5}{125}$$

4. A young man at work in a printshop runs off 1800 circulars on a printing press. Of these, $3\frac{1}{2}\%$ were spoiled through inexperience. What was the total number of circulars spoiled?

5. A well-known twist drill which lists at $9 per set, has discounts of 20%, 10%, and 5%. What is the net price of this drill?

6. An auto mechanic's helper found a slip in his weekly pay envelope stating that beginning the following week his pay would be raised 12%. His present wage is $94.50. What pay should he receive on the new basis?

7. A textbook on mathematics is listed at a school store at $4. Students, however, were allowed a discount of 5%. What is the net price to students?

8. A cast-iron pulley was found to weigh $22\frac{1}{2}$ lb. before it was machined. After the machining operations were complete it weighed exactly $19\frac{1}{2}$ lb. Calculate the percent reduction in weight as a result of these operations.

9. A boy learning the printing trade was given a job of "running off" circulars on the printing press. His foreman estimates that it would take a journeyman pressman 2 hr. to do the job. The boy begins work at 1:00 p.m. and finishes at 5:30 p.m. What is his rating on this job?

10. Baseball records show that during the year he hit 61 home runs, Roger Maris batted 590 times and made 159 hits for the Yankees. Henry Aaron of the Braves during a season was at bat 629 times and made 223 hits. What were the batting averages of these two great baseball players for the seasons?

CHAPTER 9

Formulas and Their Evaluation

9.1 Introduction

One of the most frequent uses of simple algebra and arithmetic is in the evaluation of formulas. In all phases of technical and shop work, formulas are used to find the values of certain quantities when other quantities are known.

In electrical work one may have to calculate voltage drops, currents in wires, sizes of wires. In electronics one may need to compute the frequency of an oscillator or the time constant of a circuit; in the shop one may have to compute board feet, horsepower, cutting speed, gear ratios, and so on.

All of these computations make use of particular formulas. This section will give you the knowledge necessary to work with them.

9.2 Reading a Formula

In almost every phase of technical, shop, and engineering work it is necessary to use *formulas*. Formulas are rules of computation which are written in the language of mathematics instead of in words. Formulas are written using numbers and letters. These numbers and letters are connected together by mathematical signs which tell us how to find the value of the formula when we know the number values of the letters.

We might think of mathematical formulas in the same way that a chef thinks of a recipe. To a chef, a recipe is a method of making or preparing something to eat. It tells him *what* the ingredients are, *how much* of each ingredient is needed to make a certain amount of whatever he wants to prepare, and also *how* to go about preparing it properly.

To a student of shop mathematics a formula also tells him how to find the value of a quantity whose "recipe" or formula he has, if he knows the value of the quantities that enter in the formula.

Formulas occur in almost all branches of engineering and each branch has its own set of formulas. These give a rule for computing or finding the value of some quantity when certain other quantities that appear in the formula (in mathematical form) are known.

Before beginning the study of formulas and how they are evaluated, we will take a trip into the land of algebra. This short trip will make us familiar with the way formulas are read and what the various symbols are that appear in a formula. Algebra is a very powerful mathematical tool, and you may want to study it later in your schoolwork or when you are working on the job.

In algebra, we use letters to represent numbers. Usually we select the

Bethlehem Steel Co.

One of the largest bridges in the world, the Golden Gate Bridge in California depends greatly on the practical application of mathematical formulas.

letters which have some connection with the numbers they represent. Thus we use A for Area, b for base, h for height, or altitude. We use C for circumference, r for radius, π to stand for $\frac{22}{7}$ or $3\frac{1}{7}$ or 3.14 or 3.1416 for most precise work. When we wish to multiply two numbers in arithmetic, we put a times sign between the numbers. Thus 7×8 means 7 times 8 or 56. In algebra, however, we use a *dot* frequently. Thus we can write $7 \cdot 8$ putting the dot halfway between the top and bottom of the numbers, so as not to confuse it with the decimal point. When we wish to *multiply two literal numbers,* that is, two letters which represent numbers, we simply write them next to each other without any sign between them at all. Thus, when we write bh, we mean b times h. When we write Fd we mean F times d. When we write $\pi f L$ we mean π times f times L. If we have a number which we wish to multiply by a letter, we do *not* put a times sign between them either. Thus 2π means 2 times π. Hence if we write πD we mean π times D. Of course, to get the actual numerical value of πD we would have to know what the value of D was and we would have to use $\frac{22}{7}$ or $3\frac{1}{7}$ or 3.14 or 3.1416 for the value of π, depending on the accuracy we wanted.

When we wish to indicate division in algebra we use the fraction line most frequently. Thus, to show that V is to be divided by R, we write $\dfrac{V}{R}$. We read this "V over R" or "V divided by R." Thus $\dfrac{B}{3}$ is read "B over three" or "B divided by three."

Frequently situations arise where a literal number (a letter that represents a number) must be multiplied by itself. Suppose the literal number is R. To show that R is to be multiplied by itself, we could write it as $R \times R$ or $R \cdot R$. We prefer, however, to write it as R^2. The small 2 is placed *above and to the right* of the R. It tells us that R is to be multiplied by itself, that is, R^2 means the same as $R \times R$ or $R \cdot R$. This small number is called an *exponent*. We read R^2 as "R square" or "R squared." R^2 appears in the formula for the area of a circle, where R represents the radius of the circle. If $R = 7$, $R^2 = R \times R = 7 \times 7 = 49$.

The formula for the area of a circle in terms of the radius is $A = \pi R^2$. This is read "A equals pi R squared." It tells us that to find the area of a circle when we know its radius, we must find the product $\pi \times R \times R$.

Many times a literal number appears with an exponent which is 3. Thus, in the formula for the volume of a sphere we find R^3. This is read "R cube" or "R cubed." It is a shorthand method of writing $R \times R \times R$.

Thus if $R = 6$,
$$R^3 = R \times R \times R$$
$$= 6 \times 6 \times 6$$
$$= 216$$

The formula for the volume of a sphere is $A = \dfrac{4\pi R^3}{3}$.

We read this "A equals four-thirds pi R cubed" or "A equals 4 pi R cubed over three." If we wrote it out longhand, it would appear as $A = \dfrac{4 \times \pi \times R \times R \times R}{3}$. We can all see the saving in time and space that algebra affords us by comparing $A = \dfrac{4\pi R^3}{3}$ with $A = \dfrac{4 \times \pi \times R \times R \times R}{3}$.

Every so often we may run across a formula in which some literal number has an exponent of 4 or 5 or higher. Such formulas occur in the design of machines and structures. One such formula is:
$$I = \frac{\pi D^4}{64}$$

This we read as "I equals pi D to the fourth power over 64" or "I equals pi D to the fourth power divided by 64." This would become, when written out:

$$I = \frac{\pi \times D \times D \times D \times D}{64}$$

If a literal number has an exponent which is 4 or higher, we read it "to the —— power." Thus we read n^4 as "n to the *fourth* power," t^5 we read as "t to the *fifth* power," and so on. We could also read D^3 as "D to the *third* power" if we wanted to instead of reading it as "D cube" or "D cubed."

We now give a few examples in the reading of formulas.

■ **EXAMPLE 1:**

   a) How is the formula $A = \dfrac{\pi D^2}{4}$ read?

   b) How would this formula appear if the mathematical signs were shown?

Solution and Explanation:

   a) This formula for finding the area of a circle when we know its diameter D is read "A equals pi D squared over four" or "A equals pi D squared divided by four."

   b) If written so that the signs connecting π and D^2 were shown the formula would be written $A = \dfrac{\pi \times D \times D}{4}$.

■ **EXAMPLE 2:**

   a) How is the formula $d = \dfrac{WL^3}{15EI}$ read?

   b) How would it be written so as to show the times signs which are omitted?

Solution and Explanation:

   a) This formula, which is used in the design of beams, is read "d equals WL cubed over fifteen EI" or "d equals WL cubed divided by fifteen EI."

   b) If written so the times signs are shown it would appear thus:

$$d = \frac{W \times L \times L \times L}{15 \times E \times I}$$

■ **EXAMPLE 3:**

a) How is the formula $c^2 = a^2 + b^2$ read?

b) How would it appear if the times signs that are omitted are shown?

Solution and Explanation:

a) This formula is read "*c* square equals *a* square plus *b* square."

b) If exponents were not used this formula would appear as
$$c \times c = a \times a + b \times b$$
Thus, if $a = 3$ and $b = 4$,
$$c^2 = 3 \times 3 + 4 \times 4$$
$$c^2 = 9 + 16$$
$$\mathbf{c^2 = 25}$$

■ **EXAMPLE 4:**

a) How is the formula $c = \sqrt{a^2 + b^2}$ read?

b) How would it be written if the multiplication signs were shown?

Solution and Explanation:

a) This formula, from geometry, is read "*c* equals the square root of *a* square plus *b* square."

b) It would appear as $c = \sqrt{a \times a + b \times b}$ if the multiplication signs were shown.

■ **EXAMPLE 5:**

a) How is the formula $A = \dfrac{h(B + b)}{2}$ read?

b) How would this formula appear if the omitted multiplication sign were shown?

Solution and Explanation:

a) This formula, also from geometry, is read "*A* equals *h* times the quantity large *B* plus small *b* over two" or "*A* equals *h* times the quantity large *B* plus small *b* divided by two."

b) If the omitted multiplication sign were shown, the formula would appear in the form:
$$A = \frac{h \times (B + b)}{2}$$
The part of the formula written $(B + b)$ is read "the quantity large *B* plus small *b*." The ( ) are called parentheses and indicate that

B and b are to be considered as a single quantity. Although, in the parentheses, only the second letter of the alphabet appears, it appears twice, first, as a capital letter, read "large B" and, second, as a lowercase or small letter, read "small b." Each of these letters represents a separate quantity and each must be written *as it appears, that is, capital letters must be written as capital letters and lowercase or small letters as they appear. This is a very important rule to remember.* Under *no circumstances* can we change the letters in a particular formula. *We must always write them as they appear in the particular formula.*

You have already noticed that in every instance so far, the formula begins "Something equals something else." The quantity to the *left* of the equal sign is called the *subject* of the formula, and it is the quantity whose value we find when we *evaluate* any formula. In order to do this, *it is necessary to know the values of all the other literal numbers* which appear *on the right of the equal sign.* In *every case,* when any formula is to be evaluated, *the subject must appear on the left of the equal sign by itself and nowhere else in the formula.*

Before beginning the evaluation of formulas, we give a list of expressions involving literal numbers, show how they are read and how they would appear if they were not written in the shorthand of algebra.

Algebraic form	How it is read	It stands for
L^5	"L to the fifth power"	$L \times L \times L \times L \times L$
a^3b^3	"a cube, b cube"	$a \times a \times a \times b \times b \times b$
$(D^3 - d^3)$	"The quantity large D cube minus small d cube." The parentheses are used to show that $D^3 - d^3$ must be considered as a single quantity.	$(D \times D \times D - d \times d \times d)$
$\dfrac{bh^3}{12}$	"b, h cube over 12" or "b, h cube divided by 12."	$\dfrac{b \times h \times h \times h}{12}$
$2l + 2w$	"two l plus two w"	$2 \times l + 2 \times w$
$\dfrac{PL}{AE}$	"P, L over A, E" or "P L divided by A, E."	$\dfrac{P \times L}{A \times E}$
$\dfrac{\pi SD^3}{12}$	"pi, S, D cube, over 12" or "π, S, D cube, divided by 12."	$\dfrac{\pi \times S \times D \times D \times D}{12}$

9.3 Problems Involving Literal Numbers

Read the following expressions and formulas. Write each one showing how it would appear if it were not written in algebraic shorthand.

1. a^3, c^2, x^4, L^3, h^2, B^4, I^2, W^3

2. $a^2 + b^2$, WL^3, EI, D^2, $(B + b)$, πD^2

3. $\dfrac{V}{R}$, $V^2 G$, $\frac{1}{2} bh$, at^2

4. $4\pi R^2$, $2\pi fL$, $\dfrac{MC}{I}$

5. $F = \dfrac{Wa}{g}$, $V^2 = 2gh$, $W = I^2 R$, $c = \sqrt{a^2 + b^2}$, $I = \dfrac{bh^3}{36}$

9.4 List of Frequently Used Formulas*

In geometry areas are measured in square units (sq. in., sq. ft., etc.). Widths, heights, radii, diameters, bases, semimajor axes, and semiminor axes are all measured in units of length (in., ft., yd., etc.). Volumes are measured in cubic units (cu. in., cu. ft., etc.).

Formula	Used for finding	What the letters represent
1. $A = \dfrac{bh}{2}$	Area of a triangle	A = area b = base h = height

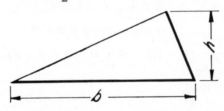

Formula	Used for finding	What the letters represent
2. $A = bh$	Area of a rectangle	A = area b = base h = height

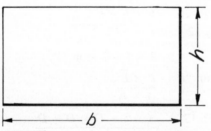

* Note the values of π to be used are $\frac{22}{7}$ 3.14, or 3.1416 depending upon the accuracy desired.

Formula	*Used for finding*	*What the letters represent*
3. $A = \dfrac{(B + b)h}{2}$	Area of a trapezoid	A = area B = large base b = small base h = height

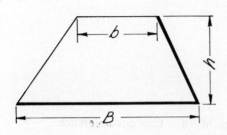

4. $A = s^2$	Area of a square	A = area s = length of a side

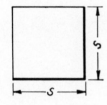

5. $A = \pi R^2$	Area of a circle using its radius	A = area $\pi = \frac{22}{7}$, 3.14, or 3.1416 R = radius

6. $A = \dfrac{\pi D^2}{4}$	Area of a circle using its diameter	A = area D = diameter

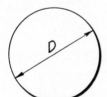

Formula	*Used for finding*	*What the letters represent*
7. $A = \pi ab$	Area of an ellipse	A = area a = semimajor axis b = semiminor axis

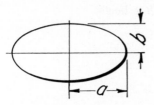

8. $C = 2\pi R$	Circumference of a circle, using its radius	C = circumference R = radius

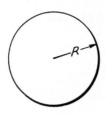

9. $C = \pi D$	Circumference of a circle, using its diameter	C = circumference D = diameter

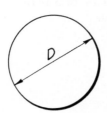

10. $S = 4\pi R^2$	Surface area of a sphere using its radius	S = area of surface R = radius of sphere

Formula	Used for finding	What the letters represent
11. $V = lwh$	Volume of a rectangular box	V = volume l = length w = width h = height

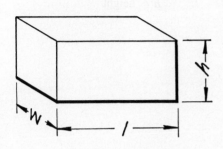

12. $V = \pi R^2 h$	Volume of a circular cylinder	V = volume R = radius h = height

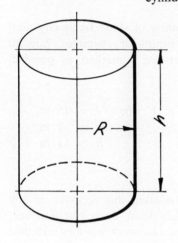

13. $V = \dfrac{Bh}{3}$	Volume of a pyramid	V = volume B = area of base h = height

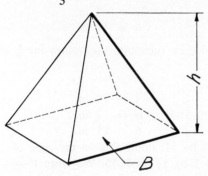

Formula	*Used for finding*	*What the letters represent*
14. $V = \dfrac{\pi R^2 h}{3}$	Volume of a circular cone	V = volume R = radius h = height

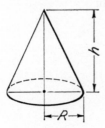

Although this list of formulas appears long, it is by no means complete. Dozens of formulas are derived and used in almost all branches of technical work.

We now turn out attention to the *evaluation* of some frequently used formulas. Our aim will be to show, by means of examples, how to evaluate a formula properly, in as blunder-free a method as possible.

■ EXAMPLE 1:

In the formula $V = lwh$ find the value of V when $l = 15$ in.

$w = 7$ in.

$h = 11$ in.

Solution and Explanation:

We will use the same procedure in evaluating this formula or any other formula. In Step 1, we write the formula down, draw a vertical line, and write down what we know in the formula. Our work will look like this:

Step 1:

$V = l \times w \times h$ $\qquad\qquad\Big|\qquad$ $l = 15$ in.

$w = 7$ in.

$h = 11$ in.

In the next step we write $V =$, and then substitute the values for l, w and h. Our work looks like this:

Step 2:

$V = l \times w \times h$ $\qquad\qquad\Big|\qquad$ $l = 15$ in.

$V = 15 \times 7 \times 11$ $\qquad\qquad\Big|\qquad$ $w = 7$ in.

$h = 11$ in.

In the next step we multiply 15 by 7 by 11, doing this on the *right* of the vertical line. We find that 15 by 7 by 11 = 1155. We write $V =$

1155 cu. in. in the third line, mark it "ans." (for answer) and put a box around it. Our work finally looks like this:

$$V = l \times w \times h$$
$$V = 15 \times 7 \times 11$$

$$\boxed{V = 1155 \text{ cu. in.} \quad \textbf{ans.}}$$

$l = 15$ in.
$w = 7$ in.
$h = 11$ in.

$$
\begin{array}{r}
15 \\
7 \\
\hline
105 \\
11 \\
\hline
105 \\
105 \\
\hline
1155
\end{array}
$$

This is all that actually needs to be written down. Notice that we
1. Wrote down the formula to be evaluated.
2. Put down what was given in the formula.
3. Substituted the numerical values for the letters in the formula.
4. Performed the arithmetic called for by the formula (here we multiplied 15 by 7 by 11).
5. Put the answer, *with the proper units,* in a box and label it "ans."
In this manner it is very unlikely that anyone would have difficulty in understanding what was done. Setting down the work in this way makes it easy for anyone to check it for correctness.

■ **EXAMPLE 2:**

Evaluate the formula $V = \frac{4}{3}\pi R^3$ for $R = 8$ in.

Solution and Explanation:

Step 1: Write down the formula, draw a vertical line to the right of it and put down what is given to the right of the line. We have:

$V = \frac{4}{3}\pi R^3$
$\pi = \frac{22}{7}$
$R = 8$ in.

Step 2: Replace the literal numbers (the letters which stand in place of the numbers) by their numerical values. The work looks like this then:

$V = \frac{4}{3}\pi R^3$
$V = \frac{4}{3} \times \frac{22}{7} \times 8^3$
$\pi = \frac{22}{7}$
$R = 8$ in.

Step 3: Write out what 8^3 is equal to. At this stage the work looks like this:

Step 4:

$V = \frac{4}{3}\pi R^3$
$V = \frac{4}{3} \times \frac{22}{7} \times 8^3$
$V = \frac{4}{3} \times \frac{22}{7} \times 8 \times 8 \times 8$
$V = \frac{4}{3} \times \frac{22}{7} \times 512$

$\pi = \frac{22}{7}$
$R = 8$ in.
$R^3 = 8 \times 8 \times 8 = 512$

Step 5: Since no cancellation is possible, we multiply 4 by 22, multiply 3 by 7, and write Step 4 as:

$V = \frac{4}{3}\pi R^3$ $\pi = \frac{22}{7}$

$V = \frac{4}{3} \times \frac{22}{7} \times 8^3$ $R = 8$ in.

$V = \frac{4}{3} \times \frac{22}{7} \times 8 \times 8 \times 8$ $R^3 = 8 \times 8 \times 8 = 512$

$V = \frac{4}{3} \times \frac{22}{7} \times 512$ $4 \times 22 = 88$

$V = \frac{88 \times 512}{21}$

Step 6: We now multiply 88 and 512 together and write the product over 21. The work looks like this so far:

$V = \frac{4}{3}\pi R^3$ $\pi = \frac{22}{7}$

$V = \frac{4}{3} \times \frac{22}{7} \times 8^3$ $R = 8$ in.

$V = \frac{4}{3} \times \frac{22}{7} \times 8 \times 8 \times 8$ $R^3 = 8 \times 8 \times 8 = 512$

$V = \frac{4}{3} \times \frac{22}{7} \times 512$ $4 \times 22 = 88$

$V = \frac{88 \times 512}{21}$ $512 \times 88 = 45056$

$V = \frac{45056}{21}$

Step 7: Now dividing 45056 by 21 we obtain the value of V. The work looks like this then:

$V = \frac{4}{3}\pi R^3$ $\pi = \frac{22}{7}$

$V = \frac{4}{3} \times \frac{22}{7} \times 8^3$ $R = 8$ in.

$R^3 = 8 \times 8 \times 8 = 512$

$V = \frac{4}{3} \times \frac{22}{7} \times 8 \times 8 \times 8$ $4 \times 22 = 88$

$512 \times 88 = 45056$

$V = \frac{4}{3} \times \frac{22}{7} \times 512$

```
              2145.5
         21 | 45056.0
              42
              ──
              30
              21
              ──
              95
              84
              ───
              116
              105
              ───
              110
              105
              ───
                5
```

$V = \frac{88 \times 512}{21}$

$V = \frac{45056}{21}$

$$\boxed{V = 2145.5 \text{ cu. in.} \quad \textbf{ans.}}$$

Again, it is not necessary to write the steps separately, that is, on separate parts of the sheet. It is, however, very important to do *one step* at a time. Some may ask why the calculations should be shown on the right of the vertical line. One reason is that it is a record of your work.

Another is that anyone else can check the computation and determine its correctness if necessary. No matter if it appears to be too detailed: it is better to do one's work neatly and without blunders than to put it down in a slovenly manner and make mistakes. As a student, two of the finest habits you can learn are the habit of *always doing neat work and the habit of going over one's work to see that it is free from blunders.* Two more examples will show the method in detail.

■ **EXAMPLE 3:**

Evaluate the formula $T = 2\pi R(H + 2R)$ if: $R = 16$
$$H = 22$$
$$\pi = 3.1416$$

Solution and Explanation:

Step 1: As in Examples 1 and 2, we write the formula, draw a vertical line to the right of it, and put the known data to the right of the line. The work appears thus:

$$T = 2\pi R(H + 2R) \qquad \begin{array}{l} R = 16 \\ H = 22 \\ \pi = 3.1416 \end{array}$$

Step 2: This consists in replacing R, H and π by the numerical values assigned to them. We have:

$$\begin{array}{l} T = 2\pi R(H + 2R) \\ T = 2 \times 3.1416 \times \\ \qquad 16(22 + 2 \times 16) \end{array} \qquad \begin{array}{l} R = 16 \\ H = 22 \\ \pi = 3.1416 \end{array}$$

Step 3: Here we find the product $2 \times 3.1416 \times 16$ and the value of the quantity inside the parentheses, which is $(22 + 32)$ or (54). We then have:

$$\begin{array}{l} T = 2\pi R(H + 2R) \\ \\ T = 2 \times 3.1416 \times \\ \qquad 16(22 + 2 \times 16) \\ \\ T = 100.5312(54) \end{array} \qquad \begin{array}{l} R = 16 \\ \\ H = 22 \\ \\ \pi = 3.1416 \end{array}$$

$$\begin{array}{rr} 3.1416 & 22 \\ 2 & +32 \\ \hline 6.2832 & 54 \\ 16 \\ \hline 37\,6992 \\ 62\,832 \\ \hline 100.5312 \end{array}$$

Step 4: In this final step, the value of T is computed by multiplying 100.5312 by 54. The work appears thus:

$$T = 2\pi R(H + 2R)$$

$$T = 2 \times 3.1416 \times$$
$$16(22 + 2 \times 16)$$

$$T = 100.5312(54)$$

$$T = 5428.6848 \quad \textbf{ans.}$$

$$\boxed{T = 5428.7 \quad \textbf{ans.}}$$

$R = 16$	3.1416	22
	2	+32
$H = 22$	6.2832	54
	16	
$\pi = 3.1416$	37 6992	100.5312
	62 832	54
	100.5312	402 1248
		5026 560
		5428.6848

■ **EXAMPLE 4:**

Evaluate the formula:

$$I = \frac{16a^3b}{175} \quad \text{if} \quad \begin{aligned} a &= 6 \\ b &= 4.5 \end{aligned}$$

Solution and Explanation:

We will confine ourselves to showing the entire problem solved according to the method explained already.

$$I = \frac{16a^3b}{175}$$

$$I = \frac{16 \times 6^3 \times 4.5}{175}$$

$$I = \frac{16 \times 6 \times 6 \times 6 \times \overset{0.9}{\cancel{4.5}}}{\underset{35}{\cancel{175}}}$$

$$I = \frac{16 \times 216 \times 0.9}{35}$$

$$I = 88.86$$

$$\boxed{I = 88.9 \quad \textbf{ans.}}$$

$$a = 6$$
$$b = 4.5$$
$$a^3 = 6 \times 6 \times 6 = 216$$

```
        216
         16
       1296
        216
       3456
        0.9
     3110.4

       88.86
35 ⌐ 3110.40
     280
     310
     280
     30 4
     28 0
      2 40
      2 10
```

Chicago Bridge & Iron Co.

Steel spheroids for storing 100,000 gallons of natural gasoline.

9.5 Problems on Evaluation of Formulas

1. Find the area of a triangle whose base is 36 in. and height is 22 in.

2. The cross section of a wooden post supporting a porch measured $5\frac{3}{8}$ by $5\frac{3}{8}$ in. What is its cross-sectional area?

3. The diameter of a steel shaft is 3 in. What is its cross-sectional area?

4. A small radar antenna reflector (called a "dish") is 4 ft. in diameter. What is its cross-sectional area? See Figure 103.

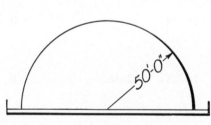

Fig. 103.   Fig. 104.

5. A recently constructed plastic and aluminum dome is in the shape of a *half sphere* (Fig. 104). If its radius is 50 ft. what is the surface area in square feet?

6. The approximate inside dimensions of a circular cylindrical water-tempering tank in the basement of an apartment building are $3\frac{1}{2}$ ft. in

diameter and 12 ft. long. How many cubic feet of water does it hold? If 1 cu. ft. contains 7.5 gal., what is the capacity of this tank in gallons?

7. On a certain construction job it was necessary to fence in a rectangular area 250 ft. by 190 ft. How many feet of fence would be needed to enclose this area?

8. To find the wavelength of a TV antenna we use the formula $l = \dfrac{936}{f}$. Here l is the wavelength in feet and f is the frequency in megacycles per second (mcs). What is l if f is 107 mcs.?

9. The formula for the area of a regular hexagon is $A = 0.866d^2$, where d is the "distance across the flats." Find the area of such a hexagon if $d = 3$ in.

10. The dimensions of a standard brick may be considered to be 8 in. by $3\frac{3}{4}$ in. by $2\frac{1}{4}$ in. What is the volume of such a brick in cubic inches?

11. The formula for the distance an object falls when it is dropped from some height above the earth is $S = 16t^2$, where S is the distance in feet and t is the time in seconds. Find the distance an object falls if the time it takes it to strike the earth is 15 sec.

Evaluate the following formulas for the values given:

12. $P = I^2R$ if $I = 6.5$
                                 $R = 3.2$

13. $V = \dfrac{\pi D^3}{6}$ if $D = 28$
                                 $\pi = \frac{22}{7}$

14. $V = \pi R^2 H$ if $R = 10$
                                 $H = 20$
                                 $\pi = 3.1416$

15. $A = \pi ab$ if $a = 10$
                                 $b = 6$
                                 $\pi = 3.1416$

16. $X_L = 2\pi f L$ if $L = 16$
                                 $f = 60$
                                 $\pi = 3.1416$

The symbol X_L is read "X sub L." The $_L$ written to the right and a little below the X is called a *subscript*.

17. $V = \dfrac{Bh}{3}$ if $B = 650$
                                 $h = 20$

18. $C = 2\pi R$ if $R = 3960$
                                 $\pi = 3.1416$

19. $I = \dfrac{V}{R + r}$ if $V = 240$
$R = 6$
$r = 2$

20. $V = \dfrac{\pi R^2 H}{3}$ if $R = 8$
$H = 7$
$\pi = \frac{22}{7}$

21. $V = \dfrac{4\pi abc}{3}$ if $a = 2.5$
$b = 3.6$
$c = 4.0$
$\pi = 3.1416$

22. $R = \dfrac{ab}{a + b}$ if $a = 800$
$b = 600$

23. $S = 4\pi R^2$ if $R = 14$
$\pi = 3.1416$

24. $E = D - \dfrac{0.64952}{n}$ if $D = 1.0000$
$n = 32$

25. $A = \dfrac{(B + b)h}{2}$ if $B = 36$
$b = 24$
$h = 25$

26. $R = \dfrac{10.4l}{A}$ $l = 500$
$A = 1020$

27. $I = PRT$ if $P = 1200$
$R = 0.04$
$T = 3$

28. $T = 2\pi R(H + R)$ if $R = 4.5$
$H = 22$
$\pi = 3.1416$

29. $T = 2\pi R(H + 2R)$ if $R = 3.5$
$H = 40$
$\pi = 3.1416$

30. $I = \dfrac{bd^3}{12}$ if $b = 3.75$
$d = 2.5$

Unit III
MEASUREMENT

CHAPTER 10

Linear Measure

10.1 Introduction

This chapter deals with the common units of linear measure and their use in connection with work that may be done by carpenters, draftsmen, householders, shopmen, technicians, and other workers.

Need frequently arises for the measurement of lengths and for computations involving linear units of various kinds. This chapter discusses these frequently used units of length and provides many examples and problems illustrating how they are used and how calculations involving them are performed.

10.2 Units of Linear Measure

Linear measure deals with measurement in one direction only, as for example, the length or the width of an object, or the distance from one place to another. Each of these involves a measurement in one direction only.

The units of linear measure most commonly used in the shop are the inch and the foot. These units are parts of a larger unit of length called the yard.

The units of weights and measures in common use in the United States are based, by act of Congress, on the metric system of units. The metric system was set up originally in France about 1787 and has been adopted by most of the non-English-speaking countries throughout the world.

In the metric system, the standard of length is the *meter*. This was originally intended to be the ten-millionth part of the meridian extending from the North Pole to the Equator and passing through Paris. This length is represented by the distance between two marks on a specially constructed platinum-iridium bar, called the "International Prototype Meter," which is kept at the International Bureau of Weights and Measures at Sèvres, near Paris, France. Subdivisions of this distance are the decimeter, or tenth of a meter; the centimeter, or hundredth of a meter; and the millimeter, or thousandth of a meter. In the metric system we thus have:

1 meter = 10 decimeters or 1 decimeter = $\frac{1}{10}$ of a meter

1 meter = 100 centimeters or 1 centimeter = $\frac{1}{100}$ of a meter

1 meter = 1000 millimeters or 1 millimeter = $\frac{1}{1000}$ of a meter

A steel rule.

Brown & Sharpe Mfg. Co.

143

These units of length are abbreviated as follows:

Unit	Abbreviation
meter	m
decimeter	dm
centimeter	cm
millimeter	mm

A copy of the International Prototype Meter, or standard meter, is kept in the Bureau of Standards at Washington, D. C. This platinum-iridium bar served as the official standard of length until 1960 when the meter was redefined in terms of the wavelength of krypton light. Our unit of length, the U. S. yard, is legally defined as $\frac{3600}{3937}$ of our official standard meter. This distance is divided into *three* equal parts called *feet*, and each of these is in turn divided into *twelve* parts, called *inches*. Thus a foot is one third of a yard; an inch is one thirty-sixth of a yard.

The following table shows the relation between these units:

$$
\begin{aligned}
12 \text{ inches} &= 1 \text{ foot} \\
3 \text{ feet} &= 1 \text{ yard} = 36 \text{ inches} \\
5\tfrac{1}{2} \text{ yards or } 16\tfrac{1}{2} \text{ feet} &= 1 \text{ rod} \\
5280 \text{ feet} &= 1 \text{ mile (1 statute mile)} \\
&= 320 \text{ rods} = 1760 \text{ yards}
\end{aligned}
$$

The word *inch* or inches is indicated by the abbreviation "in." or by the symbol ($''$). For example, the measurement 5 inches may be expressed as 5 in. or 5$''$.

The unit of measure, the *foot*, and its plural, *feet*, is abbreviated "ft.," the symbol for this being ($'$). Thus the measurement 3 feet would be expressed as 3 ft. or 3$'$.

A measurement combining feet and inches, such as 6 feet 8 inches, would be expressed as 6 ft. 8 in. or 6$'$-8$''$. Where the symbols ($'$) and ($''$) are used, it is recommended that the numbers be separated by a dash, as shown in the length 6$'$-8$''$. This is a standard practice followed in the preparation of drawings by draftsmen.

The measurement *yard* or *yards* is abbreviated "yd." Combined with feet, or inches, the measurement would be abbreviated as expressed above. For example, 5 yards 2 feet would be written 5 yd. 2 ft.; 4 yards 5 inches would be abbreviated as 4 yd. 5 in.

The word *rod* or *rods* is abbreviated as "rd." The rod is usually used in measurements relating to land.

10.3 Changing From One Denomination to Another

The units of linear measure that have been described have many uses, and it frequently becomes necessary to change units of one denomination to units of another denomination. Thus it may be necessary to change $7\frac{1}{3}$ yards to feet, or to determine the number of feet in 70 inches.

The tables showing the relations of the various units of length to each other are very useful in problems involving linear measurements.

■ EXAMPLE 1:

A young man found that, in order to build the necessary tool brackets for a portable tool carrier, he would need four pieces of 1 in. by 4-in. lumber each 33 in. long. How many linear feet of this lumber were needed?

Solution and Explanation:

Since each bracket is 33 in. long and there are 4 of them, all four would be $4 \times 33 = 132$ in. long. To change this to feet, we divide the number of inches by 12. Thus the number of linear feet $= \frac{132}{12} = 11$ ft. Hence, 11 linear feet of this type of lumber are needed.

We see from this example that to change smaller units to equivalent larger units, one should divide the number of units of the smaller denomination by the number of those smaller units required to make *one* unit of the larger denomination.

The following problems illustrate the method of changing a number of units of one denomination to an equivalent number of units of smaller denomination.

■ EXAMPLE 2:

Change 5 yd. $2\frac{1}{2}$ ft. to inches.

Solution and Explanation:

Step 1: The number of yards is changed to inches. We obtain
$$5 \times 36 = 180 \text{ in.}$$
Step 2: The number of feet is changed to inches, giving
$$2\frac{1}{2} \times 12 = 30 \text{ in.}$$
Step 3: We then have
$$5 \text{ yd.} = 180 \text{ in.}$$
$$2\frac{1}{2} \text{ ft.} = 30 \text{ in.}$$
adding: $\qquad\qquad \overline{5 \text{ yd. } 2\frac{1}{2} \text{ ft.} = 210 \text{ in.}}$

That is, 5 yd. $2\frac{1}{2}$ ft. changed to inches equals 210 in.

■ EXAMPLE 3:

How many feet of wire fence are needed to enclose a plot of land with a perimeter of 32 rods?

Solution and Explanation:

Since in each rod there are 16½ ft. the total number of feet in 32 rd. is
$$32 \times 16\tfrac{1}{2} = 528 \text{ ft.}$$
That is, there are 528 ft. in 32 rd., and consequently 528 ft. of wire fence are needed to enclose this plot of land.

The preceding problems show that in order to change units of larger denomination to an equivalent number of units of smaller denomination, we *multiply* the number of units of larger denomination by the number of the smaller units it takes to make *one* of the larger units.

The following tables are arranged as an aid to changing units of one denomination to units of another denomination.

TABLE 1

To change	to	Multiply number of
feet	inches	feet by 12
yards	feet	yards by 3
	inches	yards by 36
rods	yards	rods by 5½
	feet	rods by 16½
miles	feet	miles by 5280
	rods	miles by 320
	yards	miles by 1760

TABLE 2

To change	to	Divide number of
inches	yards	inches by 36
	feet	inches by 12
feet	miles	feet by 5280
	rods	feet by 16½
	yards	feet by 3
yards	miles	yards by 1760
	rods	yards by 5½
rods	miles	rods by 320

10.4   Application to a Shop Problem

Two common terms used in stair building are "riser" and "tread." These are illustrated in Figure 107. Stair construction and design follow

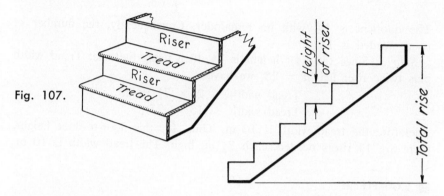

Fig. 107.

rules gained from the experience of many builders. One of these is that risers having a height of 7 to $7\frac{1}{2}$ in. have been found to be very satisfactory when combined with treads of about 10 in. These dimensions apply to main stairs generally and for house construction.

A good working rule is that the sum of the tread width and twice the height of the riser should equal 25. For example, a riser of $7\frac{1}{2}$ in. and a tread of 10 in. satisfies this rule, since $10 + 2 \times 7\frac{1}{2} = 10 + 15 = 25$.

In designing a stairs, the riser height and tread width must be determined. In doing this, a satisfactory riser height is selected. The exact height between the finish floors to be connected by the stairs is then found. This exact finish-floor to finish-floor height is then divided by the riser height. If the quotient is a whole number with no remainder, it will give the correct number of risers needed. If the quotient is not exact, the height between the finish floors is divided by the next whole number above or below the quotient. The result will then be the riser height. The tread width can then be determined by the working rule connecting riser and tread dimensions.

The following example will illustrate the calculations involved.

■ EXAMPLE 1:

Determine the number of risers and the tread width for a stair connecting two floors whose finish floor-to-floor height is 8'-9''.

Solution and Explanation:

Step 1: Changing 8'-9'' to inches, we obtain 105 in.

Step 2: Using a riser height of $7\frac{1}{2}$ in., we divide 105 by $7\frac{1}{2}$:

$$105 \div 7\frac{1}{2} = \overset{7}{\cancel{105}} \times \frac{2}{\cancel{15}} = 14$$
$$\phantom{105 \div 7\frac{1}{2} = } _1$$

The quotient is 14, with no remainder. Consequently, the number of risers needed is 14.

Step 3: Since the riser height is $7\frac{1}{2}$, then using the rule: Tread width plus twice riser height = 25, we have

$$\text{Tread width} + 2 \times 7\frac{1}{2} = 25$$
or: Tread width + 15 = 25

Therefore the tread width is 10 in. Thus, for this floor-to-floor height, there are 14 risers needed, each $7\frac{1}{2}$ in. high. The tread width is 10 in.

■ **EXAMPLE 2:**

Determine the number and height of risers needed for a stairs between a basement and first floor having a total rise of 8'-0''. How wide a tread will be satisfactory?

Solution and Explanation:

Step 1: Changing 8'-0'' to in., we obtain 96 in.

Step 2: Using a riser height of $7\frac{1}{2}$ in., we divide 96 by $7\frac{1}{2}$:

$$96 \div 7\frac{1}{2} = \overset{32}{\cancel{96}} \times \frac{2}{\cancel{15}} = \frac{64}{5} = 12\frac{4}{5}$$
$$\phantom{96 \div 7\frac{1}{2} = } _5$$

The number of risers is *apparently* $12\frac{4}{5}$. But the number of risers must always be a *whole number* and hence *cannot* be $12\frac{4}{5}$. Hence there should be 13 risers.

Step 3: We divide 96 by 13, the *nearest* whole number *greater* than $12\frac{4}{5}$. Thus $\frac{96}{13} = 7.385$ in.

Referring to a table of decimal equivalents of an inch, we find that, to the nearest $\frac{1}{8}$ of an inch, the riser height should be $7\frac{3}{8}$ in.

Using the tread-riser rule again, we have:

$$\text{Tread width} + 2 \text{ times riser height} = 25$$
$$\text{Tread width} + 2 \times 7\frac{3}{8} = 25$$
$$\text{Tread width} + 14\frac{3}{4} = 25$$

and hence tread width = $10\frac{1}{4}$ in.

We have now found that a satisfactory riser height is $7\frac{3}{8}$ in. with a tread width of $10\frac{1}{4}$ in.

Further applications are found in calculations that involve determining how many parts of a specified length may be made from a piece of stock of a given length; or in determining how many blanks of a given size may be stamped from a strip of metal of a known length. Consideration should be given to the amount of waste involved in the thickness of the saw cut, in the finishing of each piece, and in the space allowed between each stamped part. This wastage should be included in the calculations.

Computations of a similar type are used in determining the length of stock needed to make a given number of parts of a specified length.

A good procedure to follow in calculations of this kind is to make a simple neat sketch showing the various parts with the necessary dimensions. This will help visualize the particular problem and reduce blunders.

A typical calculation is illustrated in the following problem:

■ **EXAMPLE 3:**

How many pins as shown in Figure 108 can be cut from a piece of brass 2'-9" long if there is a waste of $\frac{1}{4}''$ for cutting off and finishing each pin?

Fig. 108.

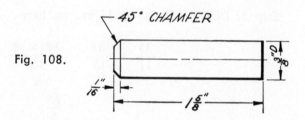

Solution and Explanation:

Problems of this type can be best solved by first changing the length of the stock into inches. Next, the length of one pin *plus* the waste on each is found. Finally, the number of pins is found by dividing the length of the stock by the total length of each pin plus the waste for each pin.

If the result of this division is a whole number plus a remainder, only the *whole number* is used and the remaining or fractional part is disregarded. The whole number gives the number of full-length pins that can be cut from the given length of stock.

Step 1: Changing 2 ft. 9 in. to inches, we have
$$2 \times 12 + 9 = 24 + 9 = 33 \text{ in.}$$

Step 2: The length of one pin plus the waste for one pin is
$$1\tfrac{5}{8} \text{ in. } + \tfrac{1}{4} \text{ in. } = 1\tfrac{7}{8} \text{ in.}$$

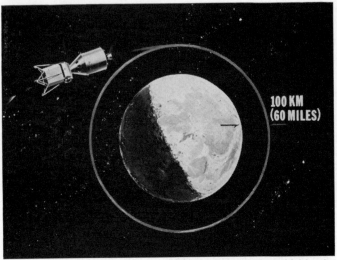

National Aeronautics & Space Administration

The U. S. moon exploration vehicle will orbit the moon 100 kilometers above the lunar surface.

Step 3: Dividing 33 in. by $1\frac{7}{8}$ in., we have

$$\frac{33}{1\frac{7}{8}} = \frac{33}{\frac{15}{8}} = \frac{\overset{11}{\cancel{33}} \times 8}{\cancel{15}} \frac{}{5}$$

$$= \frac{88}{5}$$

$$= 17\frac{3}{5}$$

Using the whole number part, we find that 17 pins can be cut from the length of stock given.

10.5 Problems Involving Changing Numbers From One Denomination to Another

1. A ball of wrapping twine contains a 450-ft. length of the twine. How many yards is this equivalent to? How many inches is this equivalent to?

2. In measuring the top of a table, a boy uses a yardstick and finds it is $1\frac{1}{4}$ yd. long and $\frac{3}{4}$ yd. wide. What is the size of the tabletop when expressed in inches?

3. What is the cost of wire fence material needed to enclose a plot of land which measures $\frac{1}{4}$ of a mile around? This fence costs $87\frac{1}{2}\cancel{c}$ per rod.

4. The lower part of a proposed lunar vehicle is 100 in. tall. How many feet is this equal to?

5. Two boys measured the distance around the base of a tree and found it to be 140 in. How many feet is this equal to?

6. A gusset plate on a structural-steel detail drawing showed rivets spaced $3\frac{1}{2}$ in. apart. If there were 14 such spaces, what was the center-to-center distance between the first and last of the rivets? Give this distance in inches and in feet and inches.

7. On an architect's drawing, a flight of stairs was marked as having 7 treads, each 10 in. wide. What is the total distance taken up by the treads? Give this length in feet and inches.

8. The length and width of a footing are given as 114 in. each. What are these dimensions in feet?

9. A stairs has a height of 4 ft. $11\frac{1}{2}$ in. and eight risers. What is the height of each riser?

10. How many pieces $5\frac{1}{2}$ in. long can be cut from a bar of stock 3 ft. 9 in. long? Allow $\frac{1}{8}$-in. waste for cutting off each piece.

11. An architect's drawing shows a flight of stairs which has 11 risers. If the total height is 6 ft. $9\frac{13}{16}$ in. what is the height of each riser?

12. Bolts (Fig. 109) are to be made from a bar of $\frac{3}{4}$-in.-square stock $8\frac{1}{4}$ ft. long. If $\frac{1}{8}$ in. is to be allowed for waste due to cutting off each bolt, how many such bolts can be made from this piece of stock?

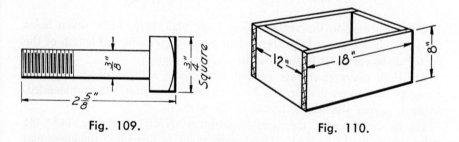

Fig. 109.   Fig. 110.

13. The sides and ends for two boxes like that shown in Figure 110 are to be cut from a board 8 in. wide and 12 ft. long. Adding $\frac{1}{8}$ in. for each piece cut, what is the total length in inches of the lumber used? What is the length in inches of the piece that remains?

14. A mortarboard is a square framework made up of boards tongue-and-grooved together on two 2-in. by 4-in. boards and used to hold mortar that is ready to use. If the width of the framework is 3 ft. 6 in. and each board is 6 in. wide, how many boards are used?

15. A partition being erected has 2 by 4-in. studding placed 16 in.

on centers. The length of the partition is 17 ft. 6 in. How many studs are needed for this, allowing one stud at each end of the partition?

16. The total rise from the finished basement floor to the finished concrete walk of a residence is 3′-9″. How many risers $7\frac{1}{2}$ in. high will be needed for the stairs leading from the basement to the walk?

17. In constructing a large concrete structure, a flight of concrete stairs was built to connect two floors having a finish-floor-to-finish-floor height of 10′-6″. If each riser was 7 in. high, how many risers were used?

18. Square steel rods measuring $\frac{5}{16}$ in. on each side weigh $\frac{1}{3}$ lb. per linear foot. Determine the total length in feet and inches of a bundle of such rods weighing $23\frac{3}{4}$ lb.

19. Calculate the width of the openings in the set of "pigeonholes" shown in Figure 111. The spaces are of equal width.

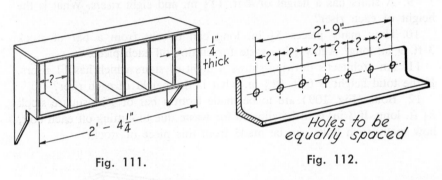

Fig. 111.   Fig. 112.

20. According to the sketch of an angle plate (Fig. 112), seven holes are to be drilled spaced equally distant apart. Determine the length of the center distances as indicated by the question marks.

21. How many risers are needed in building a flight of stairs which connects two floors that are 10 ft. apart? A $7\frac{1}{2}$ in. riser is recommended. Make a sketch showing a layout of these risers.

22. In constructing the special platform shown in Figure 113, the strips are to be $2\frac{1}{2}$ in. wide. Three cross strips of this same thickness and width are used on the bottom. What is the total length of stripping used allowing 2 ft. for the cutting waste?

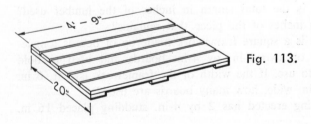

Fig. 113.

23. A temporary fence was put up using planks having a width of 9½ in. How many planks were used if the fence was 47 ft. 6 in. long?

24. One of the early rockets shot off in this country attained a maximum velocity of 3800 miles per hour. Express this velocity in:

a) miles per minute
b) miles per second
c) feet per second

25. The velocity of sound in air at sea level and at 32 deg. F is about 720 miles per hour. This is called Mach 1. Express this velocity in:

a) miles per minute
b) miles per second
c) feet per second

26. In order to escape the gravitational pull of the earth and go out into outer space, a body must have an "escape velocity" of about 7 miles per second. How many miles per hour is this?

10.6   Review Problems Involving Reduction of Measurements

1. Change 8 yd. 2 ft. 4 in. to inches. How many feet are in 8½ rd.? Change 270 in. to yards.

2. A fence encloses the plot of ground shown in Figure 114. If fence posts are located on each corner, and then spaced 8 ft. apart, how many posts will be needed?

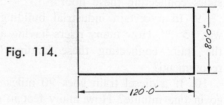

Fig. 114.

3. A rack 9¾ ft. long is to have 15 hooks placed equally distant apart. The center lines of the hooks at each end are to lie 2½ in. from the end. How far apart are the center lines of the other hooks? Draw a plan showing such an arrangement.

4. How many blanks of the following dimensions can be punched from a strip 4 ft. 8 in. long? A space of 1/16 in. is allowed between each

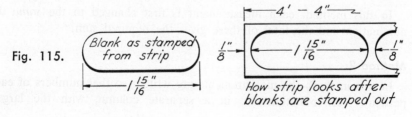

Fig. 115.

How strip looks after blanks are stamped out

punching (Fig. 115). The first blank is started $\frac{1}{4}$ in. in from the end of the strip as illustrated (Fig. 115).

5. The distance between the first and second floors as shown on a set of house plans is 11 ft. 3 in. The building specifications state that the stairs to be erected between these floors are to have 18 risers. What is the height of each of these risers?

6. What would be a suitable riser and tread in stairs which extend from the floor to a balcony, a distance of $3\frac{1}{2}$ ft.? Draw a diagram showing the general dimensions.

7. To make 10 spindles as per specifications in Figure 116, how many linear feet of material are needed? No allowance is made for finishing.

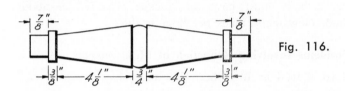

Fig. 116.

8. The finish-floor-to-finish-floor height of a certain commercial building is 11'-3". How many risers whose height is $7\frac{1}{2}$ in. will be needed for stairs connecting these floors?

9. In a certain industrial building the height between two landings was 15'-2". How many risers having a height of 7 in. will be needed for the stairs connecting these landings? How wide a tread would you recommend?

10. If a diesel train goes 90 miles per hour, how many miles does it go in one minute? How many feet in one second?

10.7 Addition of Units of Length

When several measurements involving yards, feet, and inches are to be added, two methods may be used to find the sum.

Method 1:

In this method, each measurement is first changed to the *same* denomination and the total of these gives the required sum.

Method 2:

In this method, the measurements are written so that numbers of each particular denomination are in a separate column, with the largest denomination at the *left*. The separate sums are then found and converted to the denomination desired.

The following examples will illustrate how each method is used.

■ **EXAMPLE 1:**

The inside wall-to-wall width of a building is equal to the sum of the dimensions 12'-10", 10'-8" and 12'-10". What is the total inside width?

Solution and Explanation:

Using Method 1, we can convert each dimension to its equivalent number of inches. Next we find the sum of these three measurements in inches. Dividing this sum by 12, we convert it to feet and inches.

Step 1:
$$12'\text{-}10'' = 144 + 10 = 154 \text{ in.}$$
$$10'\text{-} 8'' = 120 + 8 = 128 \text{ in.}$$
$$12'\text{-}10'' = 144 + 10 = 154 \text{ in.}$$

Step 2: Adding, we have, sum = $\overline{436 \text{ in.}}$

Step 3: Dividing this by 12, we obtain:

$$36\tfrac{4}{12} \text{ ft. or } 36 \text{ ft. } 4 \text{ in.} = 36'\text{-}4''$$

```
       _____
12 | 436
     36
     ___
     76
     72
     ___
      4
```

Thus the total inside width is 36'-4".

Using Method 2, we write

$$
\begin{array}{ll}
12 & \text{ft. } 10 \text{ in.} \\
10 & \text{ft. } 8 \text{ in.} \\
12 & \text{ft. } 10 \text{ in.} \\
\hline
34 & \text{ft. } 28 \text{ in.}
\end{array}
$$

Adding, we obtain

Since 28 in. is over 1 ft., we change 28 in. to 2 ft. 4 in. Adding this to 34 ft. we obtain 36 ft. 4 in. or 36'-4". This agrees with the answer in Method 1 but is considerably shorter.

10.8 Problems Relating to the Addition of Units of Linear Measure

1. Add 3 ft. 0 in., 1 ft. 4 in., $11\tfrac{1}{2}$ in., 6 ft. 6 in. What is the sum of 6 ft. 4 in., 4 ft. 3 in., 4 ft. 8 in., 12 ft. 0 in., and 8 in.?

2. A bill of material listed the following numbers of bars, each $1\tfrac{1}{2}$ in. wide and $\tfrac{1}{8}$ in. thick:

$$3 - 10 \text{ ft. } 6 \text{ in. long}$$
$$4 - 2 \text{ ft. } 8\tfrac{1}{2} \text{ in. long}$$
$$4 - 4 \text{ ft. } 4\tfrac{1}{4} \text{ in. long}$$

What was the total length of these bars?

3. To complete the job of making 110 pins like that in Figure 117, three pieces of stock are used which measure 4 ft. 10., 6 ft. 8 in., and

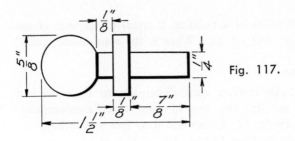

Fig. 117.

3 ft. 9 in. What is the total length of stock used on this job? How many inches were wasted?

4. To build a bookshelf for his room, a young man buys three boards measuring in length, 8 ft. 9 in., 6 ft. 8 in., and 4 ft. 6 in., respectively. What is the total length of this material?

5. A laboratory assistant in an electronics class cut some hookup wire to the following lengths:

$$
\begin{aligned}
&\text{2 pieces} - 6 \text{ in. long}\\
&\text{2 pieces} - 12 \text{ in. long}\\
&\text{3 pieces} - 18 \text{ in. long}\\
&\text{4 pieces} - 24 \text{ in. long}
\end{aligned}
$$

What was the total length of these pieces?

6. What is the perimeter of the lot shown in Figure 118?

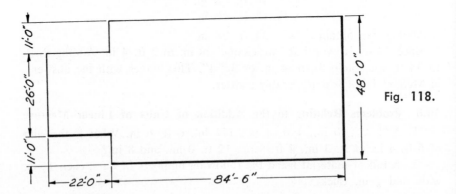

Fig. 118.

7. In selecting the border for a small room a paperhanger takes the following measurements:

1 side — 4 yd. 2 ft. 10 in.
1 side (deducting two windows) — 3 yd. 0 ft. 5 in.
1 side (deducting vent opening) — 4 yd. 1 ft. 0 in.
1 side (deducting a door) — 3 yd. 1 ft. 9 in.

How many yards of border does he need for this job?

8. In measuring a room to determine the number of feet of picture molding needed, one side is found to need 14 ft. 2 in.; another 10 ft. 3 in.; another $6\frac{1}{2}$ ft.; another 9 ft. 1 in. What length of molding is needed?

9. In one section of a sprinkler system installed in a large building the following lengths of pipes were used.

2 lengths — 13 ft. $4\frac{1}{2}$ in.
1 length — 10 ft.   0 in.
2 lengths — 13 ft. 10 in.
2 lengths — 14 ft. $2\frac{1}{2}$ in.

What is the total length of pipe used in this section of the sprinkler system?

10. The following lengths of conduit were used in connection with a light and power installation in a building.

1 length — 6 ft. 10 in.
2 lengths — 10 ft.   0 in.
1 length — 7 ft.   8 in.

What was the total length of conduit used in this installation?

11. In the construction of four steel roof trusses the following lengths of angle iron were used:

1 length — 10 ft.   6   in. long
2 lengths — 8 ft.   5   in. long
3 lengths — 2 ft. $10\frac{1}{2}$ in. long

What was the total length of the angle iron used?

12. A foundation drawing shows a number of footings with their centers spaced 10 ft. 10 in. apart. If there were 20 such spaces what was the distance from the center of the first to the center of the last footing?

13. A radio amateur constructed two high-frequency antennas in which he used the following lengths of 1-in.-dia. aluminum tubing for each:

1 piece — 9 ft. $5\frac{1}{2}$ in. long
1 piece — 8 ft. $7\frac{1}{2}$ in. long
1 piece — 8 ft. $5\frac{1}{4}$ in. long
1 piece — 8 ft. $3\frac{1}{2}$ in. long

What was the total length of tubing he needed for one antenna? for two antennas?

14. The following beams were shown on the floor plan of a steel building:

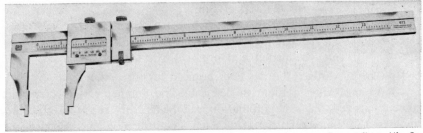

A vernier caliper measures accurately to .001 inch.

> 4 wide-flange beams — 20 ft. 10 in. long
>
> 2 wide-flange beams — 19 ft. 8 in. long

What is the total length of these six beams?

15. Determine the total length of the three timbers as listed, when they are fastened end to end. The three timbers measure 10 ft. 8 in., 11 ft. 10 in., and 8 ft. 9 in., respectively.

10.9 Subtracting Units of Different Denominations

When measurements involving units of two denominations are to be subtracted, the numbers are first arranged in columns the same as in addition; that is, with the higher denominations in the first (leftmost) column and the lower denominations in the second column, and so on.

The process of subtraction is then carried out by first subtracting the numbers of the lower denominations, and then subtracting the numbers of the higher denominations.

The following examples will illustrate how this is accomplished.

■ EXAMPLE 1:

From a steel bar 14 ft. 6 in. long, pieces totaling 9 ft. 3 in. were cut. How long a piece of the original bar remained?

Solution and Explanation:

The number of feet and inches remaining is equal to the difference between the original length and the amount that was cut off. This difference is determined by subtraction as follows.

The units are arranged as explained above and are subtracted separately as shown. The results are placed in their proper columns the same as in addition.

$$
\begin{array}{ll}
14 \text{ ft.} & 6 \text{ in.} \\
\underline{9 \text{ ft.}} & \underline{3 \text{ in.}} \\
5 \text{ ft.} & 3 \text{ in. difference}
\end{array}
$$

The length of bar remaining is 5 ft. 3 in. It will be observed that the units of higher denomination are in the first (left) column, and the units of lower denomination in the second (right) column.

This same result could have been obtained by converting the original length to inches and the total length cut off to inches and then subtracting. The result would then have been changed to feet and inches. However, three operations would have been necessary instead of one.

■ EXAMPLE 2:

Three lengths, each measuring 5 ft. 9 in., 2 ft. 8 in., and 3 ft. 6 in., are cut from a piece of drill rod 14 ft. 6 in. long. How much of the drill rod remains?

Solution and Explanation:

The combined length of the pieces used is found by adding the separate lengths as previously explained. This equals:

$$\begin{array}{rr} 5 \text{ ft.} & 9 \text{ in.} \\ 2 \text{ ft.} & 8 \text{ in.} \\ 3 \text{ ft.} & 6 \text{ in.} \\ \hline 10 \text{ ft.} & 23 \text{ in.} \end{array}$$

As 23 in. equals 1 ft. 11 in., then 10 ft. 23 in. becomes 11 ft. 11 in., which is the total amount cut from the full-length rod.

Since this amount is cut from a rod 14 ft. 6 in. long there remains an amount which is equal to the difference between the original length 14 ft. 6 in. and that which was cut off. In this subtraction the units are arranged as in the previous problem and the subtraction begins with the lower units, inches. This works out as follows:

$$\begin{array}{rr} 13 & 18 \\ \cancel{14} \text{ ft.} & \cancel{6} \text{ in.} \\ 11 \text{ ft.} & 11 \text{ in.} \\ \hline 2 \text{ ft.} & 7 \text{ in.} \end{array}$$

As shown, 11 in. cannot be subtracted from 6 in., so one unit is taken from the next higher denomination "feet," and added to the number of inches. This one unit, 1 ft., equals 12 in., so 12 in. is added to the 6 in. which changes that lower unit to 18 in. This enables the subtraction of the lower units to take place. At the same time it reduces 14 ft. to 13 ft.

The result of this subtraction, as shown, is 2 ft. 7 in.

That is, the length of the drill rod that remains after cutting off the pieces listed equals 2 ft. 7 in.

10.10 Problems Involving Subtraction of Units of Different Denominations

1. Subtract 6 ft. $5\frac{1}{2}$ in. from 11 ft. $7\frac{3}{4}$ in.

   Subtract 18 ft. 10 in. from 42 ft. 4 in.

   Subtract 4 ft. $2\frac{7}{8}$ in. from 10 ft. $6\frac{3}{4}$ in.

   Subtract $8\frac{1}{8}$ in. from 1 ft. 5 in.

   Subtract 2 ft. $0\frac{7}{16}$ in. from 6 ft. $6\frac{1}{4}$ in.

   Subtract $11\frac{1}{8}$ in. from 3 ft. $11\frac{1}{16}$ in.

2. How long a piece of tubing will be left if a 5-ft. $2\frac{1}{2}$-in. length is cut from a 12-ft. 0-in. length?

3. A thin sheet of metal is 6 ft. 0 in. wide. It is slit into 3 pieces. If two of these pieces are each 2 ft. $1\frac{1}{2}$ in. wide, what is the width of the remaining piece? No allowance is made for the width of the slits.

4. Determine the number of feet of $\frac{1}{2}$-in. stock needed in making 26 pieces as per the dimensions of the pin in Figure 119. In cutting

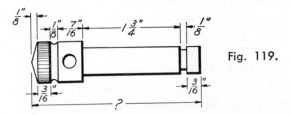

Fig. 119.

these off and finishing them to the size there is a waste of $\frac{3}{16}$ in. on each piece. At this rate how many feet of stock should remain in a 9-ft. bar from which these 26 pieces are made?

5. To build a wooden shelf, two pieces of pine each 3 ft. 10 in. long are cut from a board that measures 12 ft. 6 in. long. Neglecting the width of the saw cut, what is the length of the piece that remains?

6. From a 50-ft. 0-in. length of two-conductor cable, a radio amateur cut two pieces, one 5 ft. $7\frac{1}{4}$ in. long and the other 4 ft. $11\frac{1}{2}$ in. long. What is the length of the cable remaining?

7. What is the length of the dimension marked with a question mark in the drawing of a metal plate (Fig. 120)?

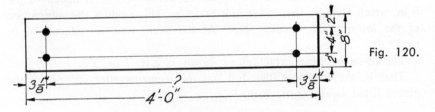

Fig. 120.

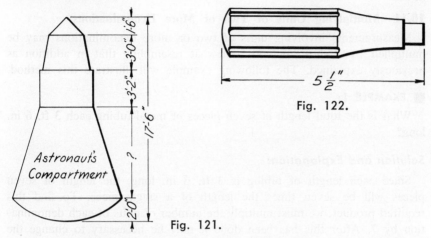

Fig. 122.

Fig. 121.

8. The drawing in Figure 121 shows the outline of a space vehicle. What is the length of the missing dimension?

9. In order to use a 10-in.-wide board for shelving, it is necessary to cut a piece 2 ft. 5 in. long off one end because of knotholes and cracks. The original length of the board was 14 ft. 3 in. What is the length of the piece that remains?

10. Stock for turning 12 screwdriver handles like those in Figure 122 is to be cut from a piece of maple 8 ft. 9 in. long. One inch is added to the length of each handle for finishing and cutting off in the lathe. What is the total amount in feet and inches used? What is the length in feet and inches of the piece that remains?

11. On the floor plan in Figure 123 determine the length of the dimensions that are noted by the question marks.

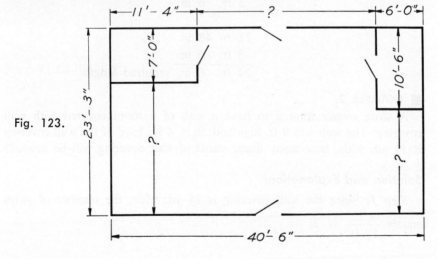

Fig. 123.

10.11 Multiplying Units of Two or More Denominations

Measurements involving units of two or more denominations may be multiplied by a short method somewhat resembling that in addition as previously explained. The following example will illustrate this method.

■ **EXAMPLE 1:**

What is the total length of seven pieces of metal tubing each 3 ft. 6 in. long?

Solution and Explanation:

Since each length of tubing is 3 ft. 6 in. long, the length of seven pieces will be seven times the length of a single piece. To find this required product, we must multiply the number of units of each denomination by 7. After this has been done it may be necessary to change the number of units in the lower denomination to their equivalent in the higher denomination and then express the final result in a commonly accepted form. This is accomplished as follows:

Step 1:
$$\begin{array}{r} 3 \text{ ft.} \quad 6 \text{ in.} \\ \times\ 7 \\ \hline 21 \text{ ft.} \quad 42 \text{ in.} \end{array}$$

Here we multiplied 6 in. by 7 to get 42 in. and we multiplied 3 ft. by 7 to get 21 ft. Since dimensions of this form are given in feet and inches, we proceed to

Step 2: Changing 42 in. to feet and inches gives 3 ft. 6 in. Adding 3 ft. to 21 ft. gives 24 ft. Hence the required length is 24 ft. 6 in.

The work can be arranged as shown:

$$\begin{array}{l} 3 \text{ ft.} \quad 6 \text{ in.} \\ \times\ 7 \\ \hline 21 \text{ ft.} \quad \cancel{42} \text{ in.} \\ 3 \text{ ft.} \quad 6 \text{ in.} \\ \hline 24 \text{ ft.} \quad 6 \text{ in. required length} \end{array}$$

■ **EXAMPLE 2:**

A store owner wanted to have a wall of a room covered with wall covering. The wall was 9 ft. high and 26 ft. 6 in. long. If the wall covering is $1\frac{1}{2}$ yd. wide, how many linear yards of wall covering will be needed?

Solution and Explanation:

Step 1: Since the wall covering is $1\frac{1}{2}$ yd. wide, the number of strips equals $\dfrac{9 \text{ ft.}}{4\frac{1}{2} \text{ ft.}} = 2.$

(The number of strips needed could also be found by dividing 3 yd., the height of the wall, by $1\frac{1}{2}$ yd., the width of one roll, that is, $\dfrac{3 \text{ yd.}}{1\frac{1}{2} \text{ yd.}} = 2$.)

Step 2: The total length of covering will be twice the length of the wall; hence, multiplying 26 ft. 6 in. by 2, we have:

$$
\begin{array}{rr}
26 \text{ ft.} & 6 \text{ in.} \\
\times\, 2 & \\
\hline
52 \text{ ft.} & \cancel{12} \text{ in.} \\
1 \text{ ft.} & 0 \text{ in.} \\
\hline
53 \text{ ft.} & 0 \text{ in.}
\end{array}
$$

Step 3: This is the length of the wall covering in feet and inches. Since the number of linear yards is required, we convert this length to yards by dividing the number of feet by 3. Hence: $\dfrac{53 \text{ ft.}}{3} = 17\frac{2}{3}$ yd.

Therefore, the number of linear yards of wall covering needed is $17\frac{2}{3}$ yd. and 18 yds. would be ordered to take care of cutting and matching.

10.12 Problems Involving Multiplication of Units of Two or More Denominations

1. A man bought 36 sections of fencing each 7 ft. 6 in. long. What was the total length of fence that he bought? If he paid $3.30 for each section, how much did he pay for the entire fence?

2. An order to a woodworking shop calls for 10 table legs as shown in Figure 124. Adding $1\frac{1}{2}$ in. to the length of each leg for waste, what is the total length of stock needed for this order?

Fig. 124.
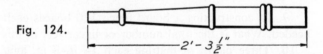
$2' - 3\frac{1}{2}''$

3. A machine shop ordered 20 bars of stainless steel each $1\frac{1}{2}$ in. in diameter and 10 ft. 9 in. long. What was the total length of this material?

4. In the installation of one section of a sprinkler system the following lengths of 2-in.-diameter pipe were used.

1 piece — 9 ft. 2 in. long
3 pieces — 12 ft. 6 in. long
1 piece — 12 ft. $8\frac{1}{2}$ in. long

What was the total length of pipe used in this section?

5. A storm door 6 ft. 10 in. high is constructed by using five boards

each 6 in. wide and 6 ft. 10 in. long. What is the total number of linear feet in the boards used in making this door?

6. A man ordered a floor covering for the kitchen-dinette in his home. The room was 12 ft. wide and 15 ft. long. The floor covering cost $5.10 for a piece 3 ft. by 12 ft. What was the cost of the floor covering?

7. Tile is a very popular type of floor covering. It comes in 9 by 9-in. squares, having an area of 81 sq. in. How many such tiles are needed to cover a floor 13 ft. 6 in. long and 11 ft. 3 in. wide? Allowing five extra tiles for waste and replacement, what would be the total number needed? If the tiles cost 35¢ each, what would be their total cost?

8. In constructing a brace like the one in the following sketch (Fig. 125), two pieces of 2 by 4-in. pine each measuring 1 ft. 10 in. long, and one piece of 2 by 3-in. pine measuring 2 ft. 5 in. long are used. What is the total length of each size needed to make six such braces?

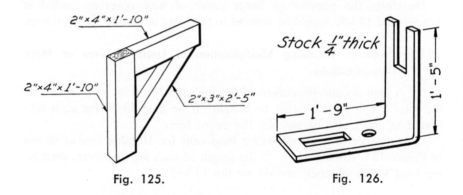

Fig. 125.   Fig. 126.

9. In constructing a board fence 120 boards each 6 ft. 5 in. long are needed. What is the total number of linear feet in this number of boards?

10. Three pieces of matting each 14 ft. 8 in. long are sewed together in one strip for a hall carpet. Deducting an allowance of 6 in. for sewing, what is the total length of this strip?

11. Fifty-four posts each 9 ft. 3 in. on center are used in building a fence enclosing a plot of ground. What is the distance around this plot?

12. To construct a board fence, a carpenter estimated that he would use 86 boards each 4 ft. 9 in. long. How many linear feet does this equal?

13. Determine the total length of flat stock needed to construct four angular braces according to the specifications in Figure 126.

14. To turn out 392 pieces like those in the sketch (Fig. 127), six pieces of stock each 10 ft. 8 in. long are used. What is the total length of material used? What is the percentage of wastage?

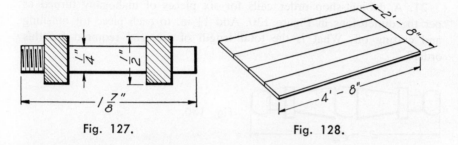

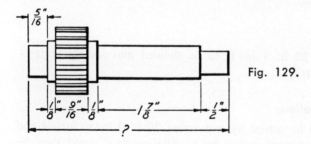

Fig. 127.   Fig. 128.

15. What is the combined length of 8-in. boards needed for the hatchway cover with measurements as illustrated in Figure 128?

16. In order to make a picture frame, 5 ft. 10 in. of picture-frame molding are needed. How many feet of this molding will be required to construct eight such frames?

17. The stockroom boy in a machine shop finds in checking his materials that he has the following ¼-in. flat stock on hand:

    3 pieces — 1   in. wide,   6 ft. 8 in. long
    5 pieces — ¾ in. wide,   8 ft. 5 in. long
    12 pieces — 1½ in. wide, 10 ft. 3 in. long

What is the total length of each size of stock?

18. Four straps of band iron are used around a heavy wooden box containing machine parts labeled "For Export Shipment." Each strip measures 8 ft. 4 in. long. What is the total length of band iron used on this box?

19. To turn out an order of 110 brass-pinion shafts as shown in Figure 129, three pieces of brass stock each 11 ft. 9 in. long were used.

Fig. 129.

What was the total length of stock used? If there was no spoilage or wastage due to cutting off each piece what was the amount of stock needed?

20. Thirty-six pieces of 4 by 4-in. oak each 2 ft. 8 in. long are needed for nine tables. What is the total length in feet and inches of these pieces?

21. A cabinet-shop order calls for six pieces of mahogany turned as per the dimensions in Figure 130. Add $1\frac{1}{4}$ in. to each piece for finishing and cutting off. What is the total length of material required for this order?

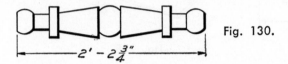

Fig. 130.

22. In punching out an order of 112 blanks as shown in Figure 131, five strips of sheet brass each 3 ft. 8 in. were used. Determine the total length of stripping used. How many inches of material were not used?

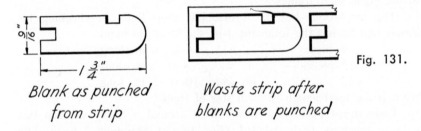

Fig. 131.

Blank as punched from strip   *Waste strip after blanks are punched*

10.13   Division Involving Units of Two or More Denominations

The division of numbers involving units of two or more denominations is carried out by a process similar to that used in multiplying linear units. The manner in which such calculations are carried out is illustrated in the following examples:

■ **EXAMPLE 1:**

A length equal to 20 ft. 9 in. is to be divided into six equal parts. How long is each part?

Solution and Explanation:

This problem could be solved by converting 20 ft. 9 in. to inches and then dividing the number of inches by 6. The quotient could then be changed back to its equivalent in feet and inches. However, the following method is shorter and more convenient.

Since the problem requires that 20 ft. 9 in. be divided into six equal spaces, to find the length of each space we must divide 20 ft. 9 in. by 6. The work is set up in the manner of short division:

$$\begin{array}{r} 2 \text{ ft. } 33 \text{ in.} \\ 6 \enclose{longdiv}{\;\;\not{20} \text{ ft. } \not{9} \text{ in.}} \\ \hline 3 \text{ ft. } 5\frac{1}{2} \text{ in.} \end{array}$$

First we divide 20 ft. by 6, obtaining 3 ft. for the partial quotient and a remainder of 2 ft. A slanting line is drawn through the number 20 to show that it has been divided, the partial quotient 3 ft. is placed *below* it and the remainder, 2 ft., is placed *above* the 20. This remainder, 2 ft., is now converted to 24 in. and is added to 9 in., giving the number 33 which is written above the 9 in.

Next we divide 33 in. by 6, obtaining $5\frac{1}{2}$ in. The complete quotient is 3 ft. $5\frac{1}{2}$ in. The length of each space is 3 ft. $5\frac{1}{2}$ in. as required.

■ EXAMPLE 2:

An iron pipe 20 ft. 6 in. long is to be cut into three equal lengths. How long is each of the pieces?

Solution and Explanation:

Proceeding as in Example 1, we set up the work as in short division. We have:

$$\begin{array}{r} 2 \text{ ft. } 30 \text{ in.} \\ 3 \enclose{longdiv}{\;\;\not{20} \text{ ft. } \not{6} \text{ in.}} \\ \hline 6 \text{ ft. } 10 \text{ in.} \end{array}$$

Now, dividing 20 ft. by 3, we write the partial quotient, 6, below the 20 ft. as shown, and write the remainder, 2 ft. above the 20 ft. The 2 ft. are now converted to 24 in., which, added to 6 in., gives 30 in. Dividing 30 in. by 3, we obtain 10 in. The entire quotient is 6 ft. 10 in.

Hence, each of the three pieces of pipe is 6 ft. 10 in. long.

10.14 Problems Involving Division of Numbers of Two or More Denominations

1. A distance of 1 ft. 9 in. is to be divided into six equal spaces. What is the length of each space?

2. A kitchen floor is 9 ft. wide. How many tiles each 9 in. wide can be laid across this width?

3. Wood joists are to be laid 16 in. apart over a distance of 24 ft. 0 in. (the center-to-center distance is 16 in.). How many joists will be needed? (One more joist must be added to the number of equal spaces to obtain the required number, assuming a joist is placed at each end of the given distance.)

4. A shelf support 18 ft. 8 in. long is to be divided into 14 equal spaces for hat hooks. How far apart will the hat hooks be spaced?

5. An angle iron 10 ft. 9 in. long is to be cut into three equal lengths. Neglecting the width of the saw cut, how long will each piece be?

6. A distance of 45 ft. 0 in. is to be divided into 6 equal spaces, called "bays." What will be the width of each bay?

7. An angle iron is 1 ft. 7½ in. long. Six rivet holes are to be equally spaced on the gauge line of one of the legs of the angle iron as shown in Figure 132. What is the center-to-center distance between the rivet holes?

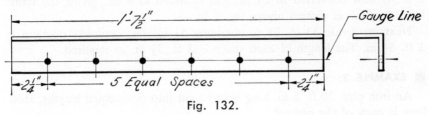

Fig. 132.

8. Seven posts are needed to support a fence 49 ft. 9 in. long. If these posts are set equally far apart (with one at each end), what will be the distance between them? Draw a diagram for this problem.

9. An iron bar 11 ft. 5 in. long is to be cut into five equal pieces. The saw cut is ¼ in. wide. (This allows for cutting and smoothing each length.) Make a layout showing how the bar should be dimensioned for cutting and compute the length of each piece.

10. A corridor 72 ft. 6 in. long has six light fixtures, spaced equally far apart, suspended from its ceiling. What is the distance between the fixtures?

11. How far apart should the light fixtures shown in Figure 133 be spaced assuming that they are equally far apart?

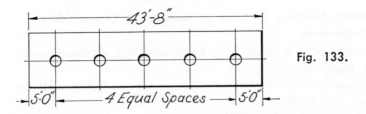

Fig. 133.

12. Figure 134 shows a steel splice plate. What is the length of each of the equal spaces indicated on the drawing? The black circles indicate rivet holes.

13. A distance of 64 ft. 9 in. is to be divided into four sections or bays. What will be the width of each bay?

14. A pipe line 41 ft. 9 in. long is made up of seven lengths of pipe,

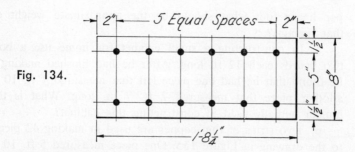

Fig. 134.

one of which is 5 ft. long. If the remaining six pieces are equal in length, how long is each of them?

15. For use in connection with electronics experiments, a laboratory assistant cut 24 ft. of wire into 9-in. lengths; another 24 ft. into 1-ft.-4-in. lengths; and 50 ft. into 2-ft.-6-in. lengths. How many lengths of each did he then have available?

16. What is the weight of 450 ft. of jacketed coaxial cable if a 10-ft. length of the cable weighs 2.5 lb.?

10.15 Review Problems Involving Addition, Subtraction, Multiplication, and Division of Linear Measure

1. Find the sum of the following measurements:
   a) 4 yd. 2 ft.; 5 yd. 10 in.; 1 ft. 4 in.
   b) 35 yd. $2\frac{1}{2}$ ft.; 16 ft. 0 in.; 8 in.
   c) 12 yd. 6 in.; 2 ft. 9 in.; 8 ft. 5 in.
   d) 9 ft. $2\frac{1}{2}$ in.; 12 ft. 3 in.; 26 ft. 11 in.

2. To make up an order of mahogany spindles, three pieces of mahogany were used. One piece measured 3 ft. long, another 2 ft. 5 in. long, and the third piece 3 ft. 10 in. long. What is the combined length of these three pieces?

3. An ornamental iron bracket requires the following four pieces for its construction:

$$
\begin{array}{lll}
1 \text{ piece} & - \ 2 \text{ ft.} & 6 \text{ in.} \\
1 \text{ piece} & - \ 2 \text{ ft.} & 8 \text{ in.} \\
1 \text{ piece} & - \ 3 \text{ ft.} & 5 \text{ in.} \\
1 \text{ piece} & - \ 1 \text{ ft.} & 11 \text{ in.}
\end{array}
$$

This stock weighs $1\frac{1}{2}$ lb. per foot of length. What is the approximate weight of this material?

4. In connection with his day's work a stockroom boy cuts from a steel bar 14 ft. 9 in. long, 3 pieces of stock measuring 2 ft. 9 in., 3 ft. 10 in., and 4 ft. 8 in., respectively. If this stock is listed as weighing 6 lb.

per linear foot what should be the approximate weight of the piece that remains?

5. In constructing a small cabinet for home use a boy purchased two boards each 12 ft. long. After he had finished making the cabinet, he found that he had one piece left that measured 1 ft. 10 in. long and another piece that measured 2 ft. 7 in. long. What is the length of lumber actually used in constructing this cabinet?

6. Two strips of thin copper are used in making 42 pieces according to the drawing in Figure 135. One piece measured 5 ft. 10 in. long and the other 4 ft. 7 in. long. How much material was wasted in making these pieces?

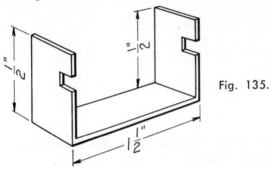

Fig. 135.

7. Three lengths of pipe, 6 ft. 8 in. long, 3 ft. 3 in. long and 2 ft. 1 in. long, respectively, were cut from a length 21 ft. 8 in. long. How much of the original length of pipe was left?

8. From two 12-ft.-0-in. lengths of aluminum tubing the following lengths were cut:

$$4 \text{ pieces} - 2 \text{ ft. } 1 \text{ in. long}$$
$$2 \text{ pieces} - 2 \text{ ft. } 2\frac{1}{4} \text{ in. long}$$
$$4 \text{ pieces} - 2 \text{ ft. } 0 \text{ in. long}$$

How much of the tubing is left over?

9. From an original stock of round tool steel, 6 ft. in length, the following pieces were used: $6\frac{5}{8}$ in., $8\frac{1}{4}$ in., 2 ft. $2\frac{3}{16}$ in., $7\frac{7}{16}$ in. The dimensions given include the wastage due to the saw cut. How much of the original stock is left for future use?

10. A steel rail weighs 660 lb. If this rail weighs 20 lb. per foot, compute its length in feet and in yards.

11. A number 10-gauge steel sheet weighs 5.625 lb. per square foot. What is the weight of a sheet 48 in. by 96 in.?

12. The distance between the center lines of two steel columns is 81 ft. 3 in. This distance is to be divided into five equal spaces or bays. What will be the length of each bay?

13. A property owner has a plot of ground measuring 127 ft. 6 in. by 42 ft. 6 in. He wishes to install a fence around this plot. If he sets a fence post at each corner, and spaces the others at distances of 8 ft. 6 in., how many posts will he need? Make a drawing showing the plot of ground and the location of the fence posts.

14. An aluminum rod 8 ft. 3 in. long is to be cut into four equal lengths. Neglecting the thickness of the saw cuts, what will be the length of each piece?

15. A round cold-finished steel bar is 12 ft. long and is to be cut into eight equal pieces. If the bar weighs 2.12 lb. per foot, what will be the weight of each piece?

16. A building is located inside a rectangular plot of ground 128 ft. 0 in. long by 104 ft. 0 in. wide. Fence posts are erected at each corner of the plot, and the other posts are located 8 ft. 0 in. apart. Make a drawing showing the location of the posts and determine how many will be needed.

17. A shipment of aluminum bars consisted of the following lots:

   a) 10 bars, 11 ft. 3 in. long, weighing 0.90 lb. per foot
   b) 24 bars, 10 ft. 9 in. long, weighing 1.49 lb. per foot
   c) 12 bars, 9 ft. 6 in. long, weighing 7.19 lb. per foot

Compute the total weight of the bars:

   a) in each lot
   b) in the three lots

18. The following steel shapes were shipped to a steel fabricating plant:

   a) 20 columns, 29 ft. 6 in. long, weighing 150 lb. per foot
   b) 48 light beams, 15 ft. 9 in. long, weighing 18.5 lb. per foot
   c) 20 base plates, weighing 1045 lb. each

Compute the weight of each set of shapes and the weight of the entire shipment.

19. What is the length of a coil of wire weighing 37.7 lb. if 26 ft. 6 in. of the wire weighs 1 lb.?

20. If the weight of a bolt with a square head and a hexagonal nut is $2\frac{3}{4}$ lb., how many bolts of this kind are there in a shipment weighing 825 lb.?

CHAPTER 11

Board Measure

11.1 Introduction

In this chapter we will consider problems involving computations with lumber. Topics dealing with board measure, kinds of lumber, calculations of board feet, estimates, and practical applications will be considered. This will provide a good working introduction to how lumber is described, measured, ordered, and used.

11.2 Calculating Board Feet

Although linear units are used in measuring *lengths* of lumber, the *amount* or *quantity* of lumber is measured in a standard unit, called a *board foot*.

This unit of lumber measure may be considered as equivalent to a board 1 in. thick, 12 in. wide, and 12 in. long, or to a board having the *same volume*. Such a board contains one board foot. This unit is abbreviated bd. ft. For example, we write 40 bd. ft., 100 bd. ft.

The number of board feet in a given piece of lumber is determined by multiplying the *thickness* in inches by the width in feet, by the length in feet. Thicknesses less than 1 in. are to be considered as 1 in. in such calculations.

Board feet = Thickness in inches × width in feet × length in feet

The abbreviation "ft. b.m." is used instead of "feet board measure." For example, we write 500 ft. b.m. for 500 feet board measure.

The following sketches will help in making clear the meaning of board measure. Each of the pieces shown (Fig. 136) is equivalent to 1 ft. b.m.

Each of the four pieces shown contains 1 bd. ft. of lumber. Piece number 1 is 1 in. thick, 1 ft. wide and 1 ft. long. Then

$$\text{bd. ft.} = 1 \times 1 \times 1 = 1$$

Thus piece No. 1 contains 1 ft. board measure. Piece No. 2 is 2 in. thick, $\frac{4}{12}$ ft. or $\frac{1}{3}$ ft. wide and $\frac{18}{12}$ ft. or $1\frac{1}{2}$ ft. long. Then

$$\text{bd. ft.} = 2 \times \tfrac{1}{3} \times 1\tfrac{1}{2}$$

or

$$\text{bd. ft.} = 2 \times \tfrac{1}{3} \times \tfrac{3}{2} = 1$$

Thus piece No. 2 contains 1 bd. ft. of lumber. This could have been computed by leaving the width as $\frac{4}{12}$ ft. and the length as $\frac{18}{12}$ ft. Thus:

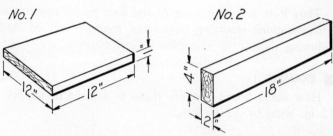

Fig. 136.

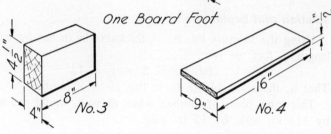

$$\text{bd. ft.} = \overset{1}{\cancel{2}} \times \frac{\overset{1}{\cancel{4}}}{\underset{\cancel{6}}{\cancel{12}}} \times \frac{\overset{\overset{1}{\cancel{3}}}{\cancel{18}}}{\underset{\cancel{3}}{\cancel{12}}} = 1$$

Piece No. 3 is 4 in. thick, 4½ in. wide, and 8 in. long. Changing the width and length to feet, we have 4½ in. $= \frac{9}{24} = \frac{3}{8}$ ft. (width).

$$8 \text{ in.} = \tfrac{8}{12} = \tfrac{2}{3} \text{ ft. (length)}$$

Using the formula for ft. b.m. we get:

$$\text{bd. ft.} = \overset{1}{\cancel{4}} \times \frac{\overset{1}{\cancel{3}}}{\underset{\underset{1}{\cancel{4}}}{\cancel{8}}} \times \frac{\overset{1}{\cancel{2}}}{\cancel{3}}$$

or
bd. ft. $= 1$

Piece No. 4 is ½ in. thick, 9 in. wide, and 16 in. long. Changing the width and length to feet, we get

$$\tfrac{9}{12} = \tfrac{3}{4} \text{ ft. (width)}$$
$$\tfrac{16}{12} = \tfrac{4}{3} \text{ ft. (length)}$$

Remembering that a thickness less than 1 in. must be considered as 1 in., we have:

$$\text{bd. ft.} = 1 \times \tfrac{3}{4} \times \tfrac{4}{3}$$
$$\text{bd. ft.} = 1$$

Thus it is seen that each of the four pieces contains one board foot. Calculations involving board-foot measure will be made clear in the following illustrative examples.

■ **EXAMPLE 1:**

How many board feet are there in a piece of lumber 2 in. thick by 12 in. wide by 12 ft. long?

Solution and Explanation:

Using the formula bd. ft. = thickness in inches by width in feet by length in feet we get:
$$\text{bd. ft.} = 2 \times 1 \times 12 = 24$$
That is, there are 24 bd. ft. in this piece of lumber.

This same piece of lumber, when **dressed,** would measure $1\frac{5}{8}$ in. thick by $11\frac{1}{2}$ in. wide by 12 ft. long.

■ **EXAMPLE 2:**

Determine the number of board feet in 60 floor joists, each 2 in. by 10 in. by 14 ft.

Solution and Explanation:

Using the formula for finding board feet, we have
$$\text{bd. ft.} = \text{thickness in inches by width in feet by length in feet}$$
$$\text{bd. ft.} = 2 \times \tfrac{10}{12} \times 14$$
$$= \tfrac{70}{3} \text{ (in one joist)}$$
In 60 joists, the total number of board feet is:
$$\text{bd. ft.} = 60 \times \tfrac{70}{3}$$
$$\text{bd. ft.} = 1400$$
This could have been computed in one step as follows:
$$\text{total bd. ft.} = 60 \times 2 \times \tfrac{10}{12} \times 14$$
$$\text{total bd. ft.} = 1400$$

11.3 Lumber Terms

Large quantities of lumber are bought and sold by the thousand board-feet measure, abbreviated M ft. b.m. or M ft., b.m. (M is the Roman 1000). Thus, long leaf yellow pine, 3 in. by 12 in., rough, in lengths up to 20 ft. sold for $139.00 per M ft., b.m. This means that this type of lumber sold for $139.00 per thousand board feet.

Certain types of lumber, including moldings, furring strips, interior trim, subflooring, and roof boards, are sold by the linear foot.

Lumber is classified according to its uses. Yard lumber is used for the building trades primarily. In this classification are included, among other sizes, 2 by 4's, 2 by 8's, 2 by 10's, and such items as flooring, moldings, common boards, siding, and other types of dimension lumber. Lumber can be purchased in either "rough stock" or "dressed stock." Rough stock is lumber that has not been planed or smoothed. It is lumber as it leaves the saw mill. *Dressed* lumber is lumber that has been *planed* or *surfaced* on one or more sides as required. Dressed lumber can be used for finished work, trim, and cabinet work.

When lumber is dressed on one side only, it is designated S1S. When it is dressed on both sides, it is marked S2S. When it is dressed on both sides and both edges it is marked S4S. The designation D and M means "dressed and matched." It is applied to wood flooring that has been tongued and grooved.

It should be remembered that when lumber is dressed, its size is reduced by the amount removed when it is run through the planer. For example, a piece of rough lumber leaving the saw mill may be a 2 by 12, that is, it is 2 in. thick and 12 in. wide. These are its nominal *dimensions*. After it is *dressed,* its size becomes $1\frac{5}{8}$ in. thick by $11\frac{1}{2}$ in. wide. A board, called a 1 by 8, that is, one whose nominal dimensions are 1 in. thick by 8 in. wide, when dressed, will be $\frac{25}{32}$ in. thick and $7\frac{1}{2}$ in. wide.

11.4 Plywood

In recent years the use of plywood for building purposes has increased tremendously. Plywood may be considered as laminated lumber, that is, lumber made up into *panels* by gluing an *odd* number of thin layers of wood veneers together. In making plywood, successive layers of thin sheets of wood, between $\frac{1}{8}$ in. to $\frac{1}{10}$ in. in thickness and coated with certain types of glues are laid crosswise to each other and pressed together. By placing various layers crosswise on top of each other, advantage is taken of the physical properties of the wood and the result is a type of wood product which is strong, light in weight, and split-proof.

In addition to these qualities, plywood is available in large *panels* and in various *plies* or thicknesses. It is easy to handle, saw, and cut with the ordinary tools available to the carpenter.

Although there are many kinds of plywood, most of the plywood used for building purposes is a softwood plywood, made from Douglas fir. Of this Douglas fir plywood, two types are in common use: interior plywood and exterior plywood.

When interior plywood is put together (after the various layers have been properly prepared) it is subjected to pressures of 50 to 70 tons per square foot at room temperature until the adhesive has set. It is then cut to size, sanded, and graded.

Exterior plywood is manufactured in the same way as interior plywood, but the adhesives used are completely waterproof. The plywood for exterior use is subjected to pressures up to nearly 20 tons per square foot, while between plates heated to temperatures of about 250 deg. F. This produces a material able to withstand repeated wetting, drying, and exposure to the elements.

Interior Douglas fir plywood is available in several widths. A width of 48 in. is in very common use, and in lengths of 72, 84, 96, 108, 120, and 144 in. Thicknesses run from $\frac{1}{4}$ in. to 1 in. in steps of $\frac{1}{8}$ in. The number of plies are 3 or 5 for thickness up to $\frac{3}{4}$ in. and 7 plies for $\frac{7}{8}$- and 1-in. thicknesses.

Plywood is also available in various grades, commonly running from A to D. It is labeled by two letters, the first referring to the *face* of the plywood and the second referring to the back of the plywood. Thus, common designations are exterior A-A, A-B, A-D, etc., or interior A-A, A-B, B-D, etc.

Plywood is sold by the *square foot*. It can be ordered as follows: Douglas fir plywood: 50 pieces, 5 ply, 48 in. by 96 in., Interior type, A-A grade, sanded 2 sides (abbreviated S2S) to $\frac{1}{2}$-in. thickness.

Plywood is used in residences for new construction or remodeling. It finds application in subfloors, interior walls and ceilings, exterior siding, and many other uses. Much plywood is used in prefabricated house construction. Other applications are found in farm buildings, in display boards, in commercial and factory buildings.

Exterior plywood is used in boat construction and in the construction of concrete forms.

The following problem deals with the ordering and cost of a quantity of plywood.

■ EXAMPLE 1:

A homeowner, wishing to make some play yards for his small children, ordered the following quantity of plywood:

Douglas fir plywood, 3 pieces, 5 ply, 48 in. by 96 in., Exterior type A-C grade. At 28 cents per square foot, what is the cost of this quantity of plywood?

Solution and Explanation:

One panel of this plywood has an area of 4 by 8 or 32 sq. ft. Three panels have an area of 3 by 32 or 96 sq. ft. At 28 cents per square foot, the cost is:

$$96 \times 0.28 = \$26.88$$

The cost of this quantity of plywood is $26.88.

11.5   Problems Involving Calculations Pertaining to Lumber and Plywood

1. How many board feet are there in each linear foot of a piece of framing lumber 2 in. thick measuring 4 in. wide; 6 in. wide; 8 in. wide; 12 in. wide?

2. Three rooms of a residence have a total area of 688 sq. ft. In order to determine the number of *board feet* of flooring needed, including a small percent for waste, 38 percent is added to this figure, making the total area 949 sq. ft., or 950 sq. ft. in round numbers. This is then equal to the number of board feet of flooring needed. If the cost of this flooring is 32 cents per board foot, what will be the total cost of the flooring?

3. The total area of three rooms of a residence equals 460 sq. ft. To find the equivalent number of board feet of flooring, this is increased by 38 percent. How many board feet of flooring will be needed? If flooring cost 30 cents per board foot, what will be the cost of the flooring for these rooms?

4. At 32 cents per *linear* foot, what will be the cost of the lumber needed to make the piece illustrated in Figure 137? Allow 20 percent for waste. All material is ¾ in. thick.

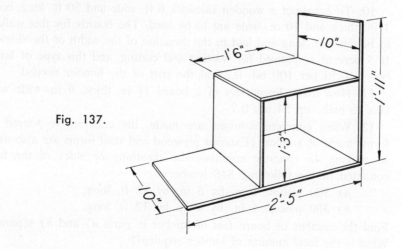

Fig. 137.

5. A builder buys 26 pieces of No. 1 Fir, 2 in. by 12 in. by 18 ft. long. Find *a*) the number of board feet in this quantity of lumber, *b*) the cost if it sold for $13.80 per 100 bd. ft.

6. What is the total cost of Douglas fir plywood: 10 pieces, 5 ply, 48 in. by 96 in., Interior type, A-D grade, sanded two sides to ⅝-in. thickness, if it sells at 28 cents per square foot?

7. A homeowner wished to soundproof his study room. The ceiling

of this room measured 11 ft. by 11 ft. He bought acoustical tile measuring 12 in. by 12 in. Find:

   a) How many pieces of tile were needed.

   b) The cost of the tile at 16 cents each.

   c) The total cost if a sales tax of 3 percent is added to the cost of the tile.

8. During the construction of a large building it was necessary to use 400 Douglas fir planks 2 in. by 12 in. by 14 ft. 0 in. for scaffolding. Find:

   a) The number of board feet of lumber in one plank.

   b) The number of board feet of lumber in the 400 planks.

9. In replacing the porch flooring in an apartment building the number of board feet needed was found by adding 33 percent to the area of the floors (expressed in square feet). If there were six porches, each 7 ft. by 18 ft., find:

   a) The area of one porch in square feet.

   b) The area of six porches in square feet.

   c) The board feet needed for the six porches.

   d) The cost of the flooring if it sold for $25.00 per hundred board feet.

10. To construct a wooden sidewalk 6 ft. wide and 50 ft. long, boards 1 in. thick and 10 in. wide are to be used. The boards for this walk are to be cut 6 ft. long and laid in the direction of the width of the sidewalk. If 5 percent is allowed for wasting and cutting, and this type of lumber cost $10.50 per 100 bd. ft., find the cost of the lumber needed.

11. How many linear feet of a board $1\frac{1}{2}$ in. thick, 9 in. wide will it take to make up 54 bd. ft.?

12. When concrete columns are made, the concrete is poured into forms made of lumber. (Exterior plywood and steel forms are also used.) In making 48 concrete columns, the sheathing or sides of the forms consisted of the following S4S lumber:

   a) 500 pieces, 1 in. by 6 in. by 12 ft. long.

   b) 300 pieces, 1 in. by 4 in. by 12 ft. long.

Find the number of board feet of lumber in parts a) and b) separately. What is the total amount of lumber required?

13. When lumber is bought in small quantities prices may be quoted by the linear foot. Find the cost of each of the following lots and the total cost:

   a) 10 planks, 2 in. by 6 in. by 14 ft. at 18 cents per linear foot.

   b) 18 planks, 2 in. by 8 in. by 12 ft. at 24 cents per linear foot.

   c) 6 planks, 2 in. by 12 in. by 12 ft. at 35 cents per linear foot.

14. How many board feet of lumber are there in 5000 railway ties each

8 in. by 8 in. by 8 ft. long? If each of these ties costs $3.80, what is the cost of 5000 of them?

15. In the construction of a railing for a walkway 30 pieces of lumber were used, each 2 in. by 4 in. by 10 ft. How many board feet of lumber are there in one piece? In the entire lot?

16. A builder bought the following quantities of clear redwood all S4S:

    a) 10 pieces, 1 in. by 12 in. by 14 ft. long.

    b) 5 pieces, 1 in. by 12 in. by 12 ft. long.

    c) 10 pieces, 1 in. by 12 in. by 10 ft. long.

If the cost of this lumber was 34 cents per board foot, find the number of board feet in each lot, the cost of each lot and the total cost.

17. Calculate the total number of board feet in the following pieces of lumber:

    150 pieces, 1 in. by 2 in. by 8 ft.

    12 pieces, 1 in. by 4 in. by 12 ft.

    10 pieces, 2 in. by 4 in. by 8 ft.

18. A load of Douglas fir lumber used for the repair of a building consisted of the following:

    a)   70 pieces, 2 in. by 8 in. by 16 ft.

    b) 120 pieces, 2 in. by 4 in. by 16 ft.

    c)   40 pieces, 4 in. by 4 in. by 16 ft.

Find the number of board feet in *a*), *b*), and *c*); find the number of board feet in the 230 pieces.

19. A man ordered the following lumber for making some home repairs:

    30 pieces, 1 in. by 3 in. by 10 ft. No. 2 spruce

    4 pieces, 2 in. by 4 in. by 16 ft. No. 1 fir

    3 pieces, 2 in. by 8 in. by 16 ft. No. 1 fir

If the cost of this lumber is 14 cents per board foot, find the total cost of the pieces listed above.

20. A man buys 40 bundles of rock lath to use as a plaster base in constructing his home. If each bundle contains six pieces 16 in. by 48 in., and the cost is 4.7 cents per square foot, find the total cost of this lath.

21. For making repairs, 200 lengths of knotty pine 1 in. by 10 in. by 18 ft. were cut into 3-ft. lengths. How many 3-ft. lengths were available? How many board feet of lumber were there in one 18-ft. length? In the 200 18-ft. lengths?

22. How many linear feet of board 1 in. thick by 6 in. wide will it take to make 68 bd. ft.?

23. Calculate the total board feet in the following bill of material:

2 pieces, fir, 4 in. by 6 in. by $8\frac{1}{2}$ ft.

2 pieces, fir, 2 in. by 8 in. by 12 ft.

5 pieces, pine, $1\frac{1}{2}$ in. by 8 in. by 10 ft.

2 pieces, pine, $\frac{7}{8}$ in. by 9 in. by 12 ft.

24. Thin strips of wood, usually of the same thickness as the lath and plaster, are attached to the framing before plastering is done. These strips are called *plaster grounds* and are sold by the lineal foot. Find the cost of 600 feet of $\frac{7}{8}$ in. by 1 in. plaster grounds if each lineal foot costs $1\frac{3}{4}$ cents.

25. How many board feet are there in 50 pieces of 1 in. by 8 in. by 12 ft. clear redwood D and M and V jointed? If this cost 33 cents per board foot, what is the cost of this amount of lumber?

26. In constructing a garage, a man ordered 30 pieces of lumber 2 in. by 4 in. by 14 ft. long. How many board feet were there in each piece? in the 30 pieces? If this lumber cost 13 cents per board foot, what was the total cost of the 30 pieces?

11.6   Review Problems Involving Calculations in Board Measure

1. Calculate the number of board feet in the following list of lumber:

   a) 10 pieces, fir, 2 in. by 8 in. by 12 ft. 0 in.

   b) 20 pieces, fir, 2 in. by 4 in. by 12 ft. 0 in.

   c) 12 pieces, pine, $1\frac{1}{2}$ in. by 9 in. by 12 ft. 0 in.

   d) 8 pieces, chestnut, 1 in. by 9 in. by 14 ft. 0 in.

2. What is the cost of 16 pieces of insulating sheathing, 4 ft. by 8 ft., if it sells at 15 cents per square foot?

3. What is the cost of Douglas fir plywood, 16 pieces, 5 ply, 48 in. by 96 in., Exterior type, A-C grade if it sells at 32 cents per square foot?

4. How many board feet of 1 in. by 8 in. sheathing 12 ft. long will be required for a partition that measures 12 ft. high and 24 ft. long? An allowance of $12\frac{1}{2}$ percent is made for waste.

5. Part of the lumber needed to construct a horse barricade used in a construction area requires the following lumber:

   1 piece, 2 in. by 6 in. by 8 ft. 0 in.

   4 pieces, 1 in. by 4 in. by 2 ft. 6 in.

   4 pieces, 2 in. by 4 in. by 3 ft. 6 in.

How many board feet are there in this quantity of lumber?

6. How many board feet of lumber are there in each of the following pieces?

   a) 20 pieces, 1 in. by 3 in. by 12 ft. long

   b) 4 pieces, 1 in. by 2 in. by 6 ft. long

   c) 4 pieces, 1 in. by 8 in. by 8 ft. long

   d) 12 pieces, 2 in. by 4 in. by 6 ft. long

What is the total number of board feet?

7. Signs for the guidance and control of traffic were mounted on wooden posts whose dimensions were 4 in. by 4 in. by 14 ft. 0 in. How many board feet of lumber are there in one post? in 100 posts?

8. In the construction of a framed wooden arch the following structural lumber was used:

  a) 4 pieces, 4 in. by 12 in. by 12 ft. 0 in.
  b) 6 pieces, 4 in. by 6 in. by 12 ft. 0 in.
  c) 1 piece, 4 in. by 6 in. by 14 ft. 0 in.
  d) 2 pieces, 2 in. by 6 in. by 14 ft. 0 in.

Find:

  1) The number of board feet of lumber in parts *a*), *b*), *c*) and *d*).
  2) The total number of board feet needed for one arch.
  3) The total number of board feet needed for eight such arches.

CHAPTER 12

Computation of Areas

12.1 Introduction

Workers in the shops and in the trades are expected to be able to compute the areas of figures commonly dealt with in their work. In almost every branch of industry, problems arise which require the computation of the areas of simple and also fairly complicated figures. It is important that the student acquire a good working knowledge of how this is done. For a clear understanding of this work we will need some of the ideas of plane geometry.

12.2 Plane Figures

Basic Definitions. A *point* may be considered as having neither length, width, nor thickness — that is, it has no size. It can be said to have position only. It is usually represented by a dot, with a letter to designate it. Thus .*A* can be read "point *A*." A *line* may be thought of as being the path of a moving point. A line has *length* only — it has no width or thickness. A line is said to be *straight* if it extends in the same direction, and it is usually marked by placing a capital letter at each of its "ends." Thus *A*——*B* is read "the line *AB*," each letter being read separately. We may also think of a point as being the intersection of two straight lines.

Angles and Angular Measurement. If we take the line *AB*, and rotate it around the point *A*, counterclockwise, to the position *C*, we form

A protractor for measuring angles.

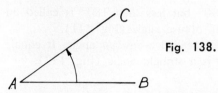

Fig. 138.

the angle *BAC* (Fig. 138). The line *AB* is called the *initial side* of the angle. The line *AC* is called the *terminal side* of the angle. The point *A* is called the *vertex* of the angle. To show the direction of rotation, we put a curved arrow between the initial and the terminal position of the line *AB*, with the *tail* of the arrow always on the *initial* side of the angle. We read the angle by three letters, the *vertex* letter being the middle one *always,* or by a single letter at the vertex.

A *degree* is the unit of angular measure most commonly used in computational work. It is $\frac{1}{360}$ of the complete rotation of a line around one of its points. The degree has its submultiples, the minute ($\frac{1}{60}$ of a degree) and the second ($\frac{1}{3600}$ of a degree or $\frac{1}{60}$ of a minute). The symbols used in angular measure are the small circle °, placed above and to the right of the number which is to be specified as *degrees,* the ', placed in a similar way, and used to denote the number of minutes, and the ", also placed in the same way as the symbol for degrees, and used to denote the number of seconds. Thus 35° 18' 45" is read thirty-five degrees, eighteen minutes, forty-five seconds. The marks ' and " are not to be confused with the same marks used to denote feet and inches.

An angle containing less than 90° is called an *acute* angle. Thus angle *BAC* is an acute angle (Fig. 139).

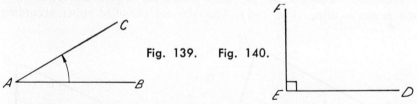

Fig. 139.   Fig. 140.

An angle containing *exactly* 90° is called a right angle. Thus angle *DEF* is a right angle (Fig. 140). The small square placed at the vertex is always used to denote a right angle. We also know that the two sides, *DE* and *EF,* are perpendicular to each other when we see the small square at *E*.

Fig. 141.

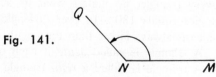

An angle containing more than 90° but less than 180° is called an *obtuse* angle. Thus angle *MNQ* is an obtuse angle (Fig. 141).

An angle containing exactly 180° is called a *straight* angle. It equals two right angles. Thus angle *UVW* is a straight angle (Fig. 142).

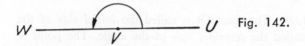

W ——————————————————— U   Fig. 142.

Polygons. The figures whose areas we will be called on to find will be plane figures. We say that a *polygon* is a plane figure bounded by three or more sides. If the number of sides is five, we call the polygon a *pentagon;* if it is six, we call it a *hexagon.* If the sides of a polygon are all of the same length, and all its angles are equal to each other, we say the polygon is a *regular* polygon. Figures 143, 144, and 145 show some

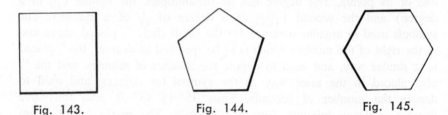

Fig. 143.   Fig. 144.   Fig. 145.

of the most common regular polygons. The square and the hexagon are used in the manufacture of nuts and bolts.

Triangles. Triangles are polygons having the fewest number of sides and angles — three (Fig. 146). Triangles are classified either according

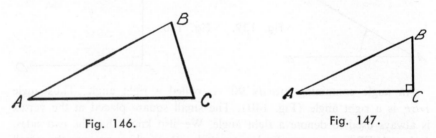

Fig. 146.   Fig. 147.

to the size of their angles or according to the length of their sides. In every triangle, no matter what its size or shape, the sum of the three angles equals 180°. In every triangle, also, the total length of any two sides is always larger than the length of the third side.

A triangle is called *acute* if each of its angles is an acute angle.

A triangle is called a *right* triangle if *one* of its angles is a right angle

(Fig. 147). The sides *AC* and *CB* are called the legs, and the side *AB,* opposite the right angle, is called the *hypotenuse.*

A triangle is called an *obtuse* triangle if *one* of its angles is an obtuse angle (Fig. 148).

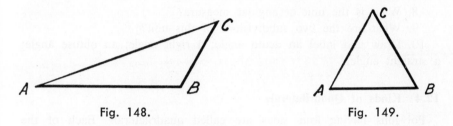

Fig. 148.   Fig. 149.

A triangle whose angles are each equal to each other (60° each) is an *equiangular* triangle (Fig. 149).

Such a triangle is also called an *equilateral* triangle because its three sides are of equal length. Thus a triangle which is equilateral is also equiangular, and vice versa.

A triangle is called *isosceles* if any two of its sides are the same in length (Fig. 150). In the isosceles triangle shown, the equal sides, called legs, are *AC* and *BC*. The angles *A* and *B*, opposite the legs, are called base angles and each is equal to the other. Thus every isosceles triangle has two of its sides equal in length and two of its angles equal in size. If we know that a triangle has any two of its sides equal in length or any two of its angles equal in size, we know it is an isosceles triangle.

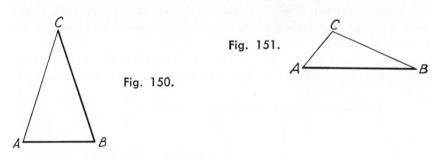

Fig. 151.

Fig. 150.

A triangle is called *scalene* if no two of its sides are equal in length (Fig. 151).

12.3 Questions on Plane Figures

1. Why is it important to know how areas are computed?
2. Describe a point in two ways. How is a point labeled?

3. Describe a line. How is a line labeled?

4. What is a straight line?

5. What is the intersection of any two straight lines?

6. How is an angle formed?

7. What are two ways of reading an angle?

8. What is the unit of angular measure?

9. What are the two subdivisions of this unit?

10. Draw and label an acute angle; a right angle; an obtuse angle; a straight angle.

12.4 Kinds of Quadrilaterals

Polygons having four sides are called quadrilaterals. Each of the common kinds of quadrilaterals has its own particular name.

A quadrilateral having *two* of its sides parallel is called a trapezoid (Fig. 152). The side *AB* is called the larger base; the side *DC,* which is

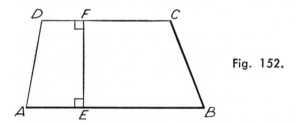

Fig. 152.

parallel to *AB,* is called the smaller base. The perpendicular distance, *EF,* between the two bases is called the altitude of the trapezoid. If the sides *AD* and *BC* happen to be equal, the trapezoid is known as an isosceles trapezoid.

A quadrilateral whose opposite sides are parallel is called a *parallelogram.* Thus, in Figure 153, if *AB* and *DC* are parallel, and *AD* and *BC*

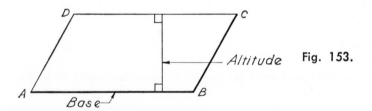

Altitude Fig. 153.

are parallel, then the quadrilateral is a parallelogram. The side *AB* is called the base, and the perpendicular distance between *AB* and *DC* is called the altitude.

A parallelogram whose angles are all right angles is called a *rectangle* (Fig. 154). We can call the longer side *AB* the base, and *BC* or *AD* the altitude of the rectangle.

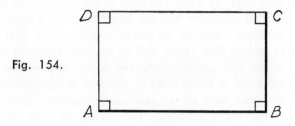

Fig. 154.

A rectangle whose sides are all of the same length is called a *square* (Fig. 155).

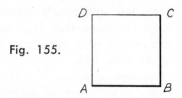

Fig. 155.

12.5 Common Units of Square Measure

In order to obtain the area of any figure, the procedure is to (1) select a unit of area; (2) see how many times this unit is contained in the figure whose area we are trying to find. Suppose the area of a rectangle 5 in. long and 3 in. high is to be found (Fig. 156). The length of the base is now divided into five equal spaces, *each 1 in. long*. Through the

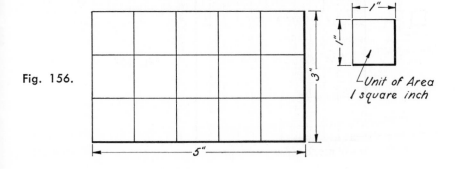

Fig. 156.

Unit of Area
1 square inch

points of division of the bases, lines are drawn parallel to the vertical sides. The height is next divided into three equal spaces, *each 1 in. long,* and lines parallel to the base are drawn through the points of division. The result is that the rectangle is now covered completely by *15* squares, each 1 in. by 1 in. The area of the rectangle is said to be 15 sq. in.

It is necessary that the length and the height of the rectangle must be in linear units of the same denomination, that is, they must both be in inches, feet, yards, and so on. The area will then be in square inches, square feet, square yards, and so on, respectively. If the length and width are given in linear units of different denominations, they must be changed to linear units of the same denomination before the area can be found.

The above procedure for finding the area of a rectangle is equivalent to determining how many squares 1 in. by 1 in. will be contained in the given rectangle. Here the *unit* of area is the square inch. For larger or smaller areas, appropriate units should be used, so that the *numerical value* of the area would be a *convenient* number to handle. It would be ridiculous, for example, to give the area of a workbench in fractions of a square mile and equally ridiculous to give the area of a farm in square inches or square feet. One number would be a small decimal and the other would be a very large one — each equally inconvenient to write and to work with.

Common sense and experience help us to select the appropriate unit of area to use when we determine the area of a particular figure.

A larger unit of area is the square foot. This is the area of a square 1 ft. by 1 ft.

Using the same procedure as for the rectangle described above, the square is divided into 144 smaller squares, each 1 in. by 1 in. (Fig. 157). Thus, 1 sq. ft. has the same area as 144 sq. in., or 144 sq. in. = 1 sq. ft.

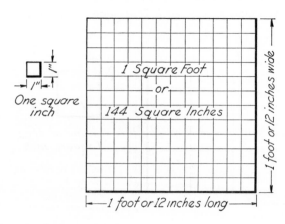

Fig. 157.

A still larger unit is the square yard (Fig. 158) This is the area of a square 1 yd. by 1 yd. If this square were divided into squares 1 ft. by 1 ft., it would be found that nine such squares would be contained in 1 sq. yd. Consequently, the area of 1 sq. yd. equals the same area as 9 sq. ft.

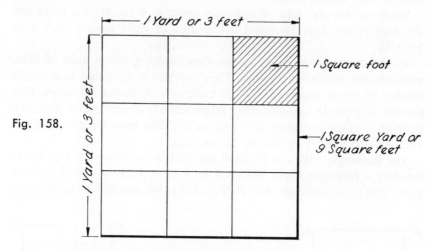

Fig. 158.

The particular unit to use depends on the size of the area to be computed. For small areas, the square inch and square foot are normally used. For larger areas, the square yard is used. In the measurement of land, especially on the farm, square rods and acres are used. In very large sections of land the square mile would be suitable as a unit of area.

The following table gives the commonly used units of area and will help in changing units of area from one denomination to another.

Table of Common Units of Square Measure

144 square inches (sq. in.)	= 1 square foot (sq. ft.)
9 square feet	= 1 square yard (sq. yd.) = 1296 sq. in.
$30\frac{1}{4}$ square yards	= 1 square rod (sq. rd.) = $272\frac{1}{4}$ sq. ft.
160 square rods	= 1 acre (A.) = 4840 sq. yd. = 43,560 sq. ft.
640 acres	= 1 square mile (sq. mi.)

12.6 Area of Common Geometric Figures

The fundamental unit of area is the square whose sides are each one linear unit in length. A square whose sides are each 1 in. long has an area of one *square* inch. A square whose sides are each 1 ft. long has an area of one *square* foot.

When we say the area of a certain figure is 8 sq. in., we mean that the area of the figure is equal to the area of eight squares each 1 in. by 1 in.

In the computation of areas, two dimensions, given in units of linear measure, are multiplied together. Their product is expressed as a certain number of *square* units. Thus, when inches are multiplied by inches, their product is given in square inches. When feet are multiplied by feet, their product is given in square feet, and so on. The most common units of area are abbreviated sq. in., sq. ft., sq. yd.

The Rectangle. We can visualize this idea in the following way. Let us consider a rectangle whose base is 5 in. long and whose altitude is 4 in. high. This is the rectangle *ABCD* (Fig. 159). We can divide this area into

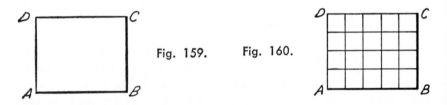

Fig. 159.   Fig. 160.

squares, 1 in. by 1 in., getting 20 squares in all (Fig. 160). Since each of these squares has an area of 1 sq. in., the area of the rectangle is 20 sq. in.

If the base of the rectangle were 5 in. and the altitude $4\frac{1}{2}$ in., we could divide the rectangle into squares $\frac{1}{2}$ in. on each side, and get ten times nine or 90 squares each $\frac{1}{2}$ in. on a side. Since it would take four of each of these little squares to equal 1 sq. in., we would have $22\frac{1}{2}$ sq. in. for the area of this rectangle. We have, then, the rule for finding the area of a rectangle (Fig. 161).

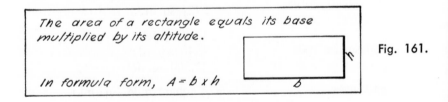

The area of a rectangle equals its base multiplied by its altitude.

In formula form, $A = b \times h$

Fig. 161.

The Parallelogram. The parallelogram *ABCD* can be shown to be equal in area to the rectangle *ABEF,* by first drawing *BE* and *AF* perpendicular to *AB* and then extending *ED* to *F*. Triangle *BCE* is exactly the same size as triangle *ADF* (Fig. 162).

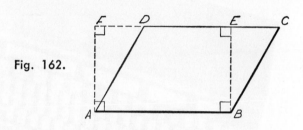

Fig. 162.

If we removed triangle *BCE* and placed it in position *ADF,* we would have rectangle *ABEF.* Hence the rule for finding the area of a parallelogram is exactly the same as for a rectangle (Fig. 163).

Fig. 163.

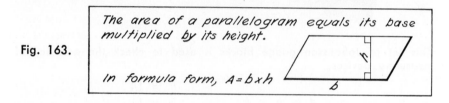

The area of a parallelogram equals its base multiplied by its height.

In formula form, $A = b \times h$

■ **EXAMPLE 1:**

Find the area of a rectangular television screen if it is 14 in. long and 11 in. high.

Solution and Explanation:

Step 1: Draw a neat figure and label it (Fig. 164).

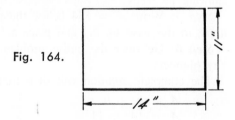

Fig. 164.

Step 2: Write down the correct formula as shown, with the formula to the left of the vertical line, and the given dimensions to the right of the line. The work will look like this so far:

This set of Johansson gauge blocks is used to check the accuracy of measuring devices.

$$A = b \times h$$

$$b = 14$$
$$h = 11$$
$$A = ?$$

Step 3: Rewrite $A =$ and put 14 in place of b and 11 in place of h. The work will look like this to this point:

$$A = b \times h$$
$$A = 14 \times 11$$

$$b = 14$$
$$h = 11$$
$$A = ?$$

Step 4: Do the arithmetical work to the *right* of the vertical line, showing all steps.

Step 5: Write $A = 154$ below the previously written $A =$, *mark the units,* in this case sq. in., and place a box around it.

Step 6: Go over the entire problem carefully, checking all steps for any blunders.

The complete solution will then look like this:

$$A = b \times h$$
$$A = 14 \times 11$$

$$\boxed{A = 154 \text{ sq. in. } \textbf{ans.}}$$

$$b = 14$$
$$h = 11$$
$$A = ?$$

$$
\begin{array}{r}
14 \\
11 \\
\hline
14 \\
14 \\
\hline
154
\end{array}
$$

The solution of this example has been carried out in detail for several reasons.

1. It shows a systematic procedure for doing the work. This reduces blunders to a minimum.

2. It shows what is given and what is to be found.

3. The arithmetical work is shown.

4. The correct units are shown.

5. The answer is placed in a box, so that whoever reads the problem cannot help but notice it.

6. The work is arranged in such a way that another person can check it completely.

Since in practically all our work someone will check it or go over it, this procedure will be found to be much better than writing the work any old way.

■ EXAMPLE 2:

The floor of a garage is a rectangle 20 ft. 9 in. by 10 ft. 9 in. What is its area (Fig. 165)?

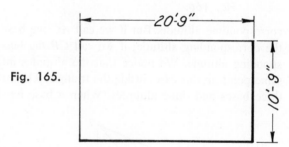

Fig. 165.

Solution and Explanation:

In this example we will show the work as it should appear on paper when completed.

$A = b \times h$

$A = 20.75 \times 10.75$

$A = 223.0625$

$$\boxed{A = 223 \text{ sq. ft.} \quad \textbf{ans.}}$$

$b = 20$ ft. 9 in.

$b = 20.75$ ft.

$h = 10$ ft. 9 in.

$h = 10.75$ ft.

$A = ?$

```
        20.75
        10.75
       ------
       103 75
       1452 5
      20750
     ---------
      223.0625
```

The dimensions were changed to feet and decimal parts of a foot, and the final answer was rounded off.

The Square. To find the area of a square we use the same formula as for finding the area of a rectangle. The length of a side of the square is used for the length of the base and for the height.

The Triangle. Let us consider the triangle ABC. The side AB we call the base. The line CD, at right angles (perpendicular) to AB, is called an altitude (or height). However, we could take any of the three sides for the base of the triangle. We could also take the perpendicular distance from any vertex to the side opposite that vertex as an altitude. Thus, in triangle ABC (Fig. 166), if we call AB the base, then CD is the

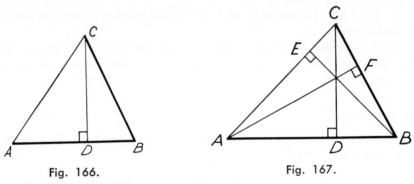

Fig. 166.   Fig. 167.

corresponding altitude. But if we call AC the base (Fig. 167), then BE is the corresponding altitude; if we call CB the base, then AF is the corresponding altitude. We notice that the altitudes intersect each other at the same point, in this case, inside the triangle. Thus triangle ABC has actually three bases and three altitudes. When a base has been selected, however,

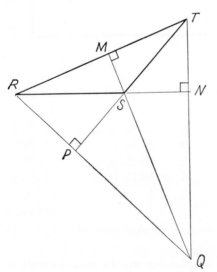

Fig. 168.

there can be only *one* altitude associated with it, and no other. Sometimes the altitudes fall outside the triangle, as in triangle *RST* (Fig. 168). Here, if we call *RS* the base, then the corresponding altitude is *TN*. If we call *RT* the base then *SM* is the corresponding altitude. If we call *ST* the base, then *RP* is the corresponding altitude. We notice in this case that the altitudes, when extended, intersect at *Q, outside* the triangle.

Now let us consider the parallelogram *ABCD* (Fig. 169). Its base is

Fig. 169.

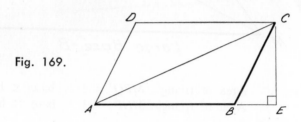

AB, its altitude is *CE* (the perpendicular distance between the upper base *DC* and the lower base *AB*). If we draw the line *AC,* called a diagonal, we know from geometry that the parallelogram is divided into two equal triangles. These are the triangles *ABC* and *ACD*. Since the area of the parallelogram is found by multiplying its base by its altitude or height, then the area of either of the two triangles must be one half the base multiplied by the height. Thus the area of triangle *ABC* is one half the base *AB* multiplied by the corresponding altitude *CE*. This will be true for any triangle whatsoever (Fig. 170).

Fig. 170.

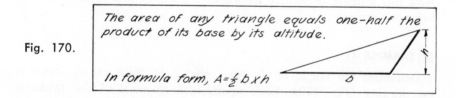

The area of any triangle equals one-half the product of its base by its altitude.

In formula form, $A = \frac{1}{2} b \times h$

The Trapezoid. The formula for the area of a trapezoid may be obtained by dividing the trapezoid into two triangles, finding the area of each triangle and adding the two areas together.

In the trapezoid *MNPQ* (Fig. 171) let us draw a diagonal *MP*. By doing so we have divided the trapezoid into two triangles, one of them being triangle *MNP* and the other being triangle *MPQ*.

Now, since the height or altitude of the trapezoid is *h,* its large base is *B* and its small base is *b,* we have:

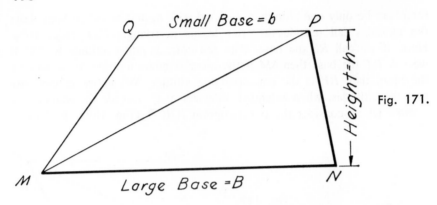

Fig. 171.

Area of triangle $MPQ = \frac{1}{2} \times$ base $\times$ height $= \frac{1}{2} bh.$
Area of triangle $MNP = \frac{1}{2} \times$ base $\times$ height $= \frac{1}{2} Bh.$

Adding, we obtain:

$$\text{Area of trapezoid} = \tfrac{1}{2} bh + \tfrac{1}{2} Bh$$
$$\text{or Area of trapezoid} = \tfrac{1}{2} \times (B + b) \times h$$

We can express this in words thus:

The area of any trapezoid equals one half the sum of its bases multiplied by its height.

How this formula or rule is applied in a practical case is shown in the following example.

■ **EXAMPLE 1:**

Determine the weight of six steel plates $\frac{3}{8}$ in. thick cut as shown in the drawing (Fig. 172). Each square inch of metal of this thickness weighs 0.106 lb.

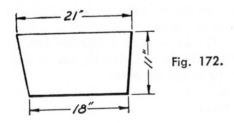

Fig. 172.

Solution and Explanation:

It is always best to do any computation in a systematic manner. In this problem there are three steps:
1. Finding the area of one plate;
2. Finding the weight of one plate;
3. Finding the weight of six plates.

Each of these steps is shown in detail below.

Step 1:

$$A = \tfrac{1}{2}(B + b) \times h$$

$$A = \tfrac{1}{2} \times (21 + 18) \times 11$$

$$A = \frac{1}{\underset{1}{2}}(\cancel{39}) \times 11$$

$B = 21$ in.	19.5
$b = 18$ in.	11
$h = 11$ in.	195
$A = ?$	195
	214.5

$$\boxed{A = 214.5 \text{ sq. in.}}$$

Step 2: Weight of one plate = Area × weight per square inch.

$$W = 214.5 \times 0.106$$

$$\boxed{W = 22.74 \text{ lb.}}$$

214.5	
0.106	
12870	
21450	
22.7370	

Step 3: Weight of six plates
$$= 22.74 \times 6 = 136.44$$

$$\boxed{\text{Weight} = 136.44 \text{ lb. } \textbf{ans.}}$$

22.74
6
136.44

Hence the computed weight of six plates is 136.4 lb. to the nearest tenth of a pound.

The Circle and the Ellipse. The circle is one of the most used geometric shapes. It may be considered as a closed curve such that all points on the curve are the same distance from a fixed point inside the

Fig. 173.

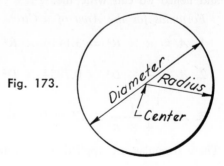

curve (Fig. 173). The fixed point inside is called the center. The length of the curve is called the circumference. The space enclosed by the curve is called the area.

In geometry the following formulas or rules of computation involving the circle are derived:

Formulas for the Area of a Circle Expressed in Words:

1. Area = π × radius × radius (π = $\frac{22}{7}$ = $3\frac{1}{7}$ = 3.1416 approximately)

2. Area = $\frac{\pi}{4}$ × diameter × diameter ($\frac{\pi}{4}$ = 0.7854 approximately)

3. Area = $\dfrac{1}{4 \times \pi}$ × circumference × circumference

This form of writing these formulas is cumbersome. However, by using a little of the language of algebra, we can shorten these considerably.

Whenever we multiply a quantity by itself, we say we have *squared* the quantity, or raised it to the second power. Thus, 3 × 3 = 9. We say 3 has been *squared* or raised to the second power, and the result is 9. Similarly with the number 8. Thus 8 × 8 = 64. We say 8 *squared* equals 64, or 8 raised to the second power equals 64. However, to show that 3 is to be squared or raised to the second power, we write a small 2 above and to the right of the 3. Thus, instead of writing 3 × 3 we write 3^2, which is the same. We read this *three squared* or *three raised to the second power* or *three to the second power,* and we do the same with any other number.

Also, instead of using the entire words Area, Radius, Diameter, Circumference, we use the letters *A, R, D, C,* respectively, to represent each of those words. This makes it possible to abbreviate the above formulas tremendously. We can thus write:

$R \times R$ or R^2 instead of radius × radius

$D \times D$ or D^2 instead of diameter × diameter and

$C \times C$ or C^2 instead of circumference × circumference

and hence we can write the:

Formulas for the Area of a Circle in Algebraic Form:

1. $A = \pi \times R^2 = 3.1416 \times R^2$

2. $A = \frac{\pi}{4} \times D^2 = 0.7854 \times D^2$

3. $A = \dfrac{1}{4 \times \pi} \times C^2 = 0.0796 \times C^2$

These formulas are applied in the following examples:

■ **EXAMPLE 1:**

What is the cross-sectional area of a round steel bar whose diameter is $4\frac{1}{2}$ in.?

Solution and Explanation:

Since we are given the diameter, we can use Formula No. 2. We have:

$A = 0.7854 \times D^2$	$D = 4\frac{1}{2} = 4.5$ in.	0.7854
$A = 0.7854 \times 4.5^2$	$A = ?$	20.25
$A = 0.7854 \times 4.5 \times 4.5$	$4.5 \times 4.5 = 20.25$	39270

$$\boxed{A = 15.90 \text{ sq. in.} \quad \textbf{ans.}}$$

```
        15708
       157080
      15.904350
```

Thus the cross-sectional area of the round steel bar is 15.90 sq. in. to two decimal places.

■ **EXAMPLE 2:**

The base of a chimney measures 50 ft. 3 in. in circumference. What is the cross-section area of this chimney at its base?

Solution and Explanation:

Since the circumference of the base is known, the formula to use is:
$$A = 0.0796 \times C^2$$

We then have:

$A = 0.0796 \times C^2$	$C = 50$ ft. 3 in. $= 50.25$ ft.
$A = 0.0796 \times 50.25^2$	$A = ?$
$A = 0.0796 \times 50.25 \times 50.25$	

$$\boxed{A = 200.99 \text{ sq. ft.} \quad \textbf{ans.}}$$

```
        50.25
        50.25
        25125
        10050
       251250
      2525.0625
        0.0796
      151503750
      227255625
      176754375
      200.99497500
```

Hence the area of the base of the chimney is 200.99 sq. ft. or 201 sq. ft. for all practical purposes.

Another geometric shape frequently used in the design and construction of gears, pulleys, bridge arches, and so on is the ellipse (Fig. 174). The ellipse has a *long* diameter, or *major axis,* and a *short* diameter, or *minor* axis. It has a center also.

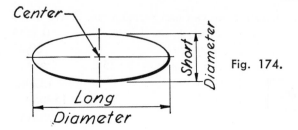

Fig. 174.

We can write the formula for the area of any ellipse in words thus:

Area of any ellipse = 0.7854 times long diameter times short diameter

We can also write this in the form:

Area of any ellipse = 3.1416 times (½ × long diameter) × (½ × short diameter)

If we represent one half the long diameter by the letter *a* and one half the short diameter by the letter *b,* then we can write the same formula in a very short form as:

$$A = 3.1416 \times a \times b = \pi \times a \times b$$

The following examples illustrate how these formulas are applied to practical problems.

■ **EXAMPLE 1:**

The arms of the pulley shown in Figure 175 are elliptical in cross section, measuring ¾ in. by 1¼ in. at the section *a-a*. What is the area of this cross section?

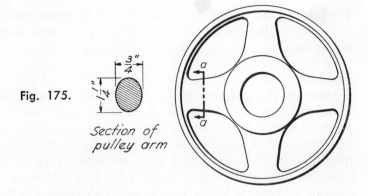

Fig. 175.

Section of
pulley arm

Solution and Explanation:

By inspecting the drawings, we find that the long diameter of the elliptical section at *a-a* is $1\frac{1}{4}$ in., and the short diameter is $\frac{3}{4}$ in.

We then have:

Area of elliptical section
= 0.7854 × $1\frac{1}{4}$ × $\frac{3}{4}$
= 0.7854 × 1.25 × 0.75

Area = 0.736 sq. in. **ans.**

Thus, the cross-sectional area of the pulley arm at *a-a* is 0.736 sq. in. or about $\frac{3}{4}$ sq. in.

long diameter = $1\frac{1}{4}$ in.
short diameter = $\frac{3}{4}$ in.
A = ?

```
        1.25
        0.75
        ────
         625
         875
       ──────
      0.9375
      0.7854
      ──────
       37500
       46875
       75000
       65625
   ──────────
  0.73631250
```

■ EXAMPLE 2:

A duct has the cross section of an ellipse in which one half of the long diameter is 21 in. and one half of the short diameter is 14 in. What is the cross-sectional area of the duct?

Using the appropriate formula, we have:

A = 3.1416 × *a* × *b*
A = 3.1416 × 21 × 14

A = 923.6 sq. in. **ans.**

a = 21 in.
b = 14 in.
A = ?

```
   21          3.1416
   14             294
   ──         ───────
   84          125664
   21          282744
  ───           62832
  294        ────────
            923.6304
```

Thus we find the area of the elliptical duct to be approximately 924 sq. in.

To change this to square feet, we divide by 144, and obtain 6.4 sq. ft. for its area.

In the calculation of surface areas of various geometric figures one frequently comes across the term *perimeter*. This is a word meaning the distance *around* a figure. For a triangle, for example, the perimeter equals the sum of the lengths of its three sides. For a square, the perimeter equals four times the length of one side, since the four sides are equal to each other in length. The perimeter of a rectangle equals twice the sum of its length and width. For other polygons, the perimeter equals the sum of the lengths of the sides. If a polygon is such that its sides are all equal in length, then its perimeter is equal to the number of sides times the length of *one* side.

For a circle we usually use the term *circumference* instead of perimeter. For any circle we can say that:

  1. Circumference = 3.1416 × diameter, or
  2. Circumference = 2 × 3.1416 × radius

If we represent circumference by C, diameter by D and radius by R, we can write the above formulas as:

  3. $C = 3.1416 \times D$ (or $C = \pi D$ or $C = 3.1416D$)
  4. $C = 2 \times 3.1416 \times R$ (or $C = 2\pi R$ or $C = 6.2832R$)

No simple formulas can be given for the perimeter of an ellipse, however.

Irregular Flat Surfaces. In most practical applications the problems relating to areas, volumes, and weights that one has to solve are frequently impossible to solve directly or in one step.

Since most of such problems must be done in steps, the computer finds it necessary to divide a particular irregular area into a number of regular shapes, each of whose areas he can determine. When each of the separate areas has been computed, their sum is found. This sum will be the area of the irregular surface.

There is no specific "recipe" for separating a given surface into simpler, regular shapes. Care and thought will be necessary, and, together with experience, will enable the student to acquire ability to solve such problems. It is quite possible for one person to divide a particular area or surface into one set of simple shapes, and for another to divide the same area or surface into a different set of simple shapes. However, *both* must obtain the *same* final answer.

By carefully choosing the fewest simple areas or shapes, the student will minimize the work. The simple areas or shapes should be formed by drawing auxiliary lines on the drawing of the given surface.

The following examples will illustrate how the areas of such irregular surfaces are computed.

■ **EXAMPLE 1:**

What is the total area of a blank made according to the drawing (Fig. 176)?

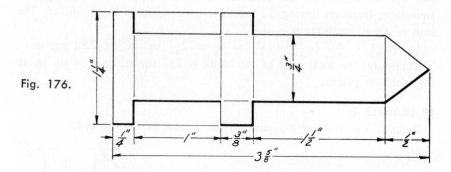

Fig. 176.

Solution and Explanation:

By studying the drawing of the blank, it can be seen that it may be divided into five parts. Of these, four will be rectangles and one will be a triangle. Furthermore, the dimensions required for computing the area of each of these separate parts are available from the drawing. Consequently, the total area can be readily determined. This may be called the *first step*.

The *second step* is to make a dimensioned drawing of each of the five parts into which the blank is to be divided, and to give each a name, or letter, or mark of some sort. A good procedure is to use the letters of the alphabet for this purpose. The five simple areas into which the entire blank is divided are shown separately (Fig. 177).

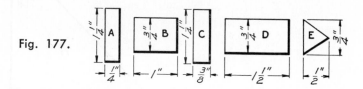

Fig. 177.

It is now evident that the parts *A, B, C,* and *D* are rectangles, and part *E* is a triangle.

The *third step* is to compute the area of each part separately, using the formulas that have been explained already.

The area of part $A = 1\frac{1}{4} \times \frac{1}{4} = \frac{5}{4} \times \frac{1}{4} = \frac{5}{16}$ sq. in.
The area of part $B = 1 \quad \times \frac{3}{4} \qquad\qquad = \frac{3}{4}$ sq. in.
The area of part $C = 1\frac{1}{4} \times \frac{3}{8} = \frac{5}{4} \times \frac{3}{8} = \frac{15}{32}$ sq. in.
The area of part $D = 1\frac{1}{2} \times \frac{3}{4} = \frac{3}{2} \times \frac{3}{4} = \frac{9}{8}$ sq. in.
The area of part $E = \frac{1}{2} \times \frac{3}{4} \times \frac{1}{2} \qquad = \frac{3}{16}$ sq. in.

The *fourth step* is to find the total area. The total area is the *sum* of the five *separate* areas. To add these areas, the five fractions are changed to equivalent fractions having 32 for their least common denominator. The sum of these fractions is:

$$\tfrac{10}{32} + \tfrac{24}{32} + \tfrac{15}{32} + \tfrac{36}{32} + \tfrac{6}{32} = \tfrac{91}{32} = 2\tfrac{27}{32} \text{ sq. in. or 2.84 sq. in.}$$

Therefore, the total area of the blank is $2\frac{27}{32}$ sq. in. or 2.84 sq. in. to two decimal places.

■ **EXAMPLE 2:**

What is the area of the gusset plate shown in Figure 178?

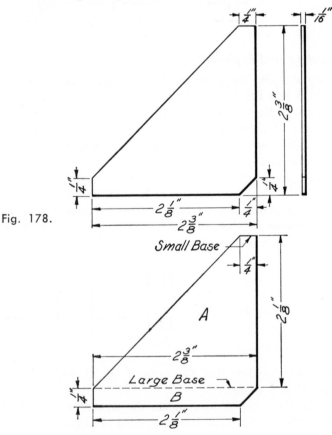

Fig. 178.

Bethlehem Steel Co.

A truss-cantilever bridge spans the Mississippi River.

Solution and Explanation:

On studying the drawing, we decide to divide the gusset plate into two parts, each of which will be a trapezoid. This is done by drawing the dotted line as shown, and marking the larger part A and the smaller part B.

Next, the area of each part is found. For part A, the large base is $2\frac{3}{8}$ in., the small base is $\frac{1}{4}$ in., and the height is $2\frac{3}{8} - \frac{1}{4}$ or $2\frac{1}{8}$ in. For part B, the large base is $2\frac{3}{8}$ in., the small base is $2\frac{3}{8} - \frac{1}{4}$ or $2\frac{1}{8}$ in., and the height is $\frac{1}{4}$ in.

Hence,

$$\text{Area of part } A = \tfrac{1}{2} \times (2\tfrac{3}{8} + \tfrac{1}{4}) \times 2\tfrac{1}{8}$$
$$= \tfrac{1}{2} \times (2\tfrac{5}{8}) \times 2\tfrac{1}{8}$$

Therefore, the area of part $A = \tfrac{1}{2} \times \tfrac{21}{8} \times \tfrac{17}{8}$
$$= \tfrac{857}{128} = 2\tfrac{101}{128}$$
$$= 2.79 \text{ sq. in.}$$

The area of part $B = \frac{1}{2} \times (2\frac{3}{8} + 2\frac{1}{8}) \times \frac{1}{4}$
$$= \frac{1}{2} (4\frac{1}{2}) \times \frac{1}{4}$$
$$= \frac{1}{2} \times \frac{9}{2} \times \frac{1}{4} = \frac{9}{16}$$
$$= 0.56 \text{ sq. in.}$$

The total area is, then, the sum of the separate areas.

Total area $= 2.79 + 0.56$

Total area $= 3.35$ sq. in. **ans.**

■ EXAMPLE 3:

What is the net area of the metal plate shown in Figure 179?

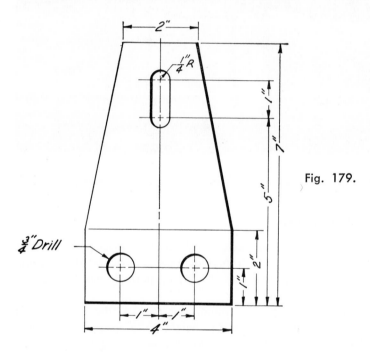

Fig. 179.

Solution and Explanation:

It can be seen by studying the drawing (Fig. 180) that the plate consists of a rectangular portion A (lower part) and a trapezoidal portion B (upper part). The net area, however, is the gross area (area without deducting holes) minus the area of the circular holes and the slotted hole.

The first step is, then, to separate the plate into two parts; one a rectangle 4 in. by 2 in.; and the other, a trapezoid whose large base is 4 in., small base is 2 in., and height is 5 in., as in Figure 180.

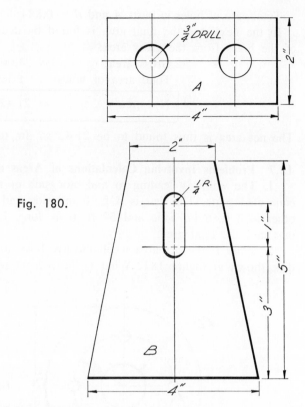

Fig. 180.

Having redrawn and dimensioned each part separately, the area of each is now found:

Gross area of part A = 4 × 2 = 8 sq. in.
Gross area of part B = $\frac{1}{2}$ × (4 + 2) × 5
= $\frac{1}{2}$ × 6 × 5 = 15 sq. in.
Total gross area = 8 + 15 = 23 sq. in.

In the next step, the areas to be deducted are computed:

Area of two $\frac{3}{4}$-in. diam. holes in part A = 2 × 0.7854 × D^2
= 2 × 0.7854 × $\frac{3}{4}$ × $\frac{3}{4}$
= 0.884 sq. in.

Area of slotted hole in part B: This consists of (*a*) rectangle 1 in. by $\frac{1}{2}$ in. and (*b*) two half circles $\frac{1}{2}$ in. in diameter. Hence:

a) Area of rectangular part of slotted hole = 1 × $\frac{1}{2}$ = $\frac{1}{2}$ sq. in.
= 0.500 sq. in.
b) Area of two half circles (considered as
one full circle) = 0.7854 × $\frac{1}{2}$ × $\frac{1}{2}$ = 0.196 sq. in.
Total area of slotted hole = 0.696 sq. in.

Total area of holes in parts A and B = 0.884 + 0.696 = 1.580 sq. in.

In the next step the final area is found by deducting the total areas of the holes from the gross area:

$$
\begin{array}{lr}
\text{Gross area} & = 23.000 \\
\text{Total area of holes} & = 1.580 \\
\hline
\text{Net area} & = 21.420 \text{ sq. in.} \quad \textbf{ans.}
\end{array}
$$

The net area is thus found to be 21.42 sq. in. to two decimal places.

12.7 Problems Involving Calculations of Areas of Flat Surfaces

1. The walkway leading to and alongside of a residence is in two connected parts. The first is 4 ft. 0 in. wide and 28 ft. long, and the other is 2 ft. 6 in. wide and 52 ft. 6 in. long. Find the area of each part and the total area.

2. What is the net area when the five holes are cut in the cast-iron disk shown in Figure 181? What is the percent reduction in area?

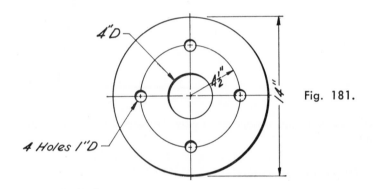

Fig. 181.

3. Find the total exterior area of the storage building shown in Figure 182.

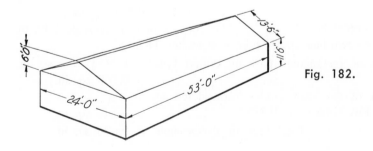

Fig. 182.

4. The drawing (Fig. 183) shows the cross section of a "wide-flange" structural-steel shape. What is the area of this cross section in square inches? How much does your answer differ from the value of 32.92 sq. in. given by the manufacturer? The drawing is a good approximation of the actual shape.

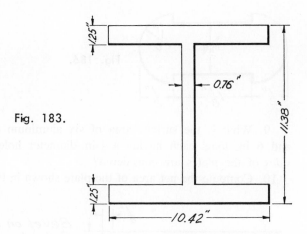

Fig. 183.

5. Determine the area of metal in the cross section of the cast-iron sleeve as shown in Figure 184.

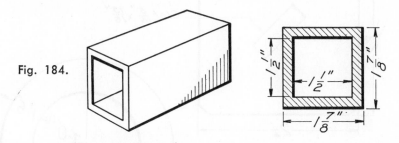

Fig. 184.

6. Calculate the cross-section area through the concrete trough as illustrated in the drawing (Fig. 185).

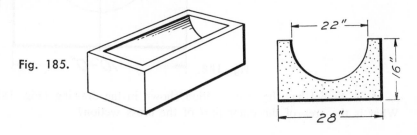

Fig. 185.

7. At 60 cents per square foot, including labor and materials, what is the cost of a concrete sidewalk 4 ft. wide and 160 ft. long?

8. Determine the area of the sheet-steel punching shown in the sketch (Fig. 186). If 10 sq. in. of this material weigh ½ lb., what will be the weight of 1200 punchings?

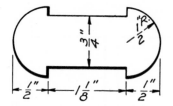

Fig. 186.

9. What is the surface area of six aluminum plates each 5 in. wide and 6 in. long, each having a ½-in.-diameter hole in its center, if *both sides* of the plates are considered?

10. Compute the net area of the plate shown in the drawing (Fig. 187).

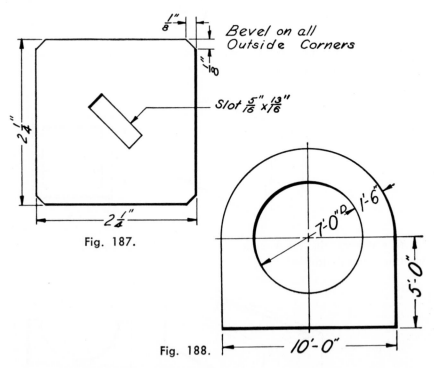

Fig. 187.

Fig. 188.

11. A tunnel has the cross section shown in the drawing (Fig. 188). What is the area of the outer part of the cross section?

12. Compute the net area of the plate shown in the drawing (Fig. 189).

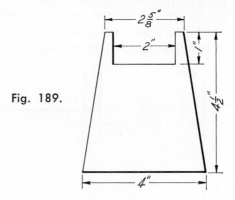

Fig. 189.

13. Calculate the cross-sectional area of a hollow fiber tube whose inside diameter is 28 in. and whose wall thickness is $\frac{3}{8}$ in.

14. A small selenium-type rectifier used in television receivers has the cross section shown in the drawing (Fig. 190). What is its cross-sectional area?

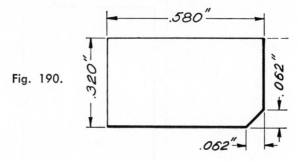

Fig. 190.

15. If the ultimate tensile strength of annealed steel wire is 80,000 lb. per square inch, how much tension will a specimen of this kind of wire sustain before breaking if it is $\frac{1}{4}$ in. in diameter?

16. Calculate the weight of 1000 washers of the following size (see Fig. 191). These are punched from strips of 18-gauge sheet iron 3 ft. long

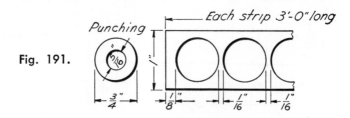

Fig. 191.

which weigh 2 lb. per square-foot area. The first "punching" in each strip lies $\frac{1}{8}$ in. from the end, and there is $\frac{1}{16}$ in. between the following blanks as shown. How many full strips are needed?

17. The inside wall dimensions of a basement storage room are shown in the drawing (Fig. 192). Find the area of the room.

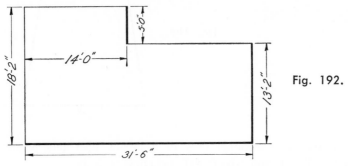

Fig. 192.

18. What is the cross-sectional area of this Z bar (Fig. 193)?

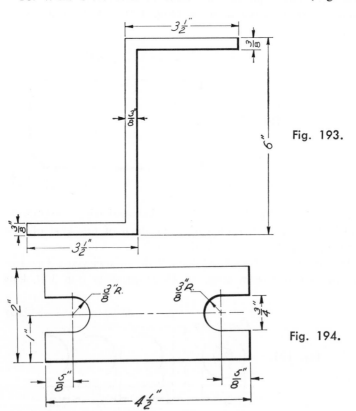

Fig. 193.

Fig. 194.

19. Calculate the net area of 125 plates having the dimensions shown in the figure (Fig. 194).

20. Calculate the cross-section area of the material in the "dovetail" slotted block as shown in the drawing (Fig. 195).

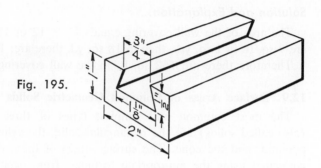

Fig. 195.

12.8   Changing Square Measurement From One Denomination to Another

In computations dealing with square measure or measurement of area, the changing from units of higher denomination to units of lower denomination is done in much the same way as in linear measure.

In changing a number of units of a larger denomination to an equivalent number of units of smaller denomination, the number of the units representing the larger denomination is *multiplied* by the number of units of the smaller denomination required to make one unit of the larger denomination.

For example, to change square feet to square inches, the area in square feet is multiplied by 144, since it requires 144 sq. in. to equal 1 sq. ft. The following examples will illustrate how the change can be made.

■ **EXAMPLE 1:**

How many square inches of material are there in a sheet of steel whose area is $4\frac{2}{3}$ sq. ft.?

Solution and Explanation:

Since there are 144 sq. in. in 1 sq. ft., in $4\frac{2}{3}$ sq. ft. there must be $4\frac{2}{3}$ times as many.

Hence: area in square inches = $4\frac{2}{3} \times 144$
$$= 672 \text{ sq. in.}$$

This is the area of the steel sheet in square inches.

■ EXAMPLE 2:

A man ordered some wall covering to install in the kitchen of his home. If the wall covering was $1\frac{1}{2}$ yd. wide and 12 yd. long, what was its area in square feet?

Solution and Explanation:

The area of the wall covering equals $1\frac{1}{2} \times 12$ or 18 sq. yd. Since there are 9 sq. ft. in 1 sq. yd., then in 18 sq. yd. there are: $18 \times 9 = 162$ sq. ft.

Therefore there are 162 sq. ft. in the wall covering.

12.9   Surface Areas of Common Geometric Solids

The most common and simplest types of three-dimensional figures (also called solids) are the rectangular solid, the cylinder, the sphere, the pyramid, and the cone. The surface areas of these figures can be easily computed using the appropriate formulas from geometry.

In many cases, however, many of the objects and machines that we manufacture, use, and work with, and even our buildings and other structures, are made up of one or more of these simple three-dimensional figures.

When computing the surface area of a complicated object for which no single formula exists, we will find it necessary to imagine the object as being made up of one or more of the common three-dimensional figures. The surface areas of these can be then computed, and their *sum* will be approximately (if not exactly) equal to the surface area of the actual object. This procedure will be explained in a later section.

Rectangular Solids.   The surface area of rectangular solids can be easily computed (Fig. 196). Since objects of this kind have rectangular or square faces, once the dimensions of the faces are known, their area can be computed. The sum of the areas of the faces is the total surface

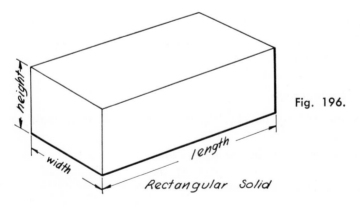

Fig. 196.

Rectangular Solid

area of the rectangular object. Calculations pertaining to the areas of such solids are frequently necessary in determining the areas and weights of sheet metal and other materials required in the manufacture of boxes, pans, trays, containers, body shapes, fenders, and so on. The following problem illustrates such a calculation:

The cabinet housing a water cooler (Fig. 197) has the shape of a

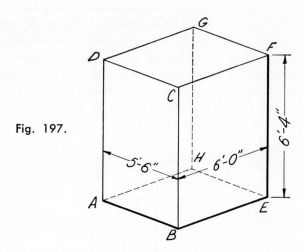

Fig. 197.

rectangular solid. If it is 5 ft. 6 in. long, 6 ft. 0 in. wide, and 6 ft. 4 in. high, what is its surface area in square feet (neglecting the bottom)?

Solution and Explanation:

Since the cabinet has the shape of a rectangular solid, its faces are rectangular. We see that the required area is made up of the following parts:

1. The faces *ABCD* and *HEFG*, which are the same size,
2. The faces *BEFC* and *AHGD*, which are the same size,
3. The top face *CFGD*.

The computed areas are, for:

Part 1. $A = 2 \times 5$ ft. 6 in. $\times 6$ ft. 4 in.   (For faces
     or $A = 2 \times 5\frac{1}{2} \times 6\frac{1}{3}$ *ABCD* and
          $A = 2 \times \frac{11}{2} \times \frac{19}{3} = \frac{209}{3}$ *HEFG*)
          $A = 69\frac{2}{3}$ sq. ft.

Part 2. $A = 2 \times 6$ ft. 0 in. $\times 6$ ft. 4 in.   (For faces
           $= 2 \times 6 \times 6\frac{1}{3}$ *BEFC* and
           $= 2 \times 6 \times \frac{19}{3}$ *AHGD*)
         $A = 76$ sq. ft.

Part 3. $A = 1 \times 5$ ft. 6 in. $\times$ 6 ft. 0 in.   (For top
$= 1 \times 5\frac{1}{2} \times 6$ face
$A = 1 \times \frac{11}{2} \times 6$ *CFGD*)
$A = 33$ sq. ft.

Since the total area is the sum of the areas of the parts, we see that
the total area $= 69\frac{2}{3} + 76 + 33$, or

$$\boxed{\text{Total area} = 178\frac{2}{3} \text{ sq. ft. } \textbf{ans.}}$$

Cylinders.   Another of the geometrical solids frequently used in the
construction of storage tanks, fuel and gas containers, receptacles for
foods and liquids is the right circular cylinder, or cylinder as it is often
called. It may be formed by taking a rectangular sheet and rolling it so
that the ends meet (Fig. 198).

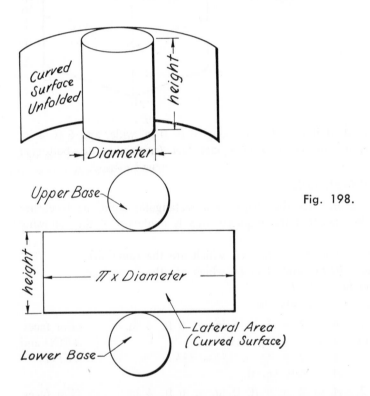

Fig. 198.

The *lateral area,* or area of the curved part of the cylinder is equal to
the length of the rectangular sheet multiplied by its height. But when the
rectangular sheet is rolled up to form the circular cylinder, the circum-

ference of the cylinder will be exactly the same as the *length* of the rectangular sheet. If we call the diameter of the cylinder *D*, then the circumference of the cylinder will be 3.1416 × *D*. Consequently, if we know how big the diameter of a cylinder is, and its height, we can calculate its lateral area by the formula:

Lateral area = 3.1416 × diameter × height

The total area, however, consists of the lateral area and the area of the ends, or bases (top and bottom). Since the bases are circles whose diameter is also *D*, their combined area is 2 × 0.7854 × *D²* or 1.5708 × *D²*.

Hence the total area of a right circular cylinder is found by using the formula,

Total area = Lateral area plus area of the two bases or:

Total area = 3.1416 × D × H + 1.5708 × D²

The following problem illustrates the application of this formula.

■ **EXAMPLE:**

Determine the number of square feet of material needed in building five cylindrical tanks 4 ft. in diameter and 6 ft. high (Fig. 199). Allow 5 percent for lapping and waste.

Solution and Explanation:

The total area of the material needed for one tank is equal to the lateral area plus the area of the two bases.

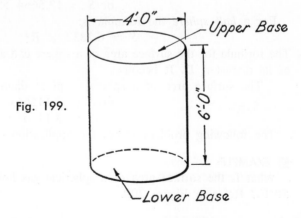

Fig. 199.

The lateral area = 3.1416 × diameter × height
= 3.1416 × 4 × 6 = 75.398 sq. ft.
The area of the two bases = 1.5708 × diameter × diameter
= 1.5708 × 4 × 4 = 25.133 sq. ft.
The total area = 75.398 + 25.133 = 100.531 or
100.5 sq. ft. (rounded off)

For five tanks, five times this amount of material is needed:
5 × 100.5 = 502.5 sq. ft.

But 5 percent must be allowed for lapping and waste. Therefore,
502.5 × 5 percent = 502.5 × $\frac{5}{100}$
= 25.125 or 25.1 sq. ft to one
decimal place.

Adding 502.5 and 25.1, the result is 527.6 or 528 sq. ft. (to the nearest square foot). Hence the number of square feet needed for five tanks 4 ft. in diameter and 6 ft. high is 528 sq. ft.

Spheres and Hemispheres. Still two other geometrical solids that are frequently used in the construction of gas, fuel, and water containers are the sphere and the hemisphere. The sphere may be considered as the solid which is formed when a circle is revolved about one of its diameters.

A sphere may also be considered as that geometrical solid having the property that all points on its surface are the same distance away from a point inside of it called the center. Lines from the center to any point on the surface are called *radii*. Any one of them is a *radius*. Lines joining any two points on the surface and passing through the center are diameters. The diameter of a sphere is twice as long as its radius.

In geometry the formula for the surface of a sphere is derived. It is found that:

The surface area of a sphere = 4 × pi × radius × radius
or $S = 4 × \pi × R^2$
or $S = 12.5664 × R^2$

For a *half sphere* the formula is:
$S = 6.2832 × R^2$

The formula for the surface area of a sphere can also be written in terms of its diameter, D. It becomes

The surface area of a sphere = pi × diameter × diameter
or $S = 3.1416 × D × D$
or $S = 3.1416 × D^2$

The following problem shows the application of these formulas.

■ **EXAMPLE:**

What is the surface area of a spherical gas holder whose diameter is 50 ft.? Refer to Figure 200.

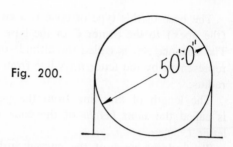

Fig. 200.

Solution and Explanation:

Using the formula for surface area in terms of the radius, we have:

$$S = 12.5664 \times R^2$$
$$\text{or } S = 12.5664 \times 25 \times 25$$

$R = 25$
$S = ?$

$$\boxed{S = 7854 \text{ sq. ft. } \textbf{ans.}}$$

Using the formula for the surface area in terms of the diameter, we have:

$$S = 3.1416 \times D^2$$
$$S = 3.1416 \times 50 \times 50$$

$D = 50$
$S = ?$

$$\boxed{S = 7854 \text{ sq. ft. } \textbf{ans.}}$$

Both formulas give the same answer, as is to be expected. Therefore, the surface area of this spherical gas holder is 7854 sq. ft.

The Cone. The cone (more accurately called the right circular cone) is another of the simple three-dimensional solid figures (Fig. 201).

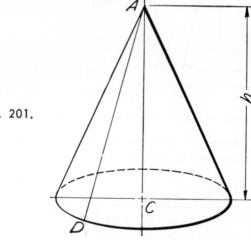

Fig. 201.

The base of this type of cone is a circle, and the line from the point A (the apex) to the center C of the base makes a 90° angle with the base. The distance AC is called the altitude or height of the cone and is usually represented by the letter h. A line from C to any point on the circle is the radius.

The length of any line from the point A to the base, such as AD, is called the *slant height* of the cone and is usually represented by the letter l.

To find the area of the curved surface, or lateral area of the cone, we use the formula:

$$S = \pi \times R \times l$$

in which $\pi = \frac{22}{7}$, 3.14 or 3.1416 (depending on the accuracy desired)

$R =$ radius of the base of the cone

$l =$ slant height of the cone

The following example illustrates the application of this formula.

■ EXAMPLE:

The nose cone of a guided missile (Fig. 202) has a slant height of 4 ft. 3 in. and the diameter of its base is 2 ft. 0 in.

What is its lateral area in square feet?

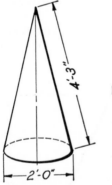

Fig. 202.

Solution and Explanation:

Since the slant height and the diameter of the base are given, the lateral area is computed as follows:

$S = \pi \times R \times l$	$R = $ 1'-0" ($\frac{1}{2}$ of the diameter of the base)
$S = 3.1416 \times 1 \times 4.25$	$l = $ 4'-3" $= 4.25'$
$\boxed{S = 13.35 \text{ sq. ft. } \textbf{ans.}}$	$S = ?$

Therefore the lateral area is 13.35 sq. ft. to the nearest hundredth of a square foot.

As a review and summary of some of the formulas that have been discussed in this section, let us find the total exposed surface of a hypothetical supersonic missile (Fig. 203).

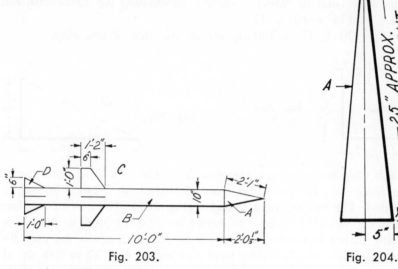

Fig. 203.   Fig. 204.

Solution and Explanation:

By studying the drawing, it is evident that the entire surface of the missile can be separated into four parts:

Part *A* is approximately a cone whose height is $24\frac{1}{2}$ in. and base 10 in. in diameter.

Part *B* is a cylinder 10 ft. long and 10 in. in diameter.

Part *C* consists of four trapezoidal wings.

Part *D* consists of four triangular fins. The calculations will be done in five steps.

Step 1: The lateral area of a cone is equal to pi × radius of base × slant height (Fig. 204). (The slant height is the distance *XY*, which is taken as 25 in.)

Therefore the area of Part $A = 3.1416 \times 5 \times 25$
$$= 392.7 \text{ sq. in.}$$

Step 2: Part B is a cylinder. The lateral area of a cylinder equals $3.1416 \times$ diameter $\times$ height (Fig. 205).

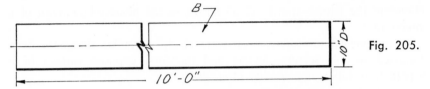

Fig. 205.

Therefore, the lateral area of the cylindrical portion equals 3.1416 × 10 × 120 = 3769.9 sq. in.

Step 3: The wings are trapezoids (Fig. 206). The area of a trapezoid equals $\frac{1}{2}$ × (sum of bases) × height. Substituting the dimensions, this gives $\frac{1}{2}$ × (14 + 6) × 12
or $\frac{1}{2}$ × 20 × 12 = 120 sq. in. for one side of one wing.

Fig. 206.

Fig. 207.

Each wing has two sides, therefore 2 × 120 = 240 sq. in. for each wing. Since there are four wings, their total area = 4 × 240 = 960 sq. in.

Step 4: The fins are right triangles (Fig. 207). The area of one face of the fins equals $\frac{1}{2}$ × base × height or $\frac{1}{2}$ × 12 × 6 = 36 sq. in.

Each fin has two sides, therefore 2 × 36 = 72 sq. in. for each fin. Since there are four fins, their total area equals 4 × 72 or 288 sq. in.

Step 5: Now that the areas have been computed, the total area of the missile can be found by adding the separate areas.

Area of cylindrical part	=	3769.9 sq. in.
Area of conical part	=	392.7 sq. in.
Area of four wings	=	960 sq. in.
Area of four fins	=	288 sq. in.
Total area	=	5410.6 sq. in.

Changing this to square feet to obtain a more convenient figure, it is found that the

$$\text{Total area} = \frac{5410.6}{144} = 37.6 \text{ sq. ft. } \textbf{ans.}$$

Hence the total surface area of this hypothetical missile is 37.6 sq. ft.

12.10 Problems Involving Reduction in Square Measure

1. One of the first man-made satellites was an instrument-carrying

sphere about 18 in. in diameter. Find the surface area of this satellite in square inches and square feet.

2. A ceiling measuring 12 ft. by 16 ft. is to be covered with insulating-board panels. The size of the insulating board is 4 ft. by 8 ft., and it sells for $4.25 a panel. Find (a) the number of panels needed; (b) the cost of covering this ceiling.

3. During the construction of a skyscraper a fence whose perimeter was 700 ft. long was erected to enclose the work site. The fence was 6 ft. high, and was to be given two coats of paint on both sides. If the first coat of paint covered 50 sq. yd. for each gallon, how many gallons of first coat paint were needed? If the second coat of paint covered 60 sq. yd., how many gallons of second coat paint were used?

4. A spherical gas holder has a diameter of 80 ft. What is its total surface area in square feet? in square yards?

5. What is the *total* surface area of a cylindrical tank 6 ft. in diameter and 24 ft. long?

6. What is the total acreage of a subdivision containing 12 lots each 60 ft. by 180 ft.?

7. If the allowable load in a certain warehouse is 2000 lb. per square yard, how many tons of small machine parts should be stored in a space 20 ft. by 36 ft.?

8. A 100-ft.-diameter inflated balloon communications satellite was put into orbit. Compute the surface area of this spherical balloon in square feet and square yards.

9. If a double roll of wallpaper measures 18 in. wide by 16 yd. long, how many square yards are there in five double rolls?

10. If a basketball court is 94 ft. long and 50 ft. wide, how many such fields this size could be covered by the material of the balloon in Problem 8?

11. A small boiler has 36 fire tubes with outside diameter of 3 in. and 3 ft. 6 in. long. What is the total exposed surface area of these tubes in square feet?

12. A cylindrical water storage tank is 32 ft. high, 36 ft. in diameter, and covered at the top. It rests on one of its circular bases. What is its total exposed area in square feet? If it is to be painted with two coats of paint which cover 60 sq. yd. per gallon (each coat), how many gallons of paint will be required?

13. The world's first active communications satellite Telstar was approximately spherical, having a diameter of $34\frac{1}{2}$ in. Find its surface area in square inches.

14. What is the area of one face of 160 of the E-shaped transformer-core laminations (Fig. 208)?

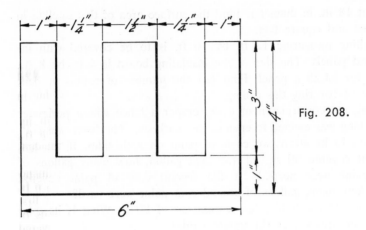

Fig. 208.

15. Determine the total surface area in square feet of this guided missile (Fig. 209). Take slant height of cone to be 36.3 in. long.

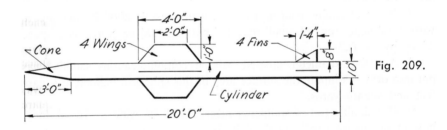

Fig. 209.

12.11   Review Problems Involving Reduction of Areas

1. A one-story industrial building is 46 ft. wide and 72 ft. long. A sidewalk 6 ft. wide is to be laid around this building. How many square yards of sidewalk surface are there in this walk?

2. What is the area of 36 gusset plates as shown in the drawing (Fig. 210)?

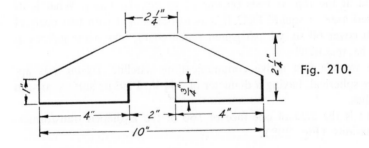

Fig. 210.

3. The cabinet housing an oscilloscope viewing monitor has the shape of a rectangular solid 28 in. high, 20 in. wide, and 21 in. deep. Find its outside surface area in square inches, neglecting the bottom.

4. How many acres are there in the plot of land shown in the drawing (Fig. 211)?

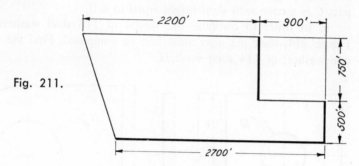

Fig. 211.

5. What is the area of the sheet-metal stamping shown in the drawing (Fig. 212)?

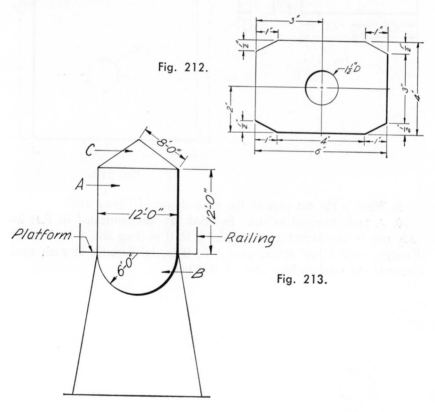

Fig. 212.

Fig. 213.

6. A smokestack on a steam electrical generating station has a diameter of 22 ft. and a height of 165 ft. What is its external surface area in square feet?

7. Find the total exposed surface of the water tank shown in the drawing (Fig. 213). Part *A* is a cylinder, part *B* is a half sphere, and part *C* is a cone with slant height equal to 8 ft.

8. In order to compute the weight of 114 steel washers shown in Figure 214, their net area must first be computed. Find the net area of one washer; of 114 such washers.

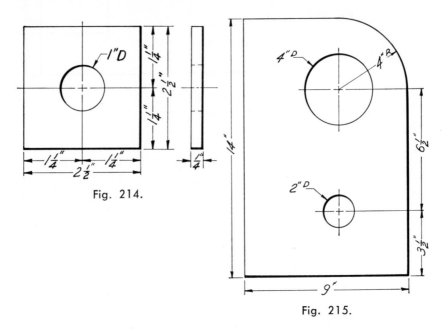

Fig. 214.

Fig. 215.

9. What is the net area of the plate shown in Figure 215?

10. A tank designed to store liquefied gas was fabricated so that its body can be considered as a cylinder 9 ft. 0 in. long and 4 ft. 0 in. in diameter, with a half sphere also 4 ft. 0 in. in diameter at each end. Compute the total surface area of this tank.

CHAPTER 13

Cubic Measure

13.1 Introduction

In this chapter you will learn how to compute volumes and weights of the common solid figures. You will learn how the volumes and weights of irregular objects can be computed. When you finish school, you may work as a draftsman, machinist, estimator, contractor, or designer. In these, as well as in many other skilled trades and occupations, your knowledge of how to make computations of volumes and weights will be of value to you. Such types of calculations occur frequently in industrial work and your working knowledge of how such computations are made should prove very helpful.

13.2 How Cubic Measure Is Determined

In our study of measurements so far, we considered first the units of linear measure or length, that is, of *one* dimension only. We followed this by the study of square measure, or area, which has *two* dimensions, length and width.

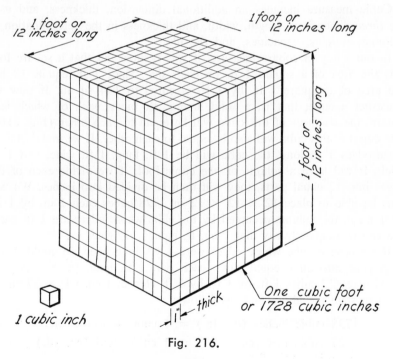

1 foot or 12 inches long

1 foot or 12 inches long

1 foot or 12 inches long

1 cubic inch

1" thick

One cubic foot or 1728 cubic inches

Fig. 216.

227

Spheres for storing pro-
pane gas under pressure
of 250 pounds per square
inch.

Chicago Bridge & Iron Co.

Cubic measure includes an additional dimension, thickness, and uses the *three* dimensions, length, width, and thickness in the determination of volumes, weights, capacities, and the like.

In our study of square measure, it was pointed out that a square foot was the area of a square 1 ft. on each side. Since 1 ft. equals 12 in., the area of a square 1 ft. by 1 ft. is equal to 144 sq. in. If now we construct a cube, that is, a solid having *six* faces, each of which is a square, the six faces of this cube will be equal to each other (Fig. 216). The edges of this cube will also be equal to each other. If we make each of these edges 1 ft. long, the cube will be 1 ft. long, 1 ft. wide, and 1 ft. thick. It will have a volume of *one* cubic foot. If we divide each of the edges into 12 equal parts, they will then be divided into inches. We will thus be able to place $12 \times 12 \times 12$ or 1728 cubes each 1 in. by 1 in. by 1 in. in the volume occupied by the cube whose edges are 1 ft. each. We can consequently say that 1 cu. ft. equals 1728 cu. in.

If we have a cube whose edges were 1 yd. long, then we could divide each edge into three equal parts, each part 1 ft. long. In this cube we could place *27* cubes 1 ft. by 1 ft. by 1 ft. Hence, 1 cu. yd. = 27 cu. ft. We can state the above facts as follows:

$$1728 \text{ cubic inches (cu. in.)} = 1 \text{ cubic foot (cu. ft.)}$$
$$27 \text{ cubic feet (cu. ft.)} \quad = 1 \text{ cubic yard (cu. yd.)}$$

A method similar to that used in linear measure and square measure can be used for changing from units of one denomination to units of a different denomination in cubic measure.

■ **EXAMPLE 1:**

In the excavation for the basements and foundation walls of a row of residences, 600 truckloads of dirt were hauled away. If the capacity of the trucks was $3\frac{1}{2}$ cu. yd. each, how many cubic yards and how many cubic feet of earth were hauled away?

Solution and Explanation:

Since each truck has a capacity of $3\frac{1}{2}$ cu. yd., and there were 600 truck loads, the volume of earth hauled away $= 3\frac{1}{2} \times 600$

$$= 2100 \text{ cu. yd.}$$

In each cubic yard there are 27 cu. ft. Therefore the volume of earth hauled away $= 2100 \times 27$

$$= 56,700 \text{ cu. ft.}$$

■ **EXAMPLE 2:**

An oil can has a capacity of 1920 cu. in. If there are $7\frac{1}{2}$ gal. in 1 cu. ft., how many gallons of oil will the can hold?

Solution and Explanation:

If we knew the volume of the can in cubic feet, we could find the number of gallons it would hold by multiplying the number of cubic feet by $7\frac{1}{2}$.

Since 1 cu. ft. $= 1728$ cu. in., we divide 1920 by 1728. Now $\frac{1920}{1728} = 1\frac{192}{1728} = 1\frac{1}{9}$ cu. ft. Since there are approximately $7\frac{1}{2}$ gals. to each cubic foot, the number of gallons in $1\frac{1}{9}$ cu. ft. will be $1\frac{1}{9} \times 7\frac{1}{2}$, or

$$\frac{\overset{5}{\cancel{10}}}{\underset{3}{\cancel{9}}} \times \frac{\overset{5}{\cancel{15}}}{\underset{1}{\cancel{2}}} = \frac{25}{3} = 8\frac{1}{3} \text{ gal.}$$

Hence, a can having a capacity of 1920 cu. in. will hold $8\frac{1}{3}$ gal.

This problem can be solved in another way. In the United States, the gallon is legally defined as containing 231 cu. in.

Hence, dividing 1920 by 231, we have:

$$\frac{1920}{231} = 8.3 \text{ gal. as before}$$

```
              8.3
      231 ⟌ 1920.0
            1848
            ─────
             72 0
             69 3
            ─────
              2 7
```

Weights of Materials

For reference in solving problems that involve weights of materials there are listed herewith the more commonly used materials and their approximate weights per unit of cubic measure.

Aluminum	weighs		.094 lb. per cu. in.
Brass	weighs		.311 lb. per cu. in.
Bronze	weighs		.317 lb. per cu. in.
Cast iron	weighs		.266 lb. per cu. in.
Copper	weighs		.321 lb. per cu. in.
Lead	weighs		.410 lb. per cu. in.
Steel	weighs		.283 lb. per cu. in.
Birch	weighs	44.	lb. per cu. ft.
Cedar	weighs	33.	lb. per cu. ft.
Chestnut	weighs	30.	lb. per cu. ft.
Concrete	weighs	150.	lb. per cu. ft.
Earth (dirt)	weighs	100.	lb. per cu. ft.
Fir	weighs	27.	lb. per cu. ft.
Hemlock	weighs	28.	lb. per cu. ft.
Oak	weighs	47.	lb. per cu. ft.
Sand (dry)	weighs	100.	lb. per cu. ft.
Spruce	weighs	28.	lb. per cu. ft.
Water (fresh)	weighs	62.425	lb. per cu. ft.

(The weight of water is often given as $62\frac{1}{2}$ lb. per cu. ft.)

Water (salt)	weighs	64.	lb. per cu. ft.
White pine	weighs	25.	lb. per cu. ft.
Yellow pine	weighs	36.	lb. per cu. ft.

To obtain a fair degree of accuracy in calculations that involve weights or volumes the answers should be carried to the second decimal place, unless otherwise specified.

13.3 Problems Involving Changing Units of One Denomination to Units of Another Denomination

1. Change 30 cu. yd. to cubic feet; $\frac{3}{4}$ cu. yd. to cubic inches; 4320 cu. in. to cubic feet; 12 cu. ft. to cubic inches; 2260 cu. in. to cubic feet.

2. In excavating for the foundation of a building, 1200 truckloads of earth were removed, using trucks holding 5 cu. yd. per load. How many cubic yards of earth were hauled away? How many cubic feet is this equivalent to?

3. In emptying a tank, 60 bucketfuls of water were removed. If each bucketful held 900 cu. in. of water, how many cubic feet of water were removed?

4. A solid iron pedestal contains $2\frac{1}{2}$ cu. ft. of metal and weighs 1150 lb. How much does a cubic inch of the metal weigh?

5. If a cubic foot of steel weighs 490 lb., what is the weight of a piece of this metal containing $42\frac{1}{2}$ cu. in.?

6. A cylindrical water tank has a capacity of 800 gal. How long will it take to fill the tank at the rate of $22\frac{1}{2}$ gal. per minute?

7. A solid metal ball has a volume of 1.183 cu. in. and weighs 0.335 lb. Compute the weight of 1 cu. in. of the metal.

8. Calculate the weight per cubic foot of an oak timber if its volume is $2\frac{1}{4}$ cu. ft. and its weight is 115 lb.

9. The foundation of a building required 120 cu. yd. of concrete. This was hauled in concrete buggies holding 3 cu. ft. each. How many buggy loads were required for the foundation?

10. A checkup shows that lubricating oil flows from the faucet of an oil tank at such a rate that it fills a can containing 1152 cu. in. in $1\frac{1}{2}$ min. If there are approximately $7\frac{1}{2}$ gal. to the cubic foot, how long will it take, at this rate, to draw 50 gal. from this tank?

13.4   Volumes of Regular Solids

The volume of the common geometrical solids, such as the cube, sphere, cylinder, rectangular prism, regular pyramid, and the right circular cone involves the product of three factors each of which is in linear units.

If the dimensions of these solids are in inches, their volume will also be in cubic inches; if they are in feet, the volume will be in cubic feet; if they are in yards, the volume will be in cubic yards.

The methods used in calculating the cubic measure of the common geometrical solids will be illustrated in detail by the problems below.

Cubes, Rectangular Prisms, and Forms Resembling Them.   In a cube, the six faces are squares and the twelve edges are equal in length. The volume of a cube, whose edge is a units long, is given by the formula: $V = a \times a \times a$, which, in shorter form, becomes

---

Formula for volume of a cube whose edge = a

$$V = a^3$$

NOTE: When a number, or a quantity, is multiplied by itself in this manner, it is said to be *cubed* or "raised to the third power." This multiplication is expressed, in the shorthand of algebra, by placing a small 3 above and to the right of the a. Thus $a^3 = a \times a \times a$, $a^2 = a \times a$, $a^4 = a \times a \times a \times a$. The small number is called an *exponent*.

The formula $V = a^3$ is read "V equals a cubed" or "V equals a cube," where a equals the length of the edge of the cube.

A rectangular solid, or rectangular prism, is a solid whose opposite faces are rectangles and equal to each other. The adjacent edges of such a solid are perpendicular to each other. The volume of such a solid is found by multiplying its three dimensions together. Since the product of the length and width gives the area of the base, the volume can be found by multiplying the area of the base by the height. The formulas for finding the volume of a rectangular solid are:

$$V = l \times w \times h$$
$$\text{or } V = B \times h$$

Formulas for volume of a rectangular prism

$l =$ **units in length**

$w =$ **units in width**

$h =$ **units in height**

$B =$ **area of base**

The following examples will illustrate these rules.

■ EXAMPLE 1:

Calculate the volume of the steel bar in the following sketch (Fig. 217), if the weight of a cubic inch of steel is 0.283 lb. per cubic inch.

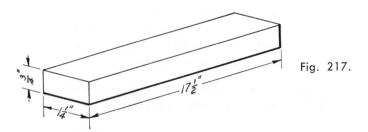

Fig. 217.

Solution and Explanation:

In solving this problem, we reason as follows: Since each cubic inch of the bar weighs 0.283 lb., we could find its weight by multiplying its volume in cubic inches by the weight per cubic inch.

Since the bar has the shape of a rectangular prism, its volume is given by: $V = lwh$

We then have:

$V = lwh$

$V = 17\frac{1}{2} \times 1\frac{1}{4} \times \frac{3}{4}$

$V = \frac{35}{2} \times \frac{5}{4} \times \frac{3}{4}$

$\boxed{V = \frac{525}{32} = 16.41 \text{ cu. in. } \textbf{ans.}}$

$l = 17\frac{1}{2}$ in.

$w = 1\frac{1}{4}$ in.

$h = \frac{3}{4}$ in.

$V = ?$

```
            16.406
   32 ) 525.000
        32
        ___
        205
        192
        ___
        130
        128
        ___
        200
        192
        ___
          8
```

Then:

$W = V \times 0.283$

$W = 16.41 \times 0.283$

$\boxed{W = 4.64 \text{ lb. } \textbf{ans.}}$

```
    16.41
    0.283
    _____
    4 923
  1 3128
  3 282
  _____
  4.64403
```

Thus we find the weight of this bar to be 4.64 lb. (to two decimal places) or 4.6 lb. to one decimal place. Notice that in doing the arithmetic, we show the work *to the right* of the vertical line. Thus we have a record of it which we can check or *anyone else* can check. If we are working in a place of business, it is most likely that our work *will* be checked. Having the information there will help *us* and the checkers also.

■ EXAMPLE 2:

Determine the inside volume of a box whose inside dimensions are as shown in Figure 218.

Solution and Explanation:

This box has the shape of a rectangular prism. Its volume is given by the formula $V = lwh$. We then proceed as in Example 1.

Fig. 218.

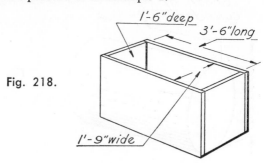

$V = lwh$

$V = 3.5 \times 1.75 \times 1.5$

$\boxed{V = 9.19 \text{ cu. ft.} \quad \textbf{ans.}}$

$l = 3$ ft. 6 in. $= 3.5$ ft.

$w = 1$ ft. 9 in. $= 1.75$ ft.

$h = 1$ ft. 6 in. $= 1.5$ ft.

$V = ?$

```
      1.75
       3.5
     ------
      87 5
      52 5
     ------
     6.125
       1.5
    -------
    3062 5
    6125
    -------
    9.1875
```

Cylinders, or Solids Resembling Cylinders.   The cylinder is one of the most frequently used geometrical shapes. It appears in shafts, rods, rivets, bolts, fasteners, tanks, wells, to mention a few common applications.

The formula for the volume of a cylinder can be stated in three ways, assuming that it is standing on *end* (Fig. 219), that is, on the circular base, or on its side if *completely full* (Fig. 220).

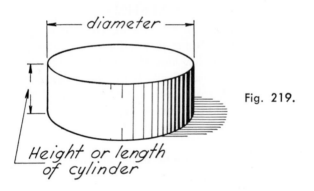

Fig. 219.

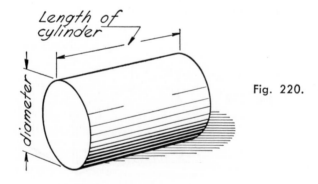

Fig. 220.

Chicago Bridge & Iron Co.

This wind tunnel can produce controlled and continuous wind from 500 to 2400 miles per hour.

$$V = \pi R^2 h \qquad\qquad (1)$$

$$V = \frac{\pi D^2 h}{4} \qquad\qquad (2)$$

R = radius
h = height
D = diameter

Now πR^2 and $\dfrac{\pi D^2}{4}$ are two forms of the formula for the area of a circle. If we call the area of the base of the cylinder B, then we could write $$V = Bh \qquad (3)$$

The particular formula to be used usually depends on the information given.

The following example will illustrate how to compute the volume of a cylinder.

■ EXAMPLE 1:

How many cubic feet of liquid are there in the tank shown in Figure 221 when the indicator shows it is half full?

Fig. 221.

Solution and Explanation:

Since we are given the height and diameter of the tank, we can use Formula 2 above, using 16 in. for D, and 13.5 in. for h (since the tank is *half* full).

We then have:

$$V = \frac{\pi D^2 h}{4}$$

$$V = \frac{\pi \times 16^2 \times 13.5}{4}$$

$$V = \frac{\pi \times 16 \times \overset{4}{\cancel{16}} \times 13.5}{\underset{1}{\cancel{4}}}$$

$D = 16$ in.

$h = 13.5$ in.

$\pi = 3.14$

$V = ?$

$$\boxed{V = 864\pi = 2712.96 \text{ cu. in. } \textbf{ans.}}$$

Since 1 cu. ft. = 1728 cu. in., to find the volume in cubic feet we divide the volume just found by 1728. We then have:

$$\boxed{V = \frac{2712.96}{1728} = 1.57 \text{ cu. ft.} \quad \textbf{ans.}}$$

This is the number of *cubic feet* the tank holds when *half full*. To find the capacity of the tank when half full we multiply the volume in cubic feet by 7.48, the number of gallons per cubic foot. Hence,

Tank capacity when half full = 1.57 × 7.48

$$= 11.7 \text{ gal.}$$

If we had used Formula 1 instead, we would have

$V = \pi R^2 h$	$R = 8$ in.	13.5	864
$V = \pi \times 8^2 \times 13.5$	$h = 13.5$ in.	64	3.14
$V = \pi \times 64 \times 13.5$	$\pi = 3.14$	54 0	34 56
$\boxed{V = 2712.96 \text{ cu. in. } \textbf{ans.}}$	$V = ?$	810	86 4
		864.0	2592
			2712.96

This is the same result we obtained using Formula 1.

Spheres or Solids Having Spherical Form. The formula for the volume of a round ball (Fig. 222), or sphere as it is called, is given by the formula:

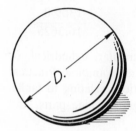

Fig. 222.

$$\boxed{V = \frac{\pi \times D \times D \times D}{6}}$$

or, in the shorthand of algebra, $V = \dfrac{\pi D^3}{6}$. (Read "pi, D cubed, over six.") If we calculate the value of $\dfrac{\pi}{6}$, we get $\dfrac{3.1416}{6} = 0.5236$. Hence we can write this formula as $\boxed{V = 0.5236 \times D^3}$ where D is the *diameter* of the sphere. Calculations involving this formula are illustrated in the following example.

■ **EXAMPLE 1:**

A cast-iron ball 5 in. in diameter is to be used in an athletic event called the "shot put." What is the weight of this ball if the weight of the cast iron is 0.25 lb. per cubic inch?

Solution and Explanation:

We compute the volume of the ball using the formula:

$$V = 0.5236 \times D^3$$

We have:

$V = 0.5236 \times D^3$

$V = 0.5236 \times 5 \times 5 \times 5$

$$V = 65.45 \text{ cu in.}$$

$D = 5$ in. $5 \times 5 \times 5 = 125$

$V = ?$

$$
\begin{array}{r}
0.5236 \\
125 \\
\hline
2\,6180 \\
10\,472 \\
52\,36 \\
\hline
65.4500
\end{array}
$$

To find the weight we multiply the number of cubic inches in the volume by the weight per cubic inch. We have:

$W = 65.45 \times 0.25$

$$W = 16.36 \text{ lb.} \quad \textbf{ans.}$$

$$
\begin{array}{r}
65.45 \\
.25 \\
\hline
327\,25 \\
1309\,0 \\
\hline
16.3625
\end{array}
$$

Volumes and weights of solids resembling rectangular, cylindrical, or spherical shapes are calculated as explained in the examples. Practical applications of such calculations occur in computations relating to tanks, columns, metal bars and rods, excavations, castings, machine parts, and construction materials.

13.5   Problems Involving Rectangular, Cylindrical, and Spherical Shapes

1. How many loads of dirt must be removed in excavating a foundation 24 ft. long, 15 ft. wide, and 12 ft. deep if the trucks used have a capacity of 5 cu. yd.?

2. What is the capacity in gallons of a cylindrical water reservoir 22 ft. in diameter and 76 ft. tall?

3. A tank that measures 8 ft. long and 6 ft. wide, holds 1260 gal. when filled to the top. How deep is this tank, assuming $7\frac{1}{2}$ gal. to 1 cu. ft.?

4. In an effort to determine the number of gallons of oil in a cylindrical tank 3 ft. in diameter, a measuring stick is lowered into the tank through a hole in the circular top until it touches the bottom. When the stick is withdrawn, the oil mark shows a depth of $1\frac{1}{2}$ ft. How many gallons of oil are there in the tank?

5. What is the capacity in gallons of a cylindrical water tank 9 ft. long and $5\frac{1}{2}$ ft. in diameter?

6. A steel ball bearing has a diameter of $\frac{1}{2}$ in. What is its volume in cubic inches? What is the weight of one such bearing if 1 cu. in. of steel

weighs 0.283 lb? What is the weight of 500 such bearings?

7. A cement-concrete roadway is 40 ft. wide, 1 ft. thick, and 10 miles long. What is its volume in cubic feet? in cubic yards?

8. How many cubic yards of earth will be removed in digging a foundation 70 ft. deep and 55 ft. in diameter?

9. A piece of steel 8 in. long is cut from a 2-in. square bar. If this material weighs 0.283 lb. per cubic inch, what is the weight of the piece 8 in. long?

10. If concrete weighs 150 lb. per cubic foot, what is the weight of a solid concrete ball which has a diameter of 18 in.?

11. What is the weight of a $\frac{1}{2}$-in.-diameter brass rod needed in making 500 screws as shown in the drawing (Fig. 223), allowing $\frac{1}{8}$ in. to each screw for cutting off and finishing?

Fig. 223.

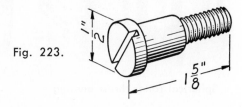

12. What is the capacity in cubic yards of a rectangular box 4 ft. 6 in. long, 2 ft. 9 in. wide, and 2 ft. deep?

13. A hemispherical copper kettle has an inside diameter of $2\frac{1}{2}$ ft. What is its capacity in gallons?

14. A flat steel bar is 3 in. wide, 1 in. thick, and 20 ft. long. What is its weight if 1 cu. in. of this steel weighs 0.283 lb.?

15. Find the weight of 2500 steel ball bearings which have a diameter of $\frac{3}{4}$ in. Use the weight per cubic inch given in Problem 14.

16. Determine the number of truckloads of earth that must be removed for an excavation 44 ft. long, 24 ft. wide, and 10 ft. deep, if the trucks used have a capacity of 5 cu. yd.

17. What is the weight of 500 wood railway ties 6 in. thick, 8 in. wide, and 8 ft. long if 1 cu. ft. of the wood weighs 50 lb.?

18. A granite paving block is 4 in. by 4 in. by 8 in. What is the weight of 50,000 such blocks if 1 cu. ft. of granite weighs 190 lb.?

19. The base plate for a column is 26 in. long, 24 in. wide, and 3 in. thick. What is the volume of this plate? Using 0.283 lb. per cubic inch for the weight of steel, what is the weight of this base plate?

20. The glass envelope of a small miniature radio tube can be considered as a cylinder having a diameter of $\frac{3}{4}$ in. and a height of $1\frac{7}{8}$ in. What is its volume in cubic inches?

Angular contact bearing.

Single row deep groove bearing.

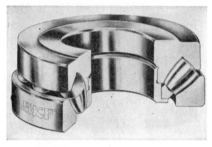

Spherical roller thrust bearing.

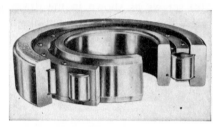

Cylindrical roller bearing.

Tapered roller bearing.

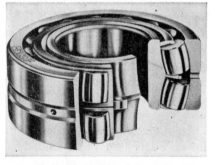

Spherical roller bearing.

SKF Industries

21. What is the weight of a round aluminum bar having a diameter of 2 in. and a length of 1 ft.? Use 0.095 lb. for the weight of a cubic inch of aluminum.

22. A half-round steel bar (a bar whose cross section is a half circle) has a diameter of 3 in. and a length of 16 ft. Find its weight, using the same value for the weight of a cubic inch of steel as in Problem 19.

23. A wide flange steel column has the following nominal dimensions: depth, 36 in.; width, 12 in. The cross-sectional area of this column is

57.11 sq. in. What does this column weigh per foot of its length? Use the same weight per cubic inch as in Problem 19.

24. A flat sheet of steel is $\frac{1}{4}$ in. thick by 5 in. wide by 16 ft. long. Calculate its weight, using 0.283 lb. per cubic inch.

25. At standard pressure and temperature, air weighs 0.08071 lb. per cubic foot. Calculate the weight of the air in a room 18 ft. long, 12 ft. wide, and 8 ft. high at these conditions.

13.6   Calculations Relating to Hollow Rectangular Solids

Rectangular Faces.   Volumes and weights of hollow rectangular forms or solids having rectangular faces (such as hollow concrete blocks, castings, in the shape of rectangular prisms, and so on) may be calculated by using the formulas and methods relating to rectangular solids. This is illustrated in the following problem.

■ **EXAMPLE 1:**

Calculate the weight of a concrete block made according to the dimensions in Figure 224.

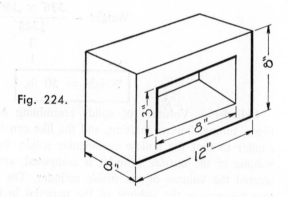

Fig. 224.

Solution and Explanation:

The weight of this block may be found in two main steps. The first step is to find the *net* volume of the block. This is done by (*a*) finding the volume of the entire block as though it were solid, and then (*b*) subtracting the volume of the hole from this.

The second step is to multiply the volume of the block by the weight of the block per cubic inch in order to obtain the weight. Proceeding as above, we have:

Step 1: *a)*

$$V = lwh$$
$$V = 12 \times 8 \times 8$$

$$\boxed{V = 768 \text{ cu. in.}}$$

$l = 12$ in.
$w = 8$ in.
$h = 8$ in.
$V = ?$

This is the volume of the block considered as though it were solid.

b)

$$V = lwh$$
$$V = 8 \times 8 \times 3$$

$$\boxed{V = 192 \text{ cu. in.}}$$

$l = 8$ in.
$w = 8$ in.
$h = 3$ in.
$V = ?$

This is the volume of the rectangular hole.

Then:

$$\boxed{\text{Net volume of block} = 768 - 192 = 576 \text{ cu. in.}}$$

Step 2: If the block is made of concrete weighing 150 lb. per cubic foot, then we can find its weight by dividing its volume by 1728 (to change it to cubic feet) and multiplying this result by 150.

Hence:

$$\text{Weight} = \frac{\overset{1}{\cancel{576}} \times \overset{50}{\cancel{150}}}{\underset{\underset{1}{3}}{\cancel{1728}}}$$

$$\boxed{\text{Weight} = 50 \text{ lb.}}$$

Cylinders. Volumes of solids resembling *hollow* cylinders, such as pipes, tubing, hollow shafting, and the like can be computed in a manner similar to that for hollow rectangular solids. In such computations, the volume of the *outside* cylinder is computed, and from this there is subtracted the volume of the *inside* cylinder. The difference between these two volumes is the volume of the material in the particular piece. The following example will illustrate how such problems are worked out.

■ **EXAMPLE 2:**

Compute the weight of the steel collar shown in Figure 225, if steel weighs 0.283 lb. per cubic inch.

Solution and Explanation:

We first find the volume of the collar as though it were solid. Using the formula for the volume of a cylinder, we have:

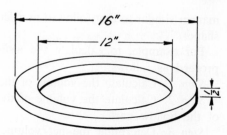

Fig. 225.

$$V = \frac{\pi \times D \times D \times H}{4}$$

$D = 16$ (outer diameter)
$H = \frac{1}{2}$
$V = ?$

$$V = \frac{\pi \times \overset{4}{\cancel{16}} \times \overset{8}{\cancel{16}} \times \cancel{\frac{1}{2}}}{\underset{1}{\cancel{4}}}$$

$V = 100.531$ cu. in.

```
  3.1416
      32
  ------
   62832
   94248
  ------
 100.5312
```

We next find the volume of the hole. Using the same formula, we have:

$$v = \frac{\pi \times d \times d \times H}{4}$$

$d = 12$ (inner diameter)
$H = \frac{1}{2}$
$v = ?$

$$v = \frac{\pi \times \overset{3}{\cancel{12}} \times \overset{6}{\cancel{12}} \times \cancel{\frac{1}{2}}}{\underset{1}{\cancel{4}}}$$

$v = 56.549$ cu. in.

```
  3.1416
      18
  ------
  251328
  31416
  ------
  56.5488
```

Subtracting, we have:

Net volume $= 100.531 - 56.549$

Net volume $= 43.982$ cu. in.

Multiplying the next volume by the weight per cubic inch, we have:

Weight $= 43.982 \times 0.283$

Weight $= 12.4$ lb.

```
   43.982
     .283
  --------
   131946
   351856
   87964
  --------
 12.446906
```

Spherical Shapes. The calculation of volumes and weights of *hollow spherical shapes* such as hollow balls and half spheres is performed in a manner similar to that followed in calculating volumes of hollow cylindrical shapes.

For example, to calculate the *weight* of a hollow sphere, one would proceed as follows:

Step 1: Calculate the volume of the sphere using the *outside* diameter.

Step 2: Calculate the volume of the hollow portion using the diameter of the hollow part.

Step 3: Determine the net volume of the material in the "spherical shell" by subtracting the volume found in Step 2 from the volume found in Step 1.

Step 4: Calculate the weight of the spherical shell by multiplying the volume of the shell by the weight per cubic inch (or cubic foot) of the material.

This procedure is illustrated in the following problem.

■ **EXAMPLE 3:**

Determine the weight of a 4-in. hollow brass ball $\frac{1}{8}$ in. thick which is to be placed on top of a flagpole.

Solution and Explanation:

Following the procedure outlined above, we have:

Step 1:

$$V = 0.5236 \times D^3$$
$$V = 0.5236 \times 4 \times 4 \times 4$$
$$\boxed{V = 33.5104 \text{ cu. in.}}$$

$D = 4$
$V = ?$

This is the volume of the ball considered as though it were solid.

Step 2: The diameter of the hollow part is $3\frac{3}{4}$ in., or $\frac{1}{4}$ in. less than the outside diameter.

Then:

$$v = 0.5236 \times d^3$$
$$v = 0.5236 \times 3.75 \times 3.75 \times 3.75$$
$$\boxed{v = 27.6117 \text{ cu. in.}}$$

$d = 3\frac{3}{4}$
$v = ?$

This is the volume of the hollow portion of the ball.

Step 3: The net volume, that is, the volume of the spherical shell:

$$= 33.5104 - 27.6117$$
$$= 5.8987 \text{ cu. in.}$$

Assuming that the brass weighs 0.30 lb. per cubic inch, the weight of the ball is

$$W = 5.8987 \times 0.30$$

$$\boxed{W = 1.77 \ \text{lb.}}$$

That is, the weight of this hollow brass ball is slightly more than $1\frac{3}{4}$ lb.

13.7 Irregular Forms

The volume and weight of *irregular solids* can be computed without difficulty by first separating the particular solid into *regular* forms. After the given solid has been divided in this manner, the volume of each part is found separately. The *total* volume is then found by adding the volumes of the various parts. The total weight is then found by *multiplying* the *total* volume by the weight per cubic inch or cubic foot of the material.

■ **EXAMPLE 1:**

Calculate the weight of 25 cast-iron angle brackets made as in the sketch (Fig. 226).

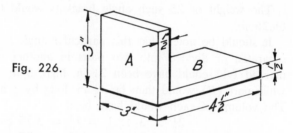

Fig. 226.

Solution and Explanation:

Inspection of this casting shows that it does not resemble any of the regular solids we have already considered. Closer examination, however, shows that it can be separated into two parts, *A* and *B,* each of which is a regular solid. Separating the bracket into these parts, and showing their dimensions, we see that these parts are rectangular prisms (Figs. 227 and 228). We next find the volume of each.

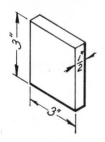

Fig. 227.
Part A

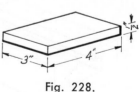

Fig. 228.
Part B

Part (*A*)

$$V = lwh$$
$$V = 3 \times 3 \times \tfrac{1}{2}$$

$$\boxed{V = 4.5 \text{ cu. in.}}$$

$l = 3$ in.
$w = 3$ in.
$h = \tfrac{1}{2}$ in.

Part (*B*)

$$V = lwh$$
$$V = 4 \times 3 \times \tfrac{1}{2}$$

$$\boxed{V = 6.0 \text{ cu. in.}}$$

$l = 4$ in.
$w = 3$ in.
$h = \tfrac{1}{2}$ in.

Next we find the *total* volume.

$$\boxed{\text{Total volume} = 4.5 + 6.0 = 10.5 \text{ cu. in.}}$$

Using 0.26 lb. for the weight per cubic inch of cast iron, we find that the

$$\text{Weight of \textit{one} bracket} = 10.5 \times 0.26$$
$$= 2.73 \text{ lb.}$$

The weight of 25 such angle brackets would then be 25×2.73 or 68.25 lb.

It should be noted that this particular angle bracket could have been separated or divided into two parts in another way. That is, the part marked (*A*) could have been $2\tfrac{1}{2}$ in. high, 3 in. wide, and $\tfrac{1}{2}$ in. thick, while part (*B*) would then be $4\tfrac{1}{2}$ in. long by 3 in. wide by $\tfrac{1}{2}$ in. thick. The volume of each would have been

$$2\tfrac{1}{2} \times 3 \times \tfrac{1}{2} = \tfrac{15}{4} = 3.75 \text{ cu. in.}$$
$$4\tfrac{1}{2} \times 3 \times \tfrac{1}{2} = \tfrac{27}{4} = 6.75 \text{ cu. in.}$$

The total volume would still be $3.75 + 6.75 = 10.50$ cu. in., the *same* as computed before. The total weight would likewise be $10.50 \times 0.26 = 2.73$ lb. for *each* bracket, and $25 \times 2.73 = 68.25$ lb. for the 25 brackets.

13.8 Problems Relating to Hollow and Irregular Forms

1. Calculate the weight of eight T-slotted cast-iron blocks as per the dimensions in Figure 229.

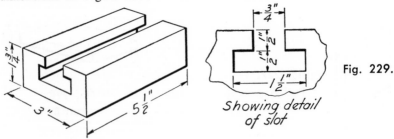

Fig. 229.

Showing detail of slot

2. What is the weight of 24 steel plates $\frac{1}{4}$ in. thick, cut according to the dimensions in Figure 230?

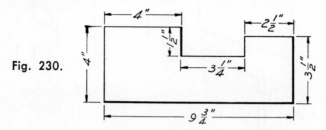

Fig. 230.

3. Determine the weight of $\frac{1}{4}$-in.-round stock needed in making 160 brass pins as shown (Fig. 231). Allow $\frac{1}{8}$ in. for cutting off each pin.

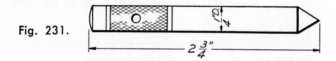

Fig. 231.

4. It is required to make 64 blanks on a foot press from sheet copper $\frac{1}{8}$ in. thick as per the sketch (Fig. 232). The strip of copper to be used measures $1\frac{1}{2}$ in. wide. An allowance of $\frac{1}{8}$ in. is to be made between the blanked pieces and at each end of the strip as shown. What is the total length of the strip of copper needed for these 64 blanks? What is the weight of the 64 blanks?

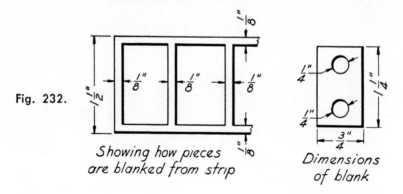

Fig. 232.

Showing how pieces are blanked from strip

Dimensions of blank

5. Determine the weight of material needed for 144 braces according to dimensions in the drawing (Fig. 233). There is a loss of $\frac{1}{8}$ in. of stock in cutting off each piece. Calculate the weight of the 144 braces if this material weighs .28 lb. per cubic inch.

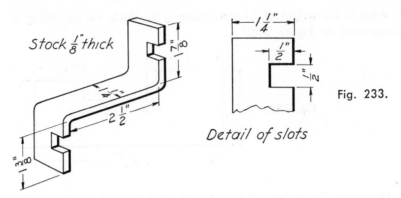

Stock ⅛" thick

Fig. 233.

Detail of slots

6. What is the weight of 1500 blanks ⅛ in. thick as shown in Figure 234? The material in these weighs .22 lb. to the cubic inch.

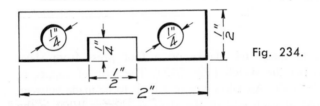

Fig. 234.

7. From the dimensions in the sketch (Fig. 235), determine the weight of the concrete in the steps illustrated.

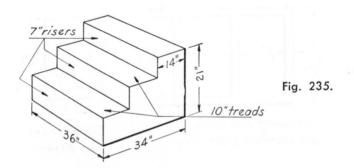

7"risers

14"

21"

Fig. 235.

10"treads

36"   34"

8. Calculate the number of tons of concrete in a footing of the dimensions shown in Figure 236. This footing is to be calculated as having no reinforcing bars.

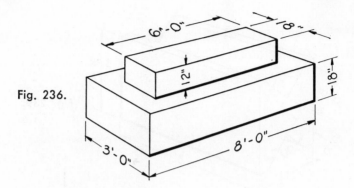

Fig. 236.

9. A copper half sphere ¼ in. thick has an outside diameter of 15 in. Determine its weight if copper weighs 0.32 lb. per cubic inch.

10. What is the weight of 25 brass castings as per the drawing (Fig. 237)?

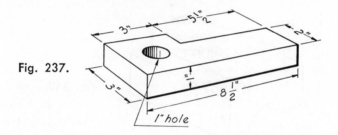

Fig. 237.

11. Determine the weight of 40 steel straps as illustrated in Figure 238.

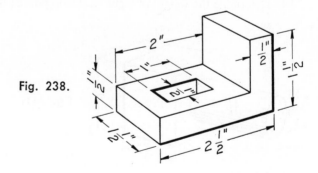

Fig. 238.

12. What is the weight of 16 steel V blocks like the one illustrated (Fig. 239)?

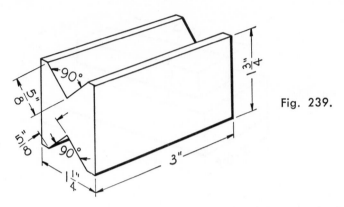

Fig. 239.

13. How many cubic feet of material are there in two concrete blocks made according to the dimensions in Figure 240? What is the weight of these two pieces?

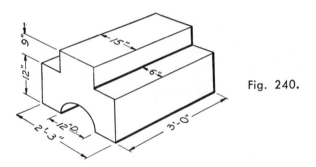

Fig. 240.

14. Determine the weight of eight steel stop pins as shown in Figure 241.

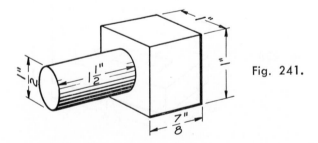

Fig. 241.

15. Calculate the weight of 10 cast-iron blocks according to the dimensions in the drawing (Fig. 242).

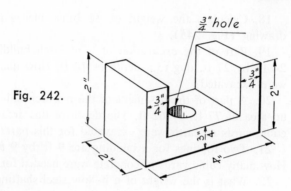

Fig. 242.

16. What is the weight of five steel straps made according to the dimensions shown in Figure 243?

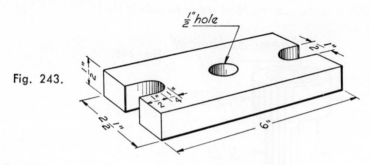

Fig. 243.

17. Four hundred aluminum pins are to be made according to the accompanying drawing (Fig. 244). Determine their total weight.

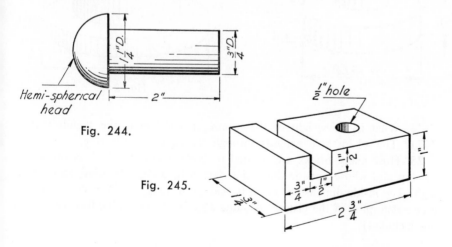

Hemi-spherical head

Fig. 244.

Fig. 245.

18. Calculate the weight of 16 brass pieces made according to the drawing (Fig. 245).

19. Part of the excavation of a research building consists of an area 24 ft. by 27 ft. dug to a depth of 14 ft. How many cubic yards of earth were excavated?

20. A part of the basement of the research building in Problem 19 has an area of 77 ft. by 62 ft. The depth of this area was 14 ft. How many cubic yards of earth were excavated for this part?

21. Two footings for a building are 9 ft. by 9 ft. and 2 ft. 6 in. thick. How many cubic yards of concrete were needed for both of these footings?

22. What is the weight of a hollow steel shafting which measures 4-in. outside diameter with a 2-in. circular hole running through its entire length of 6 ft.?

23. One-eighth of the total weight of the concrete birdbath in Figure 246 is to be cement. How many pounds is this?

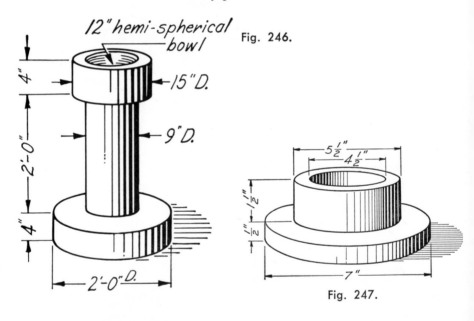

Fig. 246.

Fig. 247.

24. What is the weight of the bronze ring shown in the sketch (Fig. 247)? The 4½-in. hole extends through the center of the ring.

25. How many bricks are needed to build a cistern which is open at the top and whose outside dimensions are 8 ft. wide, 8 ft. long, and 5 ft. high? The inside dimensions are 6 ft. wide, 6 ft. long, and 4 ft. deep. Draw a complete plan of the cistern. Assume 25.6 bricks per cubic foot (mortar not included).

26. Calculate the weight of 50 steel pieces made as per the dimensions given in Figure 248.

Fig. 248.

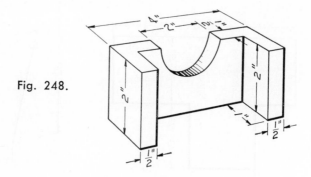

27. At the rate of 9 cents per pound, what is the cost of 20 iron castings made according to (Fig. 249)? The 1-in. hole extends through the casting.

Fig. 249.

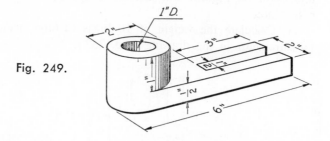

28. Determine the weight of 48 steel pieces made as per the specifications in the sketch (Fig. 250).

Fig. 250.

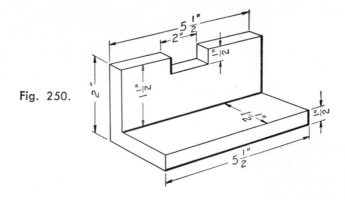

29. How many tons of earth must be removed in excavating for a cellar 5 ft. deep according to the plan in the sketch (Fig. 251)?

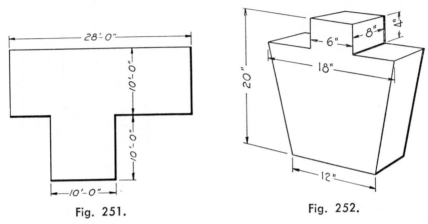

Fig. 251.

Fig. 252.

30. What is the approximate weight of a granite keystone cut to the dimensions in Figure 252? Granite weighs approximately 166 lb. to the cubic foot.

31. Calculate the weight of 10 brass castings made according to the measurements in the drawing (Fig. 253).

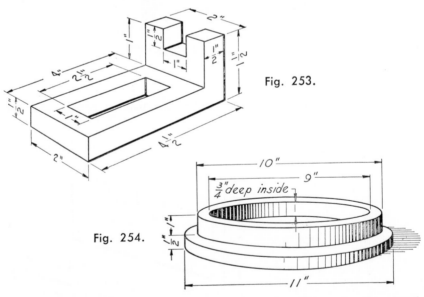

Fig. 253.

Fig. 254.

32. Determine the weight of the steel cover shown in the sketch (Fig. 254).

13.9 Review Problems Involving Regular and Irregular Shapes

1. A hollow aluminum ball measuring 8-in. outside diameter is $\frac{3}{8}$ in. thick. Calculate its weight.

2. From the following drawing determine the weight of 45 brass castings made according to the given measurements (Fig. 255).

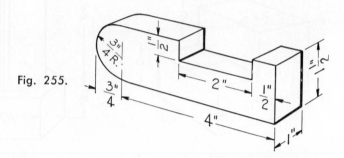

Fig. 255.

3. The following lumber is piled away to season. Because of the unseasoned condition of this lumber it is estimated as being 10 percent heavier than the weight of dry lumber as usually given. According to this what is the approximate weight of this lumber?

  24 white pine boards, $1\frac{1}{2}$ in. × 10 in. × 12 ft. long
  30 hemlock boards, 2 in. × 6 in. × 10 ft. long
  18 spruce planks,   4 in. × 8 in. × 10 ft. long

4. The average thickness of a concrete walk 6 ft. wide is 4 in. throughout its length of 142 ft. How many tons of concrete are there in this sidewalk?

5. A cylindrical iron tank weighing 24 lb. measures 18 in. in diameter and 24 in. deep inside. When it is one fourth filled with oil that weighs $7\frac{1}{4}$ lb. per gallon, what is the weight of the tank and oil?

6. From the dimensions in the drawing (Fig. 256) determine the weight of 15 cast-iron clamping blocks.

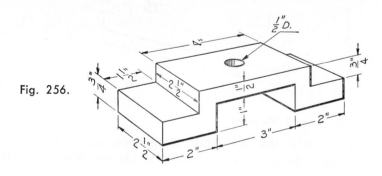

Fig. 256.

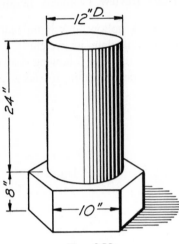

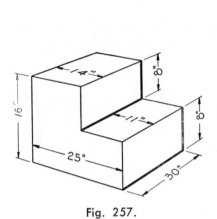

Fig. 257.   Fig. 258.

7. Calculate the weight of the concrete steps constructed according to the measurements in the drawing (Fig. 257).

8. After a rainstorm it was noted that the water in a 6-ft. diameter circular cistern had risen 8 in. The flat tin roof from which this rain was conducted to the cistern measures 18 by 32 ft. From this, calculate the approximate number of inches of rainfall per square foot.

9. What is the weight of the concrete pedestal in the drawing (Fig. 258).

10. Determine the weight of 64 forgings like that in the sketch (Fig. 259). The metal in this weighs 0.29 lb. per cubic inch.

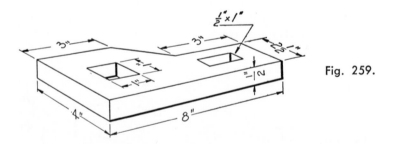

Fig. 259.

13.10   Liquid Measure

In the measurement of liquids of all kinds, such as water, oil, gasoline, turpentine, paint, we use the *gallon* as the unit of capacity. The U. S.

gallon is legally defined in terms of cubic measure as equal to a volume of 231 cu. in.

The units of liquid measure as fixed by law are related to each other according to the following table.

4 gills (gi.)   equal 1 pint (pt.)
2 pints   equal 1 quart (qt.)
4 quarts   equal 1 gallon (gal.), also 231 cu. in.
31½ gallons   equal 1 barrel (bbl.)
1 cubic foot   equals 1728 cu. in. = 7.48 gal.

Since there are 231 cu. in. in 1 gal.,

$$1 \text{ quart} = \tfrac{231}{4} = 57\tfrac{3}{4} = 57.75 \text{ cu. in.}$$
$$1 \text{ pint} = \tfrac{231}{8} = 28\tfrac{7}{8} = 28.875 \text{ cu. in.}$$

In our calculations, we will use the legally defined U. S. gallon.

13.11 Changing Units of One Denomination to Units of Another Denomination

To change units of one denomination to units of another denomination, the procedure is much the same as that followed in calculations relating to linear measure, square measure, and cubic measure.

To find the number of quarts in a number of gallons, the number of gallons is multiplied by 4, since there are 4 quarts in each gallon. To determine the number of gallons in a given number of quarts, the number of quarts is *divided* by 4. To change (or convert) a number of quarts to pints, the number of quarts is *multiplied* by 2. To convert a number of pints to quarts, the number of pints is *divided* by 2. To convert a number of cubic inches to gallons, *divide* the number of cubic inches by 231.

The following problems will illustrate the computation of volumes and capacities.

■ EXAMPLE 1:

Calculate (1) the volume in cubic inches and (2) the capacity in gallons of the fuel tank illustrated in the drawing (Fig. 260). (For the sake of simplicity the dimensions shown can be considered as being inside dimensions.)

Solution and Explanation:

Step 1: We divide the tank into three parts — *A, B,* and *C.* Parts *A* and *B* are the same, each being a half cylinder of diameter 27 in. and length 60 in. Part *C* has the shape of a rectangular solid whose length = 5 ft., height = 3 ft. 9½ in. minus 2 ft. 3 in. or 1 ft. 6½ in., and width = 2 ft. 3 in.

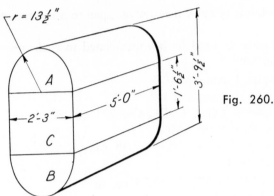

Fig. 260.

Step 2: The volume of parts A and B together is:

$$V = \frac{\pi D^2 H}{4}$$

$$V = \frac{\pi \times 2.25^2 \times 5}{4}$$

$$V = 0.7854 \times 5.0625 \times 5$$

$D = 2$ ft. 3 in. $= 2.25$ ft.

$H = 5$ ft.

$V = ?$

$$\boxed{V = 19.88 \text{ cu. ft.}}$$

Step 3: The volume of part C is:

$$V = lwh$$

$$V = 5 \times 2\tfrac{1}{4} \times 1\tfrac{13}{24}$$

$$V = 5 \times \frac{\overset{3}{\cancel{9}}}{4} \times \frac{37}{\underset{8}{\cancel{24}}}$$

$$V = \frac{555}{32}$$

$l = 5$ ft.

$w = 2\tfrac{1}{4}$ ft.

$h = 1$ ft. 6.5 in.

    $= 1\tfrac{13}{24}$ ft.

    $= \frac{37}{24}$ ft.

$V = ?$

$$\boxed{V = 17.34 \text{ cu. ft.}}$$

Step 4: The total volume $= 19.88 + 17.34$ cu. ft.

$$\boxed{\text{Total volume} = 37.22 \text{ cu. ft.}}$$

Step 5: To change the volume to an equivalent number of gallons, we multiply 37.22×7.48

$$\text{Capacity of tank} = 37.22 \times 7.48$$
$$= 278.4 \text{ gal.}$$

Tanks of these dimensions have capacities listed at 275 gal.

■ **EXAMPLE 2:**

During a period of six weeks, $34\tfrac{1}{2}$ qt. of oil were collected in the drip pans under the oil barrels in a shop supply room. How many gallons does this amount equal?

Solution and Explanation:

Since there are 4 qt. in 1 gal., then in $34\frac{1}{2}$ qt. there will be as many gallons as 4 is contained in $34\frac{1}{2}$. Hence the number of

$$\text{gallons} = 34\tfrac{1}{2} \div 4$$
$$= \frac{69}{2 \times 4} = \frac{69}{8}$$
$$= 8\tfrac{5}{8} \text{ gal.}$$

That is, $8\frac{5}{8}$ gal. were collected in the drip pans.

13.12   Problems Relating to Liquid Measure

1. How many cubic feet are there in one $31\frac{1}{2}$-gal. barrel?

2. How many quarts of linseed oil can be put into an empty cylindrical tank 15 in. in diameter and 20 in. high? When it is one half full, what is the weight of the oil in the tank? One gallon of linseed oil is listed as weighing 7.84 lb.

3. Two boys each carrying a bucket holding 10 qt. are assigned the job of filling the tank shown in Figure 261. How many bucketfuls are required to fill this tank completely? How many gallons does this equal?

Fig. 261.

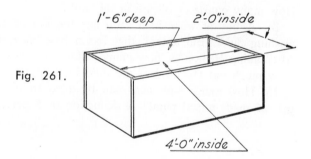

4. A cylindrical tank 18 in. in diameter, 30 in. high, and open at the top is three fourths filled with turpentine. The tank alone weighs 32 lb. If the turpentine weighs 7.26 lb. per gallon, what is the combined weight of the tank and the turpentine?

5. A cylindrical can used in a paint shop for linseed oil measures 18 in. in diameter and 24 in. high. To determine the amount of oil there was in the can a workman put a yardstick through the small opening in the top until the end of the stick touched the bottom. Upon withdrawing

the stick, the oil mark showed that there was oil up to the 15-in. mark. From this determine the number of quarts of oil in the can.

6. A spherical tank used to store liquid hydrogen has a diameter of approximately 28 ft. What is its volume in cubic feet?

7. A cylindrical bucket measures 15 in. in diameter, and is 20 in. deep. How many quarts will it hold?

8. Due to leakage and evaporation, $11\frac{1}{2}$ qt. of gasoline are lost from a 50-gal. barrel. At 34 cents per gallon, what does the loss equal?

9. What is the number of standard barrels capacity of a cylindrical tank which measures 6 ft. in diameter and $8\frac{1}{2}$ ft. high?

10. What must be the depth of a cylindrical bucket, if the diameter is to be 10 in. and it is to hold 18 qt. when completely filled?

11. From a tank of oil, 5 ft. long, 3 ft. wide, and 4 ft. deep, there are withdrawn during a certain period 225 qt. of oil. How many gallons does this equal? How much did the level of the oil in the tank drop during this time?

12. A bucket that measures 11 in. in diameter and 15 in. deep inside is used to fill a tank that measures 14 in. deep, 24 in. wide, and 6 ft. long. How many quarts does this bucket hold? How many gallons will the tank hold when completely filled?

13. To measure the amount of lubricating oil in a tank, 30 in. in diameter, a long stick marked off in inches is put down into the tank through a hole in the circular top. It showed that the oil is 14 in. deep. How many quarts of oil are in the tank?

14. A boy at work in a shop has the job of filling pint bottles with washing fluid from a tank that has a base measuring 24 in. by 36 in. After filling 50 bottles, how many gallons were withdrawn from the tank? How much did the level of the fluid in the tank drop?

15. How many $\frac{1}{2}$-pt. cans can be filled from a container holding 15 gal. of ready-mixed paint? A deduction of 5 percent is made for waste.

Unit IV
TRADE MATHEMATICS

CHAPTER 14

Mathematics Applied to the Building Trades — I

14.1 Introduction

Before any building is erected, an estimate of the cost of construction must be made. The architect uses this rough estimate as a guide in designing the structure. When the final design has been agreed on, and the building plans have been drawn up, the builder-contractors use estimates to arrive at a figure for which they will be able to undertake the construction of the building.

The builder-contractors, before submitting their bids (or price for which they will do the construction) carefully study the architect's detail drawings, and, using their knowledge of construction methods, labor, and material, and estimating the quantities of materials needed (which they determine from the architect's plans), arrive at a cost figure for which they can profitably undertake the erection of the building.

The total cost of building a home, for example, exclusive of the lot on which it stands, may be divided into the following items:

1. Excavating, backfilling, grading, and landscaping costs,
2. Concrete-work costs — footings, floors, and walks,
3. Masonry and wall construction cost,
4. Carpentry costs including millwork,
5. Roofing, gutters, and flashing costs,
6. Lathing and plastering costs,
7. Plumbing costs,
8. Heating and ventilating costs,
9. Electrical wiring costs,
10. Painting, papering, decorating, tile work, permanent floor covering work,
11. Legal fees.

Mathematics is used in each of these phases of design, estimating, and construction. In this and the following chapters, we will discuss some of these areas.

14.2 Lath

Wood Lath. The interior walls and partitions of many homes require lath and plaster for their construction. *Lath* may be considered as wood strips, metallic mesh, or plasterboards to which plaster may be applied to form the interior surface of ceilings and walls. Wood lath consists of strips of wood, 4 ft. long, $1\frac{3}{8}$ in. wide, and $\frac{3}{8}$ of an inch thick, supported on wood studs. These strips are nailed to the studs at right angles and parallel to the floor, spaced $\frac{3}{8}$ of an inch vertically from each other, and $\frac{1}{4}$ in. from each other at their ends. This spacing allows the plaster to *key* or hold on to the lath. The lath are nailed in horizontal rows, six or seven in a group, and then the next group below them is staggered over a distance equal to twice the center-to-center spacing of the studs. The purpose of this staggering is to prevent the cracking of the plaster. This type of lath is not used in present-day building, however, except possibly for repair work.

In recent years many new building materials and many new construction methods have been developed. Some of these developments were due to the scarcity of natural materials; others were due to the need for saving time and labor on construction. The demand for factories, military installations, and civilian dwellings, brought about by World War II and the years following it, gave an enormous impetus to the search for new methods, materials, and processes in building construction.

Gypsum Lath. One of the new and most widely used materials for lathing is a gypsum lath made in the form of sheets, $\frac{3}{8}$ or $\frac{1}{2}$ in. thick and 16 in. wide by 48 in. long. This type of lath is available in plain sheets and in perforated sheets. The perforated types have forty-eight $\frac{3}{4}$-in.-diameter holes in each sheet. The holes are spaced 4 in. center to center. Although plaster will adhere strongly to the plain lath, the perforations serve as a further means of anchoring the plaster to the lath. Either the plain or perforated board lath may be used on walls, but only the plain board lath is recommended for ceiling use. This material is strong and has high fire- and sound-resisting qualities. Its size makes it easy to install, and hence the cost of erection is reduced.

If the building is of frame construction, the sheets are nailed to the studs; if the walls are made of masonry or brick they are nailed to strips of wood called furring strips. When the supports to which the lath are fastened are 16 in. center to center, four nails are used at each support, making a total of 16 nails per lath. It should be remembered that, in the construction of buildings and homes, lath is put on *after* heating and ventilating ducts and pipes; wiring for power, light, heat, appliances,

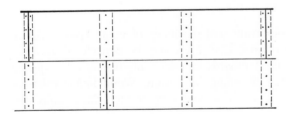

Fig. 266.

telephone, television; and pipes for water and plumbing have been put in place.

The lath are nailed with the long dimensions horizontal, as shown in Figure 266, and are butted against each other lightly. Each row is called a course and the courses are staggered as shown. All areas that are not to be covered with lath, such as windows, doors, and archways, are called "openings." It is important to note that the gypsum lath is usually reinforced at door and window openings, at inside and exterior corners, arches, and at other critical places. This is done by using strips of expanded metal lath for the reinforcing. Since each of these sheets is 16 in. wide by 48 in. long, the area of one sheet $= \frac{16}{12} \times \frac{48}{12} = 5\frac{1}{3}$ sq. ft. Six such sheets have an area of $6 \times 5\frac{1}{3} = 32$ sq. ft., and are called a *bundle*.

A complete cost estimate of installing board lath would include such items as cost of the lath, nails, metal-reinforcing lath, and labor costs. For our purpose, it will be sufficient to discuss the estimated cost of the lath only.

Estimating Amount and Cost of Board Lath. Gypsum lath may be bought by the bundle or in 1000-sq.-ft. amounts. For example, 1000 sq. ft. of $\frac{3}{8}$ by 16 by 48-in. board lath was priced at $45.00 in Chicago, $45.00 in New Orleans, and $36.25 in New York City. A bundle was sold for $1.55 in Chicago at the same time.

Let us consider the following:

■ **EXAMPLE 1:**

A living room is 20 ft. by 14 ft. and a dining room is 15 ft. by 10 ft. Each room is 8 ft. 0 in. high. A deduction of 310 sq. ft. will be made for doors and windows. How many square feet of $\frac{3}{8}$ by 16 by 48-in. gypsum lath will be needed for the walls of these rooms? How many bundles of this type of lath will be needed? Allow 10 percent for waste.

Solution and Explanation:

1. First we find the area of the walls of the living room and the dining room.

2. We then deduct 310 sq. ft. from the answer found in (1) to get the number of square feet of lath needed.

3. We divide the answer in part (2) by 32 to get the number of bundles needed.

The area of the walls of the living room = perimeter of living room × height of living room = $(20 + 14 + 20 + 14) \times 8 = 68 \times 8 = 544$ sq. ft.

The area of walls of dining room = perimeter of dining room × height
                                                      of dining room
                                = (15 + 10 + 15 + 10) × 8
                                = (50) × 8
                                = 400 sq. ft.

The total wall area   = 544 + 400 =   944   sq. ft.
Allowing 10 percent for waste   =   94.4 sq. ft.
Equivalent gross area   = 1038.4 sq. ft.
Deduction for openings   =   310   sq. ft.
Total amount of lath needed   =   728.4 sq. ft.

Since one bundle of this size lath covers 32 sq. ft., the number of
bundles needed

$$= \frac{728.4}{32}$$

$$= 22.8$$

$$= 23 \text{ bundles}$$

If a bundle costs $1.28, the cost of the lath would be

$$23 \times \$1.28 = \$29.44$$

Hence the cost of the lath is $29.44. If a sales tax at 3 percent
is included, it would amount to 0.03 × $29.44 = $0.88. The total cost
would then be $29.44 + $0.88 or $30.32.

Metal Lath.   Another and very popular type of plaster base is metal
lath. Metal lath has the great advantage that it can be shaped, cut, and
formed into many shapes and designs that would be extremely difficult
if not impossible to achieve otherwise. Metal lath in general finds much

Using metal lath in con-
structing a ceiling.

Republic Steel

use in larger buildings where large areas are to be covered and where quality construction and fireproofing are important considerations.

Metal lath is made in many different patterns and comes in several different weights, which are for a square yard of the lath. In fabricating the metal lath, steel sheets are slit or punched and then expanded, resulting in the formation of many openings of various shapes, depending on the method of slitting and punching. The openings serve as "keys" for the plaster to bond itself to the lath in an almost solid slab, making it resistant to fire and minimizing the formation of cracks in the plaster.

The common kinds of metal lath are the expanded type, the rib type, and the sheet type. For interior construction, the diamond small mesh expanded type is one of the most widely used. Metal lath is covered either with paint which inhibits the formation of rust or may be made from galvanized sheets. Metal lath is specified by its weight per square yard. Common weights are 2.5 lb. per square yard and 3.4 lb. per square yard, and common sheet sizes are 27 in. by 96 in. Metal lath weighing 2.5 lb. per square yard is used for walls and partitions; metal lath weighing 3.4 lb. per square yard can be used for walls, partitions, and ceilings.

Estimating Quantities of Metal Lath. Sheets of this size (27 × 96 in.) come in bundles of 10, covering $10 \times \frac{27}{12} \times \frac{96}{12} = 180$ sq. ft., or $\frac{180}{9} = 20$ sq. yd. 100 sq. yd. of standard diamond-mesh lath, weighing 3.4 lb. per sq. yd., in carload lots, were quoted at prices running from $44.50 to $67.20 in various parts of the country.

Metal lath may be attached to vertical wood supports with common 4-penny nails, 1-in. roofing nails, or 1-in. W&M (Washburn and Moen) gauge staples. It may be attached to horizontal forming members with $1\frac{1}{2}$-in. barbed 11-gauge roofing nails. These are attached about every 6 in. About 10 percent should be allowed for waste of the lath. Other accessories, such as corner beads would also have to be taken into consideration.

For ordinary work, not requiring special cutting and forming, it should be possible for a lather to cover about 90–100 sq. yd. of surface with metal lath in an 8-hr. day. Journeymen lathers' wages vary from $2.95 per hour to $5.20 per hour, depending on the section of the country.

■ **EXAMPLE 1:**

A five-room house has a total wall and ceiling area of 3060 sq. ft. How much will diamond-mesh wire lath weighing 3.4 lb. per square yard cost to cover this area if the lath sells at $52.00 per 100 sq. yd.?

Solution and Explanation:

Step 1: We find 10 percent of the given figure for waste:

$$\frac{10}{100} \times 3060 = 306 \text{ sq. ft.}$$

Step 2: We find the equivalent total area to be covered with lath:

$$= 3060 + 306$$
$$= 3366 \text{ sq. ft.}$$

Step 3: We convert this area to square yards:

$$\frac{3366}{9} = 374 \text{ sq. yd.}$$

Step 4: Since the lath is sold in 100-sq.-yd. amounts, we divide 374 by 100:

$$\frac{374}{100} = 3.74 \text{ hundreds of square yards}$$

Step 5: Since the cost for each 100 sq. yd. is $52.00 we multiply $52.00 by 3.74:

$$\$52.00 \times 3.74 = \$194.48$$

This is the cost of the lath not including sales tax.

14.3 Problems Involving the Computation of Quantities and Costs of Lath

1. Each of two rooms is 24 ft. long, 16 ft. wide, and 8 ft. high. How many square feet of wall and ceiling area are there in both rooms? How many bundles of board lath would be needed for both of these rooms (making no allowance for door and window openings) if one bundle (6 sheets, each 16 in. by 48 in.) covers 32 sq. ft.?

2. If a bundle of board lath costs $1.28, what is the cost of the lath needed in Problem 1?

3. A one-story frame home has a total of 1500 sq. ft. of area to be covered with board lath. How many bundles of lath are required? What is the cost of lath at $1.25 per bundle?

4. A home has two rooms each 18 ft. by 24 ft. and three rooms each 12 ft. by 18 ft. All of the rooms are 8 ft. high. Find:

a) the total wall and ceiling area in square feet,
b) the number of bundles of board lath needed to cover this area,
c) the cost of the lath at $1.28 per bundle.

5. A contractor estimates that he will have to install 27,000 sq. ft. of board lath. If a lather could install 800 sq. ft. of lath in an 8-hr. day, how many days would be needed for one man to do the work? for two men to do the work? If the work were done by two men, each receiving $3.70 per hour, how much would each of the lathers receive?

6. In remodeling an empty room into a playroom for his children, a man covered the walls with wall paneling. If the size of the room was 24 ft. long, 16 ft. wide, and 8 ft. high, and the wall panels were 4 ft. by 8 ft., how many panels would he need? (Make no allowance for the door and window openings.) If each panel costs $7.45, what would be the cost of the paneling?

7. The walls of a room 24 ft. long, 12 ft. wide, and 8 ft. high are to be paneled. The panels are 4 ft. by 8 ft. and cost $7.45 each. Find the number of panels needed and their total cost.

8. A residence has six rooms whose dimensions are:

3 rooms, each 12 ft. by 11 ft.

1 room, 13 ft. by 12 ft.

1 room, 18 ft. by 20 ft.

1 room, 16 ft. by 12 ft.

All of these rooms are 8 ft. high. If the walls and ceilings of these rooms are to be covered with board lath, find

a) the total ceiling area of the six rooms,

b) the entire wall area of the six rooms,

c) the total area of the walls and ceilings.

9. How many bundles of board lath are needed to cover the walls and ceilings of the six rooms in Problem 8? What is the cost of the lath at $1.25 per bundle?

10. A homeowner decides to cover the ceiling of his children's playroom with acoustical tile, each piece of which is 12 in. by 12 in. If the size of the playroom is 14 ft. by 20 ft., and the tile costs $14\frac{1}{2}$ cents each, what will be the cost of the tile?

11. The walls of four rooms each 14 ft. long, 11 ft. wide, and 8 ft. high are to be covered with metal lath. How many square yards of lath will be needed if each room has 50 sq. ft. of openings? Allow 10 percent for waste.

12. If one bundle of metal lath covers 20 sq. yd., how many bundles will be required for lathing the walls in Problem 11?

13. In the process of modernizing a store building it was necessary to lath and plaster the ceiling and the walls. The two side walls were 88 ft. long and 13 ft. high. The front and rear walls were 50 ft. long and 13 ft. high. There are a total of 300 sq. ft. of area allowed for windows and doors. Find the number of square feet in:

a) the area of the sidewalls,

b) the gross area of the front and rear walls,

c) the net area of the front and rear walls,

d) the ceiling area,

e) the total area (rounded off to nearest 100 sq. ft.).

14. Convert the total area in Problem 13 to square yards. If a bundle of metal lath (10 sheets, size 27 in. by 96 in.) covers 20 sq. yd., how many bundles would be needed if 5 percent extra is allowed for lapping and waste?

15. Metal lath of the type needed in Problems 13 and 14 is sold by the 100 sq. yd. How many hundred square yards would you order and

what would be the cost at $52.00 per 100 sq. yd.?

16. A contractor, in remodeling some buildings, found that the total area to be covered with metal lath was 25,700 sq. ft. If he added 5 per-cent of this amount to take care of waste in cutting, lapping, and so forth, how many square feet of lath would be needed?

17. Using Problem 16, find the number of square yards of lath that the contractor would need. Divide this figure by 100 to find the number of hundreds of square yards of lath. If the price of the lath is $44.50 per 100 sq. yd., how much would the lath cost?

18. In remodeling an office building, the contractor estimated the area to be covered with metal lath to be 5100 sq. ft. If he allowed 5 percent for cutting, waste, and so forth, how many square feet of lath would he need? How many square yards would he order?

19. The contractor ordered the lath for Problem 18. If the price was $55.00 per 100 sq. yd., what was the amount of his bill? If he received a discount of 2 percent for paying the bill in 10 days, what amount did he save?

14.4 Plastering

Plastering is applied over the lath after the lath has been put in place as described above.

Plastering over metal lath.

Republic Steel

For highest-quality work, plaster is applied in *three* coats. The first coat is called the *scratch* coat; the second coat is called the *brown* coat because of the larger proportion of sand in it. The scratch coat receives its name from the fact that a tool called a scratcher is used to scratch or roughen the surface of the first coat so that the second coat will adhere and bond to it more readily. The third coat, or *finish* coat, is put on last, when the other two coats have hardened but are not too dry. Three-coat plaster is always put on metal lath.

Where economy is an important consideration, *two-coat* plaster work is applied to gypsum lath. This is also called double-up work. In this kind of plastering, a first thickness of plaster is applied. Immediately after this the plasterer "doubles back" with mortar of the same mix to bring the plaster to the proper thickness. The total thickness of plaster varies with the base on which it is applied. This thickness may run from $\frac{3}{8}$ in. to 1 in. For example, when plaster is applied to metal lath, the plaster thickness may run from $\frac{3}{4}$ in. to $\frac{7}{8}$ in. For two-coat work the total thickness may run to $\frac{5}{8}$ in. These thicknesses are for interior plaster work. For certain types of ceilings the thickness may be as little as $\frac{3}{8}$ in.

Estimating Quantities of Plaster.   A sensible procedure in estimating quantities of plaster is to base the amounts for various thicknesses on the amount needed to cover a wall area of 100 sq. yd. or 900 sq. ft. to a thickness of 1 in. Assuming that the plaster is uniformly applied to this wall area, the volume of plaster for this thickness can be easily calculated. Since the geometric figure formed by the plaster is a rectangular solid, its volume is found by using the formula

$$V = Bh \qquad \text{where } B = \text{area of the wall}$$
$$\text{and} \quad h = \text{thickness of the plaster}$$

Since
$$B = 900 \text{ sq. ft.}$$
$$h = 1 \text{ in.} = \tfrac{1}{12} \text{ ft., we have}$$
$$V = 900 \times \tfrac{1}{12}$$
$$V = 75 \text{ cu. ft.}$$

Disregarding losses due to waste, this would be the number of cubic feet of plaster needed to cover a wall area of 900 sq. ft. or 100 sq. yd. to a thickness of 1 in. To obtain the amount needed for any other thickness, this basic quantity is *multiplied* by the thickness in question. Thus, for a thickness of $\frac{1}{2}$ in., we multiply 75 cu. ft. by $\frac{1}{2}$ and find that 37.5 cu. ft. of plaster will be required. For a thickness of $\frac{5}{8}$ in., we multiply 75 cu. ft. by $\frac{5}{8}$ and obtain 46.9 cu. ft. or 47 cu. ft. more approximately.

If one were to allow a small percentage for waste, say 5 to 7 percent, this would mean that from 3.7 to 5.3 cu. ft. extra would be required for a thickness of 1 in. These computations can be put in a tabular form for handy reference.

Cubic Feet of Plaster Required for 900 Sq. Ft. of Surface Area

Plaster thickness, in.	$\frac{1}{16}$	$\frac{1}{8}$	$\frac{3}{16}$	$\frac{1}{4}$	$\frac{3}{8}$	$\frac{1}{2}$	$\frac{5}{8}$	$\frac{3}{4}$	$\frac{7}{8}$	1
Cu. ft. of plaster, no waste	4.7	9.4	14.1	18.8	28.1	37.5	46.9	56.3	65.6	75.0
Cu. ft. of plaster, 7% waste	5.0	10.0	15.0	20.1	30.1	40.1	50.2	60.2	70.2	80.3

The following examples show how this table may be used.

■ **EXAMPLE 1:**

How many cubic feet of plaster are needed for an area of 4500 sq. ft. if the thickness is $\frac{3}{4}$ in.? Give the amounts if no waste is assumed and if 7 percent is assumed.

Solution and Explanation:

For 900 sq. ft. of wall area and $\frac{3}{4}$-in. thickness the table gives 56.3 cu. ft. Since there are 4500 sq. ft. to be covered, we multiply 56.3 by 5, getting 281.5 cu. ft., if no waste is assumed. For 7 percent waste, the table gives 60.2 cu. ft. for an area of 900 sq. ft. Since the area to be covered is five times that given in the table, we multiply 60.2 by 5, getting 301 cu. ft.

Therefore, the amounts needed are 281.5 cu. ft. if no waste is assumed and 301 cu. ft. if 7 percent waste is assumed.

■ **EXAMPLE 2:**

How many cubic feet of plaster are required for an area of 1800 sq. ft. if the plaster has a thickness of $\frac{5}{8}$ in. and there is 7 percent waste?

Solution and Explanation:

Reference to the table shows that 50.2 cu. ft. are needed for an area of 900 sq. ft. and a thickness of $\frac{5}{8}$ in. Since the area to be plastered is 1800 sq. ft., we multiply 50.2 by 2, obtaining 100.4 cu. ft., with 7 percent waste assumed.

14.5   Problems Dealing With Estimating Quantities of Plaster

1. How many cubic feet of plaster are needed for an area of 3600 sq. ft. if the plaster thickness is $\frac{5}{8}$ in. and there is an allowance of 7 percent for waste?

2. A surface area of 9000 sq. ft. is to be plastered to a thickness of

$\frac{3}{4}$ in. If 7 percent is assumed, how many cubic feet of plaster will be required?

3. A building has an area of 18,000 sq. ft. in its walls, which are to be plastered to a thickness of $\frac{3}{4}$ in. If 7 percent waste is allowed, how many cubic feet of plaster will be required?

4. A large building has an area of 6000 sq. yd. which is to be plastered. If the cost of plastering is $2.50 per square yard, what will be the total plastering cost?

5. An area of 260 sq. yd. is to be plastered. For this type of work the cost is $3.10 per square yard. What is the cost of plastering?

NOTE: The reader will find detailed information on materials and their proportions for plaster mixes in books dealing with lathing, plastering, and construction costs.

14.6 Brickwork

Introduction. The use of brick as a building material goes back to ancient times. It is, from the standpoint of usefulness, one of the oldest of man's building materials. Brick is easy to manufacture and to erect. It is available in different sizes, colors, and textures. It can be laid in very simple and very complicated patterns, and stands up well against the elements. It can be used both for exterior and interior construction. These are some of the many reasons why it finds wide acceptance in many types of construction.

Types and Sizes of Brick. Two very widely used types of brick are the standard *common* brick and the *face* brick. Common brick is used largely for those parts of a building, such as the side walls, which are not in public view or where appearance is not a prime consideration. It is also used as a "backing" for walls more than one brick thick, and whose exterior is built of brick of higher quality called face brick. Common brick is considerably less expensive than facing brick. The size of standard common brick is taken to be $3\frac{3}{4}$ in. by $2\frac{1}{4}$ in. by 8 in.

Face brick is usually used on those exterior parts of a structure which are exposed to public view. In the process of manufacture, face brick can be made in a large number of colors and textures, so that the exterior of a brick building or residence can be made to have an unusually attractive appearance. Standard face bricks are also $3\frac{3}{4}$ in. by $2\frac{1}{4}$ in. by 8 in. in size. In recent years many new types of facing brick have been manufactured. Bricks of these types have unusual decorative colors and textures and make possible the construction of dwellings of great beauty. Among these may be mentioned the Roman bricks, having an actual size of $11\frac{5}{8}$ in. by $2\frac{3}{8}$ in. by $1\frac{5}{8}$ in. which are widely used for both residential and small commercial buildings.

Prices for brick are usually quoted on the basis of 1000 bricks. For common building brick they are about $31.00 per M (per thousand) and up. For facing brick they may run from $60.00 to $95.00 per M. Roman brick run from $90.00 to $120.00 per M, and other unusual types of brick run over $300.00 per M. It should be remembered that *prices of building materials vary with the locality*.

Types of Brick Bonds.   There are many ways in which bricks are put together or "laid" with mortar. In most cases, the method of putting bricks together or *bonding* them depends on the type of structure that is being built. In some instances, where a particular appearance is desired, the bonding patterns may be changed so as to produce unusual designs. The purpose of arranging or bonding bricks in certain ways is to give strength to the particular structure being built and enable it to withstand shocks and the elements.

Two of the most frequently used methods of bonding bricks together are the *running* bond and the *common* bond. In the *running* bond, the bricks are laid with their ends together in rows called stretchers.

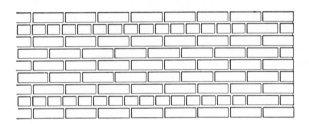

Fig. 267.
Common bond.

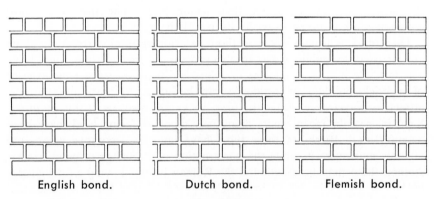

English bond.   Dutch bond.   Flemish bond.

Fig. 268.

The mortar, which holds the brick together as a single block, is laid in "beds" or horizontal layers, and also in vertical or head joints. These joints are $\frac{1}{4}$ in., $\frac{3}{8}$ in., or $\frac{1}{2}$ in. thick usually, depending on the structure.

Another commonly used brick bond is called *common* bond. In this type of bond, a number of stretcher courses are laid, then a header course is laid. Next come the same number of stretcher courses, followed by another header course. The number of stretcher courses may be as many as five, six, or seven. For such a bond, the number of bricks needed is increased by $\frac{1}{5}$ (20 percent), $\frac{1}{6}$ ($16\frac{2}{3}$ percent), or $\frac{1}{7}$ ($14\frac{2}{7}$ percent), respectively. See Figure 267.

Many other types of bonds are used, as stated before, depending on the structure and the appearance and pattern desired (Fig. 268).

Estimating Quantities of Brick.   The dimensions of a common or building brick are $3\frac{3}{4}$ in. by $2\frac{1}{4}$ in. by 8 in. (Fig. 269). The face of such a

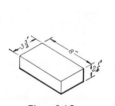

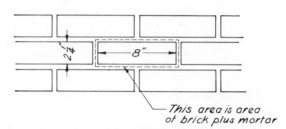

This area is area of brick plus mortar

Fig. 269.   Fig. 270.

brick has an area of $2\frac{1}{4}$ in. by 8 in. or 18 sq. in. If we assume a wall area of 100 sq. ft., and make the end joints and the horizontal mortar joints $\frac{1}{4}$ in. in thickness, the area of one brick, including these joints becomes $2\frac{1}{2}$ in. by $8\frac{1}{4}$ in. $= \frac{5}{2}$ in. by $\frac{33}{4}$ in. $= \frac{165}{8}$ sq. in. (Fig. 270).

Now in 100 sq. ft. there are 100×144 sq. in. Hence the number of brick in this wall area $= \dfrac{100 \times 144}{\frac{165}{8}} = \dfrac{100 \times 144 \times 8}{165}$

$$= \frac{7680}{11}$$

$$= 698$$

For end joints and horizontal mortar joints which are $\frac{3}{8}$ in. in thickness, we find that the area of one brick is $2\frac{5}{8}$ by $8\frac{3}{8} = \frac{21}{8}$ by $\frac{67}{8}$ sq. in. In 100 sq. ft. of wall area the number of bricks would be

$$\dfrac{100 \times 144}{\frac{21}{8} \times \frac{67}{8}} = \dfrac{100 \times \overset{48}{\cancel{144}} \times 8 \times 8}{\underset{7}{\cancel{21}} \times 67}$$

$$= 655$$

For a thickness of $\frac{1}{2}$-in. end and horizontal joints, the area of one brick becomes $2\frac{3}{4}$ by $8\frac{1}{2} = \frac{11}{4}$ by $\frac{17}{2}$ sq. in. The number of bricks in a wall area of 100 sq. ft. for this case, is, then,

$$\frac{100 \times 144}{\frac{11}{4} \times \frac{17}{2}} = \frac{100 \times 144 \times 4 \times 2}{11 \times 17}$$

$$= 616$$

The above calculations were made on the basis of a wall one brick in thickness, or what is known as a 4-in. wall. For a wall two bricks thick, or what is called an 8-in. wall, the numbers of bricks should be doubled. For a wall three bricks thick the number of bricks should be tripled.

The following table summarizes this information:

Table Showing Number of Standard Common Brick Needed for a Wall Area of 100 Sq. Ft.

Vertical and Horizontal Mortar Joint Thickness	Wall Thickness		
	4″	8″	12″
$\frac{1}{4}″$	698	1396	2094
$\frac{3}{8}″$	655	1310	1965
$\frac{1}{2}″$	616	1232	1848

This table is for brick laid in running bond and makes no allowance for breakage.

Other Types of Brick. In recent years unusual types of bricks have come into wide use in the construction of residences, small offices, stores, and other similar buildings. Among these types of bricks, one of the most popular is the Roman brick. The dimensions of this type of brick are $3\frac{5}{8}$ in. by $11\frac{5}{8}$ in. by $1\frac{5}{8}$ in. Brick of this type, when $\frac{3}{8}$-in. mortar joints are used, occupies an exposed wall area of 12 in. $\times$ 2 in. or 24 sq. in. In 100 sq. ft. of wall area, the number of bricks required, for a wall of one-brick thickness, is $\frac{100 \times 144}{24} = 600$.

The amount of mortar needed for 1000 such bricks can be found as follows:

1. The volume of 1000 bricks $= 3\frac{5}{8} \times 11\frac{5}{8} \times 1\frac{5}{8} \times 1000$

$$= \frac{29}{8} \times \frac{93}{8} \times \frac{13}{8} \times 1000$$

$$= 68,479 \text{ cu. in.}$$

2. The volume of 1000 bricks and $\frac{3}{8}$-in. mortar joints all around except the back of the brick (the surface on the interior of the wall)

$$= 12 \times 2 \times 3\frac{5}{8} \times 1000$$

$$= 87,000 \text{ cu. in.}$$

3. The volume of mortar $= 87,000 - 68,479$

$$= 18,521 \text{ cu. in.}$$

4. The volume of mortar $= \frac{18,521}{1728} = 10.7 \text{ cu. ft.}$

This makes no allowance for any mortar that is wasted.

The application of this information to typical problems will be taken up.

■ EXAMPLE 1:

A man builds a wall, one brick thick, 4 ft. 8 in. tall, and 30 ft. long, using $\frac{1}{2}$-in. mortar joints, running bond. How many bricks should he order, allowing 4 percent for waste?

Solution and Explanation:

Changing 4 ft. 8 in. to feet, we have $4\frac{2}{3}$ ft. The area of the wall = $4\frac{2}{3} \times 30 = \frac{14}{3} \times 30 = 140$ sq. ft. From the table, a wall of one-brick thickness (a 4-in. wall) and $\frac{1}{2}$-in. mortar joints, having an area of 100 sq. ft. requires 616 bricks. Since the wall in this problem has an area of 140 sq. ft., the number of bricks needed is $\frac{140}{100} \times 616 = 862.4$ bricks.

Allowing 4 percent for waste, $\frac{4}{100} \times 862.4 = 34.496 = 34.5$ bricks Hence the total number of bricks required = 862 + 35 = 897 bricks. He would then order 900 bricks.

■ EXAMPLE 2:

A wall having an area of 600 sq. ft. is to be constructed of common building brick. It is to be two bricks in thickness, and have $\frac{3}{8}$-in. mortar joints in running bond. Find:

a) The number of bricks needed, allowing 3 percent for waste.

b) The cost of the brick at \$33.00/M (for quantities of 2500 or more).

Solution and Explanation:

a) From the table, we find that, for a wall thickness of 8 in. and with $\frac{3}{8}$-in. mortar joints, there are 1310 bricks for 100 sq. ft. of wall area. Since the area of this wall is 600 sq. ft., we have

$$6 \times 1310 = 7860$$

Allowing 3 percent for waste,

$$\frac{3}{100} \times 7860 = 236$$

The total brick needed

$$= 8096 \text{ or } 8100$$

b) Since each thousand of bricks costs \$33.00, the cost is

$\frac{8100}{1000} \times \$33.00 = \$267.30$, exclusive of sales tax.

■ EXAMPLE 3:

A small residence was built using facing brick (veneer) over wall areas totaling 380 sq. ft. and with $\frac{3}{8}$-in. mortar joints. If the brick costs $95.00 per M, what will be the total cost of the brick? Allow 3 percent for waste.

Solution and Explanation:

A veneer brick wall is made with a single thickness of brick. From the table, 655 bricks are needed for 100 sq. ft. of 4-in. wall and with $\frac{3}{8}$-in. mortar joints. Hence:

$$\text{No. of brick} = \tfrac{380}{100} \times 655 = 2489$$
$$\text{Adding 3 percent for waste} = \tfrac{3}{100} \times 2489 = \underline{75}$$
$$\text{Total} = 2564$$
$$\text{Cost, at } \$95.00/\text{M}, = \$95.00 \times \tfrac{2564}{1000} = \$243.58$$

The total cost of the brick is, therefore, $243.58.

■ EXAMPLE 4:

Masonry walls are frequently built by using a veneer of brick and a backing of concrete blocks. One of the most widely used types of these blocks has the following dimensions:

$$\text{Length} \quad = \quad 15\tfrac{5}{8} \text{ in.}$$
$$\text{Height} \quad = \quad 7\tfrac{5}{8} \text{ in.}$$
$$\text{Thickness} = \quad 3\tfrac{5}{8} \text{ in.}$$

Find:

a) the area of the face of one of these blocks when set in $\frac{3}{8}$-in. mortar joints,

b) the number of these blocks in 100 sq. ft. of wall area.

Solution and Explanation:

a) The area of the face of one of these blocks, including the $\frac{3}{8}$-in. mortar joints, is 16 in. $\times$ 8 in. or 128 sq. in. This area is equal to $\frac{128}{144} = \frac{8}{9}$ sq. ft.

b) The number of these blocks in 100 sq. ft. of wall area is found by dividing 100 sq. ft. by the area of one block.

We have
$$100 \div \tfrac{8}{9}$$
$$= 100 \times \tfrac{9}{8}$$
$$= 112.5 \text{ or } 113 \text{ blocks.}$$

Hence each of these blocks has a face area of $\frac{8}{9}$ sq. ft. and 113 of these blocks occupy an area of 100 sq. ft. when set in $\frac{3}{8}$-in. mortar joints.

14.7 Problems Dealing With Estimating Quantities of Bricks

1. The two sidewalls of a storage building have a total length of

96 ft. and a height of 12 ft. They are made of double thickness of common brick with ⅜-in. joints. If 5 percent allowance is made for breakage, find, using running bond:

  a) the area of the wall,
  b) the number of building bricks needed,
  c) the cost of the bricks at $32.50/M.

2. A man built a two-brick thickness wall around part of his property. If this wall was 5 ft. 6 in. high and 60 ft. long and was made of building bricks using ½-in. joints, find:

  a) the area of the wall,
  b) the number of bricks needed, allowing 3 percent for breakage,
  c) the cost of the brick at $47.50/M.

3. Two walls of a building have a length of 32 ft. 9 in. and a height of 16 ft. 9 in. each. They are made of common double bricks (8-in. thickness) using ½-in. joints in running bond. Find:

  a) the total area of the walls,
  b) the number of bricks needed, allowing 3 percent for breakage,
  c) the cost of the bricks at $44.00/M.

4. The two sidewalls of a rectangular warehouse building are 90 ft. long and 15 ft. high. The rear wall is 40 ft. wide and 15 ft. high. The walls are three bricks thick (12-in. walls) and use ½-in. thick mortar joints in running bond. If 2 percent is allowed for waste, and there are 184 sq. ft. of openings, find:

  a) the total gross area of the sidewalls,
  b) the gross area of the rear wall,
  c) the total net wall area,
  d) the number of bricks needed for the walls,
  e) the cost of the bricks at $41.50/M.

5. A rectangular store building has side walls 56 ft. 0 in. long and front and rear walls are 24 ft. 0 in. long. The height of all these walls is 12 ft. 0 in. The side and rear walls are 8 in. thick and use common building bricks in running bond with ⅜-in. mortar joints. The total area of doors and windows in the side and rear walls is 110 sq. ft. If an allowance of 3 percent is made for breakage, find:

  a) the gross area of the two sidewalls,
  b) the gross area of the rear wall,
  c) the net area of the side and rear walls,
  d) the total number of bricks needed,
  e) the cost of the bricks at $38.00/M.

6. The front wall of a residence is made of veneer brick. It is 38 ft. 0 in. long and 9 ft. 2 in. high, and has door and window openings of

108 sq. ft. If the veneer brick (face brick) are laid with $\frac{3}{8}$-in. mortar joints, find:

   a) the gross wall area,
   b) the net wall area,
   c) the number of bricks needed,
   d) the cost of the bricks at $88.00/M.

7. A one-story office building has a length of 56 ft. and a width of 42 ft. Its walls are 10 ft. in height. The side and rear walls have openings whose total area is 210 sq. ft., and are of double-brick construction, using $\frac{3}{8}$-in. mortar joints. Find:

   a) the total gross area of these walls,
   b) the total net area of these walls,
   c) the number of bricks needed,
   d) the cost of the bricks at $32.70/M.

8. An exterior wall of a one-story building is made up of one thickness of brick and one thickness of concrete-block backing. The wall is 14 ft. high, with no openings, and 60 ft. long. Find the number of bricks needed and the cost at $32.00 per M if $\frac{3}{8}$-in. mortar joints are used and 5 percent allowance is made for breakage.

9. A small factory building has a sidewall 48 ft. long and 14 ft. high. The construction is brick facing backed with one thickness of concrete blocks. Find:

   a) the area of the wall,
   b) the number of concrete blocks needed if 113 of them occupy an area of 100 sq. ft.

Consider the wall as having no openings and allow 5 percent for breakage.

10. One wall of a storage building is 90 ft. long and 18 ft. high, with door and window openings of 180 sq. ft. The wall is made of a brick facing backed up by concrete blocks $7\frac{5}{8}$ in. by $7\frac{5}{8}$ in. by $15\frac{5}{8}$ in. When $\frac{3}{8}$-in. mortar joints are used, 113 of these blocks can be set in an area of 100 sq. ft. Find:

   a) the gross area of the wall,
   b) the net area of the wall,
   c) the number of concrete blocks needed, allowing 4 percent for waste.

CHAPTER 15

Mathematics Applied to the Building Trades — II

15.1 Roofing

General. The roof of a home, like the foundation, is one of its most important parts. Roofs carefully designed and constructed will add to the comfort of the occupants both in summer and winter, and add to the appearance of the home. By roofing is meant the material used for actual covering above the rafters and roof sheathing.

There are many varieties of roofing. Some are relatively simple to install; others are considerably elaborate. For homes with slanting roofs, some type of shingle roofing is usually used. For apartments and larger public buildings, built-up roofing is used. This consists of several layers of roofing felt with alternate layers of tar or asphalt. Many of these types of roofs are covered with gravel, slag, and marble chips. Other types of roofs use slate, tile, and metals such as aluminum, copper, tin for the roofing materials.

Shingle Roofing. Shingle roofs are one of the most popular types of roofs used for small residences. Roofing of this type is usually done in the following steps:

1. The metal drip edges along the eaves are put in place.
2. The roof sheathing is covered with a layer of roofing felt.
3. The starter strips are put in place.
4. The shingles are nailed to the roof sheathing or roof deck.

One of the popular types of shingles used for residential roofing is the strip shingle (Fig. 277). Strip shingles are made by impregnating a felt

Fig. 277.

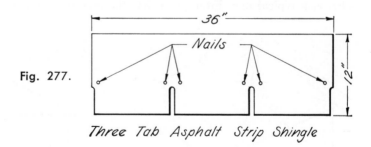

Three Tab Asphalt Strip Shingle

base with asphalt. The exposed or weather side of the shingle is coated with mineral granules which give the shingles a particular color and also serve to protect the shingles from flying sparks. The strip shingles are cut in various sizes, such as individual shingles, 3-tab, or 4-tab shingles, and are available in many colors.

Estimating Areas of Roofs. Although the type of roof may depend on the location of the residence, most homes have sloping roofs of one type or another. In estimating the area of the roof for purposes of determining the cost of roofing, the unit of area measure is the *square*. This is equivalent to an area of 100 sq. ft., and is the unit used to order quantities of shingles.

For example, if a particular plain roof has an area of 800 sq. ft., we would say that eight squares of strip shingles would be needed to cover it.

Let us now consider the simple dwelling illustrated in this drawing (Fig. 278), having a gable roof.

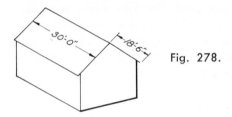

Fig. 278.

Each part of the roof, neglecting any chimney and vent openings, has a length of 30 ft. 0 in., and a width of 18 ft. 6 in., or an area of $30 \times 18\frac{1}{2} = 555$ sq. ft. Since there are two parts, the total area of the roof is 2×555 or 1110 sq. ft. Dividing this number by 100 to change it to "squares," we find that there are 11.10 squares of roofing in this particular roof.

Next, consider a garage with a roof as shown in the drawing (Fig. 279). This type of roof is called a *hip* roof. It consists of four triangles, of which ABE is a typical one. From geometry, the area of a triangle is equal to

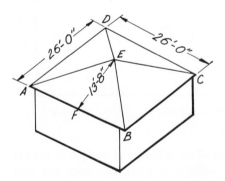
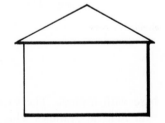

Fig. 279.

one half the length of its base multiplied by its height. In the triangles forming this roof, the distance EF (this distance is assumed to be measured on the roof) is equal to 13 ft. 8 in. or to $13\frac{2}{3}$ ft. Hence the area of one triangle $= \dfrac{26 \times 13\frac{2}{3}}{2} = 178$ sq. ft. The area of the entire roof $= 4 \times 178 = 712$ sq. ft. In terms of roofing squares, this area equals $\frac{712}{100} = 7.12$ roofing squares.

In practice, the various dimensions of a particular roof can be obtained directly from the architect's drawings or they may be computed without too much difficulty.

A still different type of roof is the one shown in Figure 280. This is also a type of hip roof.

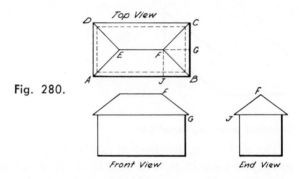

Fig. 280.

As can be seen from these drawings, the roof consists of the two parts $ABFE$ and $DEFC$, which are trapezoids, and the other two parts AED and BCF, which are triangles. In order to find the entire roof area, we need to know the lengths AB, BC, EF, and, in addition, the distances FG and FJ. Let us assume the following lengths:

$$AB = DC = 62 \text{ ft.}$$
$$BC = AD = 36 \text{ ft.}$$
$$EF = 26 \text{ ft.}$$
$$FG = FJ = 19 \text{ ft.}$$

Then the area of the trapezoid $ABFE$
$$= \tfrac{1}{2} \text{ (sum of its bases)} \times \text{ its altitude}$$
$$= \tfrac{1}{2} (EF + AB) \times (FJ)$$
$$= \tfrac{1}{2} (26 + 62)(19) = \tfrac{1}{2} \times 88 \times 19$$
$$= 836 \text{ sq. ft.}$$

The area of the triangle $BCF = \tfrac{1}{2}$ (its base) $\times$ (its altitude)
$$= \tfrac{1}{2} (BC) \times (FG)$$
$$= \tfrac{1}{2} \times 36 \times 19$$
$$= 342 \text{ sq. ft.}$$

Hence one half the area of the roof = 836 + 342 = 1178 sq. ft. and the area of the entire roof = 2 × 1178 = 2356 sq. ft. In terms of roofing squares, this equals $\frac{2356}{100}$ = 23.56 or 24 roofing squares.

The following problems illustrate the use of these procedures in the calculation of roof areas.

■ EXAMPLE 1:

What is the area of the roof of the building shown in Figure 281? How many roofing squares is this equivalent to?

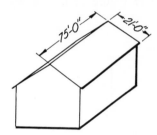

Fig. 281.

Solution and Explanation:

The roof of this building, as can be seen by inspection, consists of two rectangles, each 75 ft. 0 in. long by 21 ft. 0 in. wide. Since the area of a rectangle = length × width, we have:

$$A = 75 \times 21$$
$$A = 1575 \text{ sq. ft.}$$

Hence the total area = 2 × 1575 = 3150 sq. ft. This is equivalent to $\frac{3150}{100}$ = 31.5 roofing squares.

Hence the area of this roof is 3150 sq. ft. and is equivalent to 31.5 roofing squares.

■ EXAMPLE 2:

Compute the area of the roof of the residence shown in Figure 282. The slant heights AB and CD are each 16 ft. 0 in. long.

Solution and Explanation:

The area of this roof consists of two trapezoids and two triangles. For the trapezoids, we have:

$$B = \text{large base} = 60 \text{ ft. 0 in.}$$
$$b = \text{small base} = 30 \text{ ft. 0 in.}$$
$$h = \text{altitude} = 16 \text{ ft. 0 in.}$$

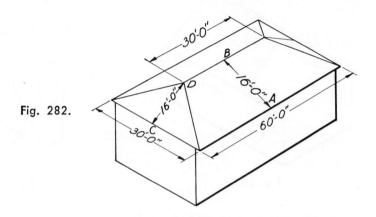

Fig. 282.

Hence the area of each of the trapezoids:

$$A = \frac{(B + b)h}{2}$$

$$A = \frac{(60 + 30) \times 16}{2}$$

$$A = \frac{90 \times 16}{2} = 720 \text{ sq. ft.}$$

The two trapezoids then have an area of 1440 sq. ft. The triangles making up the two gables have a length of 30 ft. 0 in. and an altitude of 16 ft. 0 in. (This is the distance CD in the drawing.) Since, for a triangle:

$$A = \tfrac{1}{2} bh$$
$$\text{and} \quad b = 30 \text{ ft. 0 in.}$$
$$h = 16 \text{ ft. 0 in.,}$$

we have:

$$A = \tfrac{1}{2} \times 30 \times 16 = 240 \text{ sq. ft.}$$

For the two gables the area = 480 sq. ft. Hence the total roof area
$$= 1440 + 480$$
$$= 1920 \text{ sq. ft.}$$

This is equivalent to $\frac{1920}{100}$ = 19.2 roofing squares. Hence the total roof area = 1920 sq. ft. or 19.2 roofing squares.

15.2   Problems Involving Computation of Roof Areas

1. What is the area of the roof of the storage shed shown in the drawing (Fig. 283). How many roofing squares is this equivalent to?

2. Six refreshment stands each have roof dimensions as shown in Figure 284. Find:

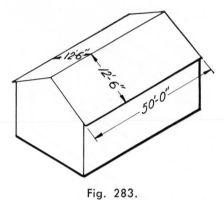

Fig. 283.

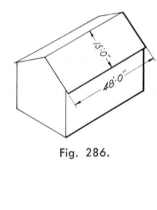

Fig. 284.

a) the area of each roof in sq. ft.,
b) the total roof area,
c) the number of roofing squares in each roof,
d) the total number of roofing squares.
3. The drawing (Fig. 285) shows the roof plan of a flat roof multi-

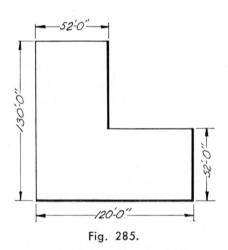

Fig. 285.

Fig. 286.

story apartment building. There is a total of 380 sq. ft. of opening for ventilation, heating, and so on. What is the gross roof area of this building in square feet? What is its net roof area? How many roofing squares is this equivalent to?

4. A builder erected six homes with roofs as shown in this drawing (Fig. 286). Find:

a) the total area of each roof,

b) the number of roofing squares in each roof.

c) the total area of the six roofs,

d) the total number of roofing squares in the six roofs.

Both parts of the roof have the same dimensions.

5. A manufacturing plant has a flat roof plan as shown in the drawing (Fig. 287). Openings for heating, ventilating, and illumination total

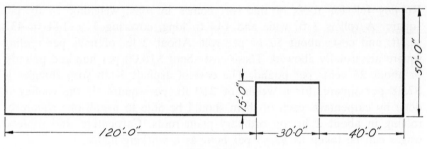

Fig. 287.

800 sq. ft. What is the gross area of the roof? What is the net area of the roof? How many roofing squares is this equivalent to?

6. In this view of a private residence (Fig. 288), the following dimensions are given:

$$AB = 37 \text{ ft. } 0 \text{ in.}$$
$$CD = 64 \text{ ft. } 0 \text{ in.}$$
$$DE = 27 \text{ ft. } 0 \text{ in.}$$
$$BF = 14 \text{ ft. } 6 \text{ in.}$$

Fig. 288.

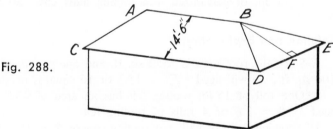

NOTE: The entire roof has another part the same size as *ABDC* and another part the same size as *BDE*.

What is the area of the trapezoid *ABDC*? What is the area of the gable *BDE*? How many square feet are there in the total area of the roof? How many roofing squares is this equivalent to?

15.3   Calculation of Roofing Costs

In ordinary residential roofing, where asphalt strip shingles are used, the roofing materials needed are:

> asphalt-impregnated roofing felt
> asphalt strip shingles
> roofing nails

Roofing felt for roofs of this sort comes in rolls, weighing 15 lb. per square. A roll is 3 ft. wide and 144 ft. long, covering $3 \times 144 = 432$ sq. ft. and costs about $2.75 per roll. About 2 lb. of nails per roofing square are usually allowed. These cost about $18.00 per hundred pounds, or about 25 cents per pound. The cost of asphalt 3-tab strip shingles is $7.88 per square, for a weight of 210 lb. per square. If the roofing is done by carpenters, each of them should be able to install one square of roofing in about 2 hr. on ordinary plain roofs. Carpenters' and roofers' wages can be taken as $3.65 per hour as a working figure.

In addition to these expenses, there are, of course, several others. Among these are overhead, insurance for the workers, cost of scaffolding, social-security payments. In the problems considered here these expenses have not been included. Let us consider the following simple problem.

■ **EXAMPLE 1:**

What is the cost of materials for a plain roof whose area is 1550 sq. ft.? Assume:

> 1 square of 3-tab asphalt strip shingles costs $7.88,
> 1 roll 15-lb. roofing felt costs $2.75,
> 1 lb. of galvanized iron roofing nails costs $0.25.

Solution and Explanation:

1. Since the roof area is 1550 sq. ft. and one square of roofing covers 100 sq. ft., we will need $\frac{1550}{100} = 15.5$ or 16 squares of shingles.

2. One roll of 15-lb. roofing felt has an area of 432 sq. ft. We will need $\frac{1550}{432} = 3.6$ or 4 rolls of roofing felt.

3. Allowing 2 lb. of nails per roofing square, $2 \times 16 = 32$ lb. of nails will be needed.

Using the above unit prices, the cost of the required materials will be:

16 squares of 3-tab asphalt strip shingles at $7.88/sq. = $126.08
4 rolls of 15-lb roofing felt at $2.75/rolls   =   11.00
32 lb. of nails at $0.25/lb.   =   8.00
                                        Total cost   = $145.08

Hence the cost of the materials, exclusive of sales tax and any delivery charges, is $145.08.

■ EXAMPLE 2:

A residence has a roof area equal to 1950 sq. ft. If the materials and prices are the same as in Example 1, find the cost of the materials for this roof.

Solution and Explanation:

1. For this roof, the number of squares of shingles is $\frac{1950}{100} = 19.5$. We will order 20 squares to allow for waste.

2. The number of rolls of roofing felt needed is $\frac{1950}{432} = 4.5$. We will order five rolls to allow for waste.

3. Since 2 lb. of nails per square are allowed, we will need $2 \times 20 = 40$ lb. of nails.

The cost of the materials will be:

20 squares of 3-tab asphalt shingles at $7.88/sq.	=	$157.60
5 rolls of 15-lb. roofing felt at $2.75/roll	=	13.75
40 lb. of nails at $0.25/lb.	=	10.00
Total cost	=	$181.35

Hence the total cost of the materials is $181.35.

■ EXAMPLE 3:

If two carpenters were employed to install the roof in Example 1, what would be their wages for the work? What would the total cost of the roofing be?

Solution and Explanation:

Allowing 2 hr. per square for each carpenter, each should be able to install four squares per 8-hour day. For two carpenters, eight squares per day should be installed, which means the 16 squares in Example 1 would take the two men 2 days.

The labor cost is, then, at $3.65/hr., $2 \times 2 \times 8 \times \$3.65 = \$116.80$. The total cost of the roof is the cost of the materials and labor.

Materials cost	=	$145.08
Labor cost	=	116.80
Total cost	=	$261.88

Hence the labor cost is $116.80 and the total cost of the roofing is $261.88.

15.4 Problems Involving Calculation of Roofing Costs

1. A builder ordered the following materials for roofing two homes: 50 squares of three-tab asphalt strip shingles costing $7.80 per square: six rolls of 15-lb. roofing felt at $2.75 per roll: 100 lb. of galvanized iron nails at $18.25 per 100 lb. What is the cost of these roofing materials?

2. A small residence has a roof area of 1200 sq. ft. Using the same prices for shingles and roofing felt as in Problem 1, and nails costing 25 cents per pound, find:

   a) the number of squares of roofing this is equivalent to,
   b) the number of squares of three-tab asphalt strip shingles required,
   c) the number of pounds of nails required,
   d) the number of rolls of roofing felt required,
   e) the cost of the roofing materials.

3. A builder erected six homes, each having a roof area of 1450 sq. ft. Using the prices in Problem 1, find the cost of the roofing materials.

4. A small residence has a roof area of 1400 sq. ft. Using the same prices as in Problem 1, find the cost of the roofing materials.

5. A western-type residence has a roof area of 1700 sq. ft. What is the cost of the roofing materials if the prices are:

   a) galvanized iron nails — 30¢/lb.,
   b) 3-tab asphalt strip shingles — $8.25/sq.,
   c) 15-lb. roofing felt — $3.20/roll.

6. The roof of a large residence has an area of 3400 sq. ft. If the price of materials is the same as in Problem 5, what is the cost of the roofing materials?

15.5 Painting

Many factors enter into and influence the cost of painting. Among these may be listed:

1. The kind and area of the surfaces to be painted — whether they are of wood, brick, plaster, metal, or other materials,

2. The shape of the surfaces to be painted — whether they consist of large or small areas and whether they are flat or curved,

3. The quality of the paint used.

4. The number of coats applied,

5. The skill of the painters,

6. The wage rate of the painters.

There are other factors which must be considered when hazardous jobs are undertaken, such as the painting of towers, smokestacks, tall buildings, and bridges.

Paint may be considered as a mixture of a *pigment* (such as white lead, zinc ozide, titanium dioxide) and a liquid called a *vehicle* (such as linseed oil or tung oil) which acts as a drier. A thinner (such as turpentine) is used to bring the paint to a suitable consistency so it can be easily applied to the surfaces to be painted.

For most interior surfaces, paint called flat paint is used. It is called flat paint because it produces a dull, soft finish. Glossy paint is usually put on exterior surfaces. In considering the cost of painting, it is sound practice to keep in mind that, in the long run, the better the quality of the paint, the more satisfactory and longer lasting will be the paint job.

Exterior Painting.

First Coat. If the surface to be painted is new wood, three coats are necessary. The first coat of paint put on is called a primer coat. This is used as a base on which to put the other two coats, and should consequently be carefully applied. The primer coat should be thin enough with sufficient linseed oil and turpentine to enable it to soak into the wood and leave a surface with a flat finish sufficiently rough for the second coat to adhere to.

Second Coat. The second coat is put on after the first coat has dried and any nail holes have been covered with putty. The second coat should be put on in a thin layer and dry with a surface such that the final coat will be able to adhere to it.

Third Coat. The final coat is put on when the second coat has dried. Enough oil is put into this coat so that the paint, when dry, will have a glossy surface which will be able to resist the elements effectively.

Interior Painting. Paint used for interior purposes is different from paint used for exterior purposes. However, if the surface to be painted is new plaster, a special type of priming or sealer paint is used for the first coat. Its purpose is to seal the pores of the plaster so that they will not pull in the paint applied to it and also to provide a uniform surface for the second coat.

The second coat is applied when the primer coat has dried, and finally the third coat is put on.

Calculation of Areas to Be Painted. In calculating the surface area of a residence or small structure to be painted, the dimensions of the walls, roof, gables, and openings such as doors and windows may be measured on the structure itself, or they can be obtained from the architect's plans.

A good procedure for exterior painting is to consider all surfaces such as walls and gables as having no openings unless these openings have a total area of 100 sq. ft. or more. However, for ordinary doors and windows in residences, an allowance of 35 sq. ft. to 40 sq. ft.* for each door or window should prove sufficient, and these areas should be added

---

* This allowance is for one side only.

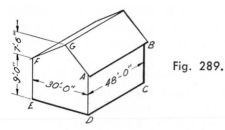

Fig. 289.

to the surface area to be painted. With this in mind, let us calculate the area to be painted for the house shown in the drawing (Fig. 289), the roof being excluded. There are 2 doors and 16 windows in the house.

Step 1: In this type of simple structure, a good procedure is to compute the entire outside wall area and to this add the area of the two gables.

The perimeter of the house = 30 + 48 + 30 + 48   =   156 ft.
The wall height   =   9 ft.
The entire wall area = perimeter × height = 156 × 9 = 1404 sq. ft.
The area of one gable = $\frac{1}{2}$ × 30 × $7\frac{1}{2}$ = 112.5 sq. ft.
Both gables have an area   =   225 sq. ft.

The total area to be painted = 1404 + 225 = 1629 sq. ft., which we can round off to 1630 sq. ft.

Step 2: If this is to receive three coats, then we must know how many square feet a gallon of the first coat (or primer) will cover, how much a gallon of the second coat will cover, and how much a gallon of the third coat will cover. For a building with frame siding, satisfactory working areas per gallon are:

> First coat (or primer) 450 sq. ft./gal.
> Second coat   500 sq. ft./gal.
> Third coat   600 sq. ft./gal.

In addition, it must be remembered that the painting of door and window frames and trim is time-consuming work; hence, in addition to the paint needed for this work, an allowance for painting time should be made.

Step 3: To find the number of gallons of paint needed for each coat, we have

Number of gallons
  needed for first $= \dfrac{\text{area in sq. ft.}}{\text{no. of sq. ft. covered by 1 gal.}} = \frac{1630}{450} = 3.6$ gal.
coat

Number of gallons of second coat $= \frac{1630}{500} = 3.3$ gal.

Number of gallons of third coat $= \frac{1630}{600} = 2.7$ gal.

Hence 4 gal. of primer and 6 gal. of exterior house paint would be required for this part of the painting.

Step 4: The areas of the doors and windows will now be considered. A good working rule for ordinary doors and windows is to consider each as having an area of 35 sq. ft. to 40 sq. ft. Since there were 16 windows, the total window area = 16 × 35 = 560 sq. ft.

Total door area   = 2 × 35 =   70 sq. ft.

Total window and door area   = 630 sq. ft.

Step 5: Proceeding as in Step 3, and using the same paint coverage, we find that the:

$$\text{Number of gallons of the first coat} = \frac{\text{area of exterior trim in sq. ft.}}{\text{no. of sq. ft. covered per gal.}} = \frac{630}{450} = 1.4 \text{ gal.}$$

Number of gallons of the second coat $= \frac{630}{500} = 1.3$ gal.

Number of gallons of the third coat $= \frac{630}{600} = 1.1$ gal.

Thus 1.5 gal. of primer and 2.5 gal. of exterior house paint would be required for this part of the painting. The total amount would then be 5.5 gal. of primer and 8.5 gal. of exterior house paint.

The above procedure can be summarized as follows:

Step 1: Determine the wall area to be painted.

Step 2: Knowing the kind of surface to be painted, the kind of coat to be applied, and the area in square feet covered by a gallon, find the number of gallons required for each coat.

Step 3: Assume each door and window has an area of 35 to 40 sq. ft. Find the total area of the windows and doors. This area will be painted with exterior trim paint. From the coverage allowed for each coat of this type of paint, calculate the number of gallons of each coat needed.

Step 4: Using the results of Steps 2 and 3, compute the total amount of each kind of paint needed.

Step 5: Knowing the cost per gallon of each kind of exterior paint determine the total cost of the paint. Prices* of house paint may be taken as follows:

> For frame siding . . . . . $5.35 to $ 8.00 per gal.
> For exterior trim . . . . . $6.50 to $12.00 per gal.
> For exterior brick (oil paint) . $5.50 to $ 8.80 per gal.
> For exterior house paint for
>   shingle siding . . . . . . $3.50 to $ 5.50 per gal.

15.6 Problems Involving Cost of Painting

1. The porches of a large apartment building were given two coats of paint. If this paint covered an average of 500 sq. ft. per gallon and

---
* Prices and costs quoted here will vary according to economic conditions and locality.

the area of the porches was 4500 sq. ft., how many gallons of paint were needed? If a gallon of this paint cost $5.35, how much would the required paint cost?

2. One floor of a bilevel residence has an area of 800 sq. ft. and is to be varnished. If the varnish used covers 560 sq. ft. per gallon, how many gallons of varnish should be ordered? If varnish is available in gallon cans at $5.30 each and in quart cans at $1.45 each, what will be the cost of the varnish?

3. A homeowner painted the exterior of his wood garage, whose total wall area was 850 sq. ft. If the paint used covered 550 sq. ft. per gallon, how many gallons would be required? If each gallon cost $6.95, what would the required paint cost?

4. A house owner wishes to cover the walls in his kitchen and dining area with two coats of paint. The first coat is to be an enamel under-coating and the second coat is to be enamel. The wall area is 480 sq. ft. The enamel undercoating costs $5.75 per gallon and each gallon covers 500 sq. ft. The enamel for the second coat costs $6.95 per gallon, and each gallon covers 600 sq. ft. How many gallons of each coat should he buy and what will be the total cost for both coats?

5. A storage yard has a board fence whose total area (of one side) is 30,000 sq. ft. It is to be painted on both sides with one coat of paint covering 380 sq. ft. per gallon. How many gallons are needed? If one gallon costs $5.35, what will be the cost of the paint?

6. The exterior walls of a wood storage shed have a total area of 2600 sq. ft. and are to be painted. If the paint will cover 350 sq. ft. per gallon when used for two coats, how many gallons will be needed? If the cost per gallon averages $5.95, what will be the cost of the paint?

7. A steel structure is to be painted. The painters will use brushes in doing the painting. If the weight of the structure is 1200 tons, and each ton has an estimated surface area of 220 sq. ft., how many square feet of surface area will be painted? If one gallon of the paint covers 400 sq. ft., how many gallons will be needed?

15.7 Wallpapering

Introduction. The use of wallpaper goes back to the ancient Chinese. From China it was introduced into Europe, then into England, and into our country before the Revolutionary War. Today wallpaper design has been developed into a highly skilled art. Recently large photographic murals, some 45 by 65 in. and others $6\frac{1}{2}$ by 15 ft. have become available for use in homes, offices, eating establishments, stores, banks, and other locations, providing scenes of unusual decorative effect and beauty.

Wallpaper is available in many styles and qualities. Its cost can run from 75 cents to $20.00 per single roll. Wallpaper usually comes in single rolls which are 18 in. wide and by 24 ft. long, covering 36 sq. ft., and in double rolls which are 18 in. wide by 48 ft. long, covering 72 sq. ft.

In the hanging of wallpaper, the first procedure is to make sure that the surface to be papered is clean, smooth, and free from cracks, lumps, and other irregularities. On newly plastered walls a wall sizing is applied. The wall sizing used today comes in a concentrated liquid form which is diluted with water, and which allows the wallpaper to adhere to the wall more effectively.

After the walls have been properly prepared, the paper is cut into several strips. The back of each of these strips is covered with paste and trimmed (unless it is trimmed already). The hanging of each of the strips is the next operation, care being taken to see that the strips are properly aligned, matched, and trimmed. Wallpaper is also available in prepasted form.

Calculations of Quantities of Materials and Costs of Wallpapering. Excluding the cost of the equipment needed for wallpapering (such as ladders, paste tables, pails, sponges, yardsticks, patching plaster, and brushes) the materials for wallpapering will include:

a) wall sizing
b) paste
c) wallpaper
d) border paper (if used)

The cost of these can be assumed to be: wall sizing — $1.50 per quart (enough for an average room), paste — 55 cents for 2 lb. (enough for an average room), sidewall paper — prices running from 75 cents to several dollars per single roll. Good-quality paper may be purchased at $1.00 to $2.00 per single roll.

Good-quality ceiling paper runs from 80 cents to $1.50 per single roll. Wallpaper border runs from 8 cents to 15 cents per linear yard. Kits containing the necessary tools for home wallpapering are available at from $2.00 to $3.00 each.

Although the amount of wallpaper needed can be calculated in more than one way, the following method should prove satisfactory.

Step 1: Measure the perimeter (distance around) of the room in feet and multiply this by the height of the room in feet. This gives the gross area of the walls in square feet. This area is called gross sidewall area.

Step 2: Divide this area by 30 sq. ft. to obtain the number of single rolls of wallpaper needed. This figure takes care of waste due to spoilage, matching, and so on.

Step 3: For every *two* ordinary sized windows or doors, subtract one single roll from the number obtained in Step 2, or subtract one single roll for every 30 sq. ft. of opening.

Step 4: Multiply the length of the room by its width. Divide this area by 30 sq. ft. to get the number of single rolls needed for the ceiling.

Step 5: Divide the perimeter of the room in feet by 3 ft. to obtain the number of linear yards of border needed.

Step 6: Multiply the cost of a single roll of the sidewall paper by the number of rolls to get the cost of the sidewall paper.

Step 7: Multiply the cost of a single roll of ceiling paper by the number of rolls to get the cost of the ceiling paper.

Step 8: Multiply the cost of a linear yard of the border paper by the number of linear yards to get the cost of the border paper.

Step 9: Add the figures of Steps 6, 7, and 8 to get the total paper and border cost. To this add the cost of sizing, paste, and tools for the final total cost.

The following example will make use of and illustrate the above discussion.

■ EXAMPLE 1:

A man wishes to paper the walls and ceiling of a room 10 ft. by 12 ft. by 8 ft. high. This room has two doors and two windows of ordinary size. Sidewall and ceiling paper* costing $1.20 per single roll is to be used. Find:

   a) the gross area of the sidewalls,
   b) the number of single rolls of sidewall paper needed,
   c) the net area of the ceiling,
   d) the number of single rolls needed for the ceiling,
   e) the total number of single rolls needed,
   f) the total cost of the wallpaper.

Solution and Explanation:

   a) The gross area of the sidewalls = perimeter × height
   $$= (10 + 12 + 10 + 12) \times 8$$
   $$= (44) \times 8 = 352 \text{ sq. ft.}$$

   b) The number of single rolls of sidewall paper needed (if there were no openings) $= \frac{352}{30} = 11.7 = 12$

---

* In recent years there has been a decline in the papering of ceilings; hence most of the problems on papering deal with the papering of sidewalls except as specified.

Since there are *two doors* and *two windows,* we *deduct* two single rolls. Number of single rolls of sidewall paper needed $= 12 - 2 = 10$

d) The number of single rolls needed for the ceiling $= \dfrac{120 \text{ sq. ft.}}{30 \text{ sq. ft.}} = 4$

e) The total number of single rolls needed $= 10 + 4 = 14$

f) The total cost of the paper $= \$1.20 \times 14 = \$16.80$

■ EXAMPLE 2:

A homeowner wishes to paper a room (sidewalls and ceiling) 13 ft. by 15 ft. by 8 ft. high with wallpaper costing $1.50 per single roll. The room has 180 sq. ft. of door and window openings. Find:

a) the gross sidewall area,
b) the number of single rolls of sidewall paper needed,
c) the ceiling area,
d) the number of single rolls of ceiling paper needed,
e) the total number of single rolls needed,
f) the total cost of the wallpaper.

Solution and Explanation:

a) The gross sidewall area $=$ perimeter of room in ft. $\times$ height of room in ft.
$= (13 + 15 + 13 + 15) \times 8$
$= (56) \times 8 = 448$ sq. ft.

b) Number of single rolls needed for the sidewalls (assuming no openings). $= \frac{448}{30} = 15$

Since there are 180 sq. ft. of openings, and the deduction is one single roll per 30 sq. ft., six rolls are deducted. Hence the actual number of single rolls for the sidewalls $= 15 - 6 = 9$

c) The ceiling area $=$ room length in ft. $\times$ room width in ft.
$= 15 \times 13 = 195$ sq. ft.

d) Number of single rolls needed for the ceiling $= \frac{195}{30} = 6.5$
He will buy 7 rolls.

e) The total number of single rolls = 9 + 7 = 16

f) The cost of the paper   = 16 × $1.50

= $24.00

■ **EXAMPLE 3:**

A homeowner wishes to paper two rooms, each 12 ft. by 12 ft. by 8 ft. high. Each room has two ordinary-sized doors and two ordinary-sized windows. He buys a wallpapering kit for $3.00, 5 lb. of paste at 28 cents per pound and 2 qt. of wall sizing at $1.50 per quart. The sidewall and ceiling paper costs $1.00 per roll. Find:

a) the gross sidewall area of each room,

b) the number of single rolls of sidewall paper needed for each room,

c) the number of single rolls of ceiling paper needed for each room,

d) the total number of single rolls needed for each room,

e) the total number of single rolls needed for both rooms,

f) the total cost of the wallpaper,

g) the cost of the sizing,

h) the cost of the paste,

i) the total cost, including the kit.

Solution and Explanation:

a) The gross area of the sidewalls = perimeter of room in ft. × height of room in ft.

= (12 + 12 + 12 + 12) × 8

= (48) × 8

= 384 sq. ft.

b) The number of single rolls needed (no deductions) = $\frac{384}{30}$ × 12.8 or 13

Since there are two doors and two windows in each room, we deduct two rolls. Hence, number of single rolls of sidewall paper = 13 − 2 = 11

c) The ceiling area of each room = length of room in ft. × width of room in ft.

= 12 × 12

= 144 sq. ft.

The number of single rolls needed for the ceiling = $\frac{144}{30}$ = 4.8 or 5

d) The total number of single rolls for each room = 11 + 5 = 16

e) The total number of single rolls for *both* rooms   = 2 × 16 = 32

f) The total cost of the wallpaper = $1.00 × 32 = $32.00

g) The cost of the sizing   = 2 × $1.50   =   3.00

h) The cost of the paste   = 5 × 28¢   =   1.40

i) The cost of the kit   =   3.00

The total cost   = $39.40

15.8 Problems Involving Calculation of Amounts and Costs of Wallpapering

1. A room is 16 ft. long, 12 ft. wide, and 8 ft. high. It has door and window openings amounting to 90 sq. ft. Find:

    a) the sidewall area of this room,

    b) the number of single rolls of wallpaper needed for the sidewalls,

    c) the number of single rolls of wallpaper needed for the ceiling,

    d) the total number of single rolls of wallpaper needed,

    e) the cost of the paper at $1.05 per single roll (for sidewalls and ceiling).

2. A homeowner wishes to wallpaper his living room, which is 13 ft. long, 13 ft. wide, and 8 ft. high. He measures the door and window openings and finds that they have an area of 120 sq. ft. Answer the same questions for this problem as for Problem 1, if the wallpaper costs 90 cents per single roll (for sidewalls and ceiling).

3. What is the total cost of wallpapering a room 13 ft. long by 11 ft. wide by 8 ft. high if the wallpaper costs $1.25 per single roll for sidewalls and the cost of the wallpaper tool kit, sizing, and paste comes to $4.75? There are 120 sq. ft. of door and window openings in the room.

4. A man bought four colored murals for his children's room. Each of these cost $9.00. His other expenses for mounting them were $4.80. What were his total expenses?

5. Four large murals (6½ ft. high by 15 ft. long) costing $110.00 each were mounted on the main floor walls of a financial institution. The other expenses for doing this work were $280.00. What was the total cost for this work?

6. A room 11 ft. long, 11 ft. wide, and 8 ft. high is to be wallpapered. The room has door and window openings amounting to 60 sq. ft. If the sidewall paper costs $1.05 per single roll, find the cost of the wallpaper required for the sidewalls. Follow the same steps as in Problem 1, omitting item *c*).

7. The room shown on the partial floor plan (Fig. 290) is to be

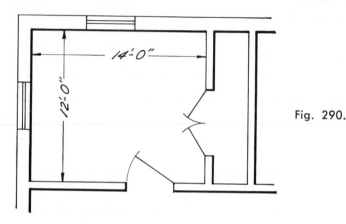

Fig. 290.

wallpapered with paper costing $1.50 per single roll. The ceiling is 8 ft. high and the door, window, and closet openings amount to 90 sq. ft. Proceed as in Problem 1 and find the cost of the sidewall paper required.

8. A room 11 ft. long by 10 ft. wide by 8 ft. high is to be wallpapered. The paper costs $2.39 per single roll for the sidewalls. The door and window openings have a total area of 90 sq. ft. Proceed as in Problem 1 and answer items *a*) through *e*), omitting *c*).

9. A homeowner decides to wallpaper a room 18 ft. long, 16 ft. wide, and 8 ft. high. The paper for the walls costs $1.89 per single roll. The door, window, and closet openings have an area of 150 sq. ft. Find the items as in Problem 1, omitting *c*).

10. The owner of a rather large home bought these materials in the process of wallpapering two of the rooms:

　　20 rolls of paper at $1.29 per roll,
　　24 rolls of paper at $1.69 per roll,
　　Other materials costing $6.80.

What were his total expenses in connection with the papering of these rooms?

15.9 Review Problems Relating to the Building Trades

1. One of the brick walls of a manufacturing building is to be painted. The wall is 120 ft. long and 18 ft. high, with no openings. If the paint covers 350 sq. ft. per gallon, how many gallons of paint will be needed?

2. The windows in the dining room of a certain home have glass panes with the following dimensions:

　　　　4 panes — 32 in. wide by 24　in. high
　　　10 panes — 32 in. wide by 11　in. high
　　　　1 pane　— 66 in. wide by $56\frac{1}{2}$ in. high

What is the total area of these panes in square feet? Give answer to nearest square foot.

3. A man buys the following materials and equipment in connection with wallpapering a room:

        12 single rolls of sidewall paper at $1.49 per roll
        20 yards of border at 12 cents per yard
         1 tool kit at $2.95
           sizing and paste, $2.05

What is the total cost of the paper and materials for wallpapering this room?

4. The ceilings of three rooms of a home are to be painted with two coats each. The first ceiling is 12 ft. by 16 ft., the second ceiling is 10 ft. by 15 ft., and the third ceiling is 9 ft. by 14 ft. What is the total area of the three ceilings? If a gallon of each coat covers 500 sq. ft., how many gallons of each will be needed? What will be the total cost of the paint if the first coat cost $4.95 per gallon and the second coat costs $6.29 per gallon?

5. The front and back walls of a barn are 40 ft. by 30 ft. The two sidewalls are 65 ft. by 30 ft. What is the total wall area of this barn? If a gallon of first-coat paint covers 500 sq. ft., how many gallons will be needed to give the walls one coat of paint? How many gallons will be needed to give the walls a second coat if the second coat covers 550 sq. ft. per gallon? What will be the total cost of the paint if the average cost per gallon is $7.10?

6. The area of the roof of a house is 1600 sq. ft. How many squares of 3-tab 12 in. by 36 in. shingles will be required to cover this roof? What will be the cost of the shingles if each square costs $8.50?

7. It is necessary to buy roofing felt for the roof in Problem 6. If each roll of roofing felt covers 432 sq. ft., how many rolls would be ordered? What would the roofing felt cost at $3.15 per roll?

8. A homeowner wanted to cover the ceiling of a room with acoustical tile. Each tile is 12 in. by 12 in. If the ceiling is 10 ft. by 12 ft., how many tiles should he buy? If each tile cost 16 cents, how much is the total cost?

9. In doing some remodeling of his home, the owner decided to cover the walls of one room with wall paneling. The room was 12 ft. long, 8 ft. wide, and 8 ft. high. Each wall panel was 4 ft. wide and 8 ft. high and cost $5.40. He made no deductions for door or window openings because he wanted to use the amounts left over for other repairs. How many pieces of wallboard did he need? What was the total cost of the wallboard?

10. A homeowner bought three wall murals 45 in. high by 65 in. long to be mounted on the walls of his living room. Each of these murals costs

$8.95. He also bought a wallpaper tool kit, sizing, and paste totaling $3.70. What was the total cost of the murals and materials?

11. In the construction of a room, it was necessary to use 10 bundles of rock lath, each of which cost $1.50 per bundle. In addition, 6 lb. of nails were bought at 40 cents per pound. If a charge of $3.00 was made for delivery, what was the total cost of these materials?

12. A brick wall serving as a fence on one side of a storage yard is 8 ft. high and 50 ft. long. This wall is 12 in. thick and uses $\frac{1}{2}$-in. mortar joints. (Three times as many bricks are needed per square foot of this wall as for a wall 4 in. thick.) How many bricks were needed for this wall? Allow 2 percent for waste. A running bond was used in the wall construction.

13. What is the cost of the bricks in Problem 12 if each 1000 costs $39.00?

14. A contractor orders the following quantities of materials:

       120 squares of 3-tab strip shingles at $7.85 per square

        28 rolls of roofing felt at $2.90 per roll

       250 lb. of roofing nails at $0.27 per lb.

What is the total cost of these materials?

15. Steel structures totaling 2600 tons in weight are to be painted. Each ton of this steel has a surface area of 220 sq. ft.

    a) What is the total surface area of the steel?

    b) If a gallon of paint covers 400 sq. ft., how many gallons of paint will be needed?

    c) If a gallon of paint costs $7.00, what will be the cost of the paint?

CHAPTER 16

Mathematics Applied to Printing — I

PAPER — TYPE SIZES AND AREAS

16.1 Introduction

Without doubt, among the very old arts practiced almost universally by man are the graphic arts, and of these, writing and printing are among the oldest.

Thousands of years ago the ancient Egyptians made a type of paper from the fibers of the papyrus plant which grew along the banks of the Nile River, and many examples of their writing on this kind of material are still in existence. The early Chinese made paper from the fibers of bamboo and wood and used linen and silk in the making of paper.

In later times, skins of animals were used to make vellum and parchment. In the early 1800's machines were invented for the manufacture of paper. Today the printing industry is one of the most important in the world, giving employment to millions of people and serving in the spreading of news, culture, and knowledge to all parts of the inhabited earth.

Among the many important things a printer should know are how to select, order, and use various kinds of paper.

16.2 Kinds of Printing Paper

Most of the paper that we use today is machine-made. The basic material may be wood pulp, cornstalks, and vegetable fibers for the cheaper grades of paper, and linen or cotton fibers for the better grades of paper.

Although there are literally hundreds of kinds of papers, the majority can be classified for material and basic ream (500 sheets) sizes as follows:

> *Newsprint* (25 in. by 38 in.)
> *Book paper* (25 in. by 38 in.)
>   Uncoated (offset)
>   Coated (enamel)
> *Wrapping paper*
> *Cardboard* ($25\frac{1}{2}$ in. by $30\frac{1}{2}$ in.)
>   Bristol
>   Bogus Bristol
> *Blotting paper* (19 in. by 24 in.)
> *Bond paper* (17 in. by 22 in.)
>   Sulphite — Wood pulp
>   Rag — Cotton
>   25%, 50%, 75%, 100% rag content
> *Paper used for covers* (20 in. by 26 in.)

303

The standard sizes of the papers listed above are given in parentheses in inches. Sizes and weights of paper are discussed later in this chapter.

In the manufacture of paper, the fibers of rag or wood which make up the paper are arranged chiefly in one direction. The lining up of these fibers along this direction gives the paper a *grain*. The printer must take into consideration the direction of the grain of the paper when he cuts, prints, folds, and assembles the printed matter. For best folding results, printing is done in the direction of the grain of the paper. This direction will determine the way in which stock-size sheets are to be cut.

Paper folds easily *along* the direction of the grain. If it is folded *across* the direction of the grain, it may have to be scored or creased in order that a smooth, accurate, and straight fold may be made.

16.3 Type-Size Measurement

In the composition and laying out of type it is important to have a working knowledge of type sizes and how they are measured. The system used by printers today is one which is due to the efforts of such men as John Marder and Nelson C. Hawks. This system was approved by the United States Typefounders Association in 1886.

The system of type units is called the *point system;* a point is equal to 0.013837 in. or very nearly $\frac{1}{72}$ in. (0.013889 in.)

We are all familiar with the inch marks on a 12-in. ruler. Each of the inch spaces is divided into halves, quarters, eighths, sixteenths, and thirty-seconds of an inch. On a comparative basis, the printer divides one inch into 72 equal spaces known as points and his line gauge (or ruler) shows $\frac{1}{6}$ in. as 12 points (called a pica) and 12 spaces called nonpareils, which are 6 points each. To summarize:

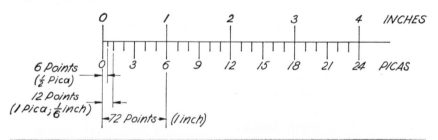

H. B. Rouse & Co.

Fig. 291. A printer's line gauge.

The smallest unit of type measure is the point, which for all practical purposes equals $\frac{1}{72}$ in. The other units in common use were selected so that:

$$6 \text{ points} = \tfrac{1}{2} \text{ pica or 1 nonpareil}$$
$$12 \text{ points} = 1 \text{ pica}$$
$$6 \text{ picas} = 1 \text{ in.}$$
$$72 \text{ points} = 1 \text{ in.}$$
$$72 \text{ picas} = 12 \text{ in.} = 1 \text{ ft.}$$

Figure 291 shows a comparison of the first part of a printer's rule or line gauge with an ordinary inch rule.

16.4   Correlation and Expression of Type Sizes in Points and Inches

The common type sizes in terms of points are 6, 8, 10, 12, 14, 18, 24, 30, 36, 42, 48, 60, and 72 points. Other sizes are also available, running from 4 to 144 points.

The use of these units of type measure is illustrated in the following examples:

■ **EXAMPLE 1:**

The size of a certain type is 48 points. Express this in picas and in inches.

Solution and Explanation:

Since 12 points = 1 pica, 48 points must equal 4 picas. Also, since 72 points = 1 in., 48 points must equal $\frac{48}{72}$ in. or $\frac{2}{3}$ in.

In printing, when a page size or form size is specified, the first dimension is the width (horizontal dimension); the second dimension (called the depth) is the height of the page or form.

■ **EXAMPLE 2:**

A border is 18 picas wide and 30 picas deep. What is the size of this border in inches?

Solution and Explanation:

Since 6 picas = 1 in., 18 picas = 3 in., 30 picas= 5 in. Hence, the border has a width of 3 in. and a depth of 5 in.

■ **EXAMPLE 3:**

Part of the printed material on an advertising blotter occupied a space of $6\frac{3}{4}$ in. by 2 in. What is the size of this space in picas?

Solution and Explanation:

In each inch there are 6 picas. Hence, in $6\frac{3}{4}$ in. there are $6\frac{3}{4} \times 6$ or

$\frac{\overset{27}{\cancel{27}}}{\cancel{2}} \times \overset{3}{\cancel{6}} = \frac{81}{2} = 40\frac{1}{2}$ picas. In 2 in. there are $2 \times 6 = 12$ picas.

Therefore the size of this space is $40\frac{1}{2}$ picas by 12 picas.

16.5 Problems Involving Type-Size Computations

1. How many points are there in $3\frac{1}{2}$ in.; 5 in.; 9 in.; 12 in.?

2. A line of type is $16\frac{1}{2}$ picas long (horizontal length). What is this length in points? in inches?

3. A pica is equal to what fractional part of an inch?

4. Reduce the sum of 3 in. plus 3 picas plus 36 points to points.

5. The printing on an announcement occupies a space 5 in. wide (horizontal distance) by 3 in. deep (vertical distance). Express the dimensions of the space in picas.

6. Express each of the following in inches: 24 picas; 43 picas; 72 points; 396 points; 36 picas.

7. The size of a printed page is 24 picas by 43 picas. Express the size of this page in inches.

8. The size of the printed form is $5\frac{1}{2}$ in. by 7 in. Express this size in picas.

9. The size of a certain type is $\frac{1}{2}$ in. What is its size in points?

10. The type area of a page is 3 in. by 6 in. Express the size of this page in picas.

11. How many points are there in $1\frac{1}{2}$ in.? How many picas?

12. A page size is 7 by 10 in. Allowing a margin of 3 picas on the left-hand side and a margin of 4 picas on the right hand side, what will be the width of the type area in picas?

13. A page size is 6 in. by 9 in. The type area is 5 in. by $7\frac{1}{2}$ in. or 30 picas by 45 picas. How many lines of 12-point type can be set on this page, assuming that the type is set with no additional spacing between lines?* How many lines of 10-point type can be set on this page?

14. How many lines of 12-point type can be set in a depth of 1 in.?

16.6 Type-Spacing Material

In setting up or composing type by hand, a tool called a composing stick is used. This is a light, open metal frame shaped like a shelf and

---

* When additional spacing is inserted between lines of type, it is said to be "opened up" for easier readability. Thus, 12-point type may be cast with an additional 2 points of spacing between lines and is specified as 12 on 14 (commonly written 12/14). This avoids the necessity of leading (pronounced "ledding"), which is discussed later.

A composing stick for
setting type by hand.

H. B. Rouse & Co.

carrying a scale marked in picas and often in half picas. This frame
is provided with a movable clamp so as to allow adjustment to lines
of various lengths which are set up in the stick.

As the printer sets the type into lines to make sentences and paragraphs
and "makes up" these lines along with any illustration into pages, it is
necessary for him to use spacing material so that, among other things,
he may:

a) separate the words from each other,

b) separate each line from the other,

c) indent for paragraphs,

d) center the type on the line (for headings, etc.),

e) fill in the space left by a line which does not go to the end of the
stick.

The spacing material he uses between lines is of various sizes and
lengths, all measured in units of points or picas. (For example, a 3-point
lead $= \frac{1}{4}$ pica, a 6-point lead $= \frac{1}{2}$ pica.) The level of this material is
below the printing surface of the type; consequently, it does not make
contact with the paper and the result is a blank (or white) space on the
printed sheet.

Where type is composed or set on a machine, the spacing may be done
mechanically. Generally, spacing material can be put into two classes:

1. *Strip material* (for spacing between lines). This consists of type
metal of various lengths and thicknesses. Those in 1-, 2-, or 3-point
thickness are called *leads* (pronounced "leds") and those available in 6-,
9-, or 12-point thickness are called *slugs*. The most commonly used strips
for spacing lines are the 2-point leads.

2. *Quads and spaces* (for spacing between words and sentences in a
line). These are pieces of type metal, of the same point size in depth as
the type used, but of varying widths. The widths commonly used are:

a) The *em quad* (also called mutton quad) is the basic unit of
spacing material and is a square whose vertical dimensions cor-
respond to the point size of the type with which it is being used.
Thus, if 10-point type is used, then an *em quad* is 10 points.
Usually these are called ems, the word *quad* being omitted.

b) The *2-em* quad is twice as wide as it is high. A 2-em quad of
12-point type would be 24 points wide and 12 points high.

c) The *3-em quad* is three times as wide as it is high. A 3-em quad of 8-point type would be 24 points wide and 8 points high. The 2- and 3-em quads can be used for filling out blank spaces and lines which do not run to the end of the stick.

d) The *en quad* (nut quad) is half the width of an em quad of the same point size. An en quad of 10-point type would be 5 points wide.

e) *The spaces.* These are of the same height as the point size of type used, but their widths (horizontal lengths) are certain fractional parts of the type size "em."* The fractional parts are $\frac{1}{3}$, $\frac{1}{4}$, and $\frac{1}{5}$ of an em. Those $\frac{1}{3}$ of an em are called 3-em spaces; those $\frac{1}{4}$ of an em are called 4-em spaces; those $\frac{1}{5}$ of an em are called 5-em spaces.

These spaces are also called 3-to-em, 4-to-em, 5-to-em spaces, and are used for the horizontal spacing of words within a line so as to provide proper "justification" of the line. They are also used in various arrangements to provide appropriate spacing.

When type is set by hand, it is necessary to adjust the spacing of the words on each line so all lines occupy the width of the composing stick. Adjustment is called justification and each line so arranged is said to be justified.

For the printer, it is important to know how much space his copy (the material to be set in type) will occupy when it has been set in a particular size of type to fit into a page of specified dimensions. He must know this in order to estimate the total size of a book, magazine article, advertising piece, and the like. This information will allow him to estimate costs or determine whether it will be necessary to cut the copy, reduce the type size, increase the measure (width to which the copy is set), increase the page size, and so on.

16.7   How the Number of Ems in a Line of Type is Computed

If one were computing the area of a wall he would probably use the square foot for the unit of area. If he were computing the volume of an engine cylinder he would most likely use the cubic inch for the unit of volume. The printer, in computing the area that will be covered by a line of type, measures the width of the line and uses for the unit of area a unit called an *em*. The *em* is a *square* of any size of type. It may be considered as the space taken up by the capital or uppercase letter *M* of any size of type.

Thus, a 12-point em is 12 points by 12 points; a 10-point em is 10

---

* In printing, the em may be considered as a unit of area or as a unit of type measure. It is a square whose dimensions are of a particular type size. Thus a square 12 points by 12 points is called a 12-point em; a square 8 points by 8 points is called an 8-point em, and so on.

points by 10 points; an 8-point em is 8 points by 8 points. *When no type size is mentioned, the printer assumes the em to be a 12-point em.*

In computing the number of ems of a particular point size in a line of type, the procedure is to divide the number of points in the width of the line by the point size of type. This can be stated in a formula in the following ways:

$$\text{1. No. of ems} = \frac{\text{No. of picas in width of line} \times 12}{\text{Point size of type}}$$

$$\text{2. No. of ems} = \frac{\text{No. of inches in width of line} \times 72}{\text{Point size of type}}$$

The number of ems found by using these formulas is for one line of type.

The following examples will illustrate the application of these formulas.

■ EXAMPLE 1:

How many ems of 6-point type are there in a line of type 24 picas wide?

Solution and Explanation:

Since we know the width of the line, we can use Formula 1.

$$\text{No. of ems} = \frac{\text{No. of picas in width of line} \times 12}{\text{Point size of type}}$$

$$= \frac{24 \times \overset{2}{\cancel{12}}}{\underset{1}{\cancel{6}}}$$

$$= 48 \text{ ems}$$

Therefore there are 48 ems of 6-point type in this line of type.

■ EXAMPLE 2:

A line of type is 6 in. wide. How many ems of 8-point type are there in this line?

Solution and Explanation:

In this problem we are given the width of the line in inches. Using Formula 2:

$$\text{No. of ems} = \frac{\text{No. of inches in width of line} \times 72}{\text{Point size of type}}$$

$$= \frac{6 \times \overset{9}{\cancel{72}}}{\underset{1}{\cancel{8}}}$$

$$= 54 \text{ ems}$$

Therefore there are 54 ems of 8-point type in this line of type.

16.8 Problems Involving Computation of Number of Ems of Type in a Line of Type

1. How many ems of 8-point type are there in a line 34 picas wide?

2. A line of 12-point type is 45 picas wide. How many ems are there in this line?

3. A line of 24-point type is 6 in. wide. How many ems are there in this line?

4. How many ems of 14-point type are there in a line of type 4 in. wide?

5. A line of type 4 in. wide is composed of 18-point type. How many ems of this size type are there in this line?

6. How many ems of 14-point type are there in a line 28 picas wide?

7. The lines of type in a technical book are $5\frac{1}{2}$ in. wide and composed with 12-point type. How many ems of this size type are there in each of these lines?

8. For a certain job the type is set in columns 30 picas wide and is 12-point in size. How many ems of this size type are there in each line of such a column?

9. A workbook is set in 14-point type in columns 28 picas wide. Compute the number of ems of this size type in each line of this book.

10. A textbook uses 12-point type set in lines 27 picas wide. How many ems of this size type are there in each line of this text?

16.9 How the Number of Ems in a Given Width and Depth of Type Set Solid Is Computed

In the calculation of the area of a rectangle, we multiply the number of units in its length by the number of units in its width and obtain its area in square units.

In printing, the unit of *type area* is the em of the point size of type used. To determine the number of ems of type, we must know the width and depth of the type matter, and the point size of the type used. From this information we calculate the number of ems in the width of each line and in the depth of the type matter. *The product of these two quantities gives the total number of ems in the type matter.*

This rule can be put into the following forms:

1. No. of ems of type set solid = No. of ems in width × no. of ems in depth

2. No. of ems of type set solid = $\left(\dfrac{\text{Width of line in picas} \times 12}{\text{Point size of em}}\right) \times \left(\dfrac{\text{Depth of printed matter in picas} \times 12}{\text{Point size of em}}\right)$

$$\text{3. No. of ems of type set solid} = \frac{\left(\dfrac{\text{Width of line in inches} \times 72}{\text{Point size of em}}\right) \times}{\left(\dfrac{\text{Depth of printed matter in inches} \times 72}{\text{Point size of em}}\right)}$$

In common practice the type area is *first* calculated as 12-point ems. The square area of 12-point type being 144 square points, that is, 12×12, a comparative coefficient is then determined by the percentage of the actual typeface in question. Thus an area 8 points by 8 points or 64 square points is contained in 144 square points 2.25 times $(\frac{144}{64} = 2.25)$.

Hence to determine the total number of 8-point square ems in 12-point square ems, multiply the area in 12-point square ems by 2.25.

If the 8-point type is set on a 10-point body (for spacing) the square is figured as 8×10 and the comparative percentage of "multiplying factor" becomes $\frac{144}{80} = 1.80$. (NOTE: See Section 16.11 on the computation of leaded type.)

Two other forms of this rule are:

4. No. of ems of type set solid $= \dfrac{W \times 12}{\text{Point size of em}} \times \dfrac{D \times 12}{\text{Point size of em}}$

 W = Width of line in picas
 D = Depth of printed matter in picas

5. No. of ems of type set solid $= \dfrac{W \times 72}{\text{Point size of em}} \times \dfrac{D \times 72}{\text{Point size of em}}$

 W = Width of line in inches
 D = Depth of printed matter in inches

The following examples will illustrate the use of these formulas.

■ **EXAMPLE 1:**

Calculate the number of 8-point ems in a paragraph 32 picas wide and 24 picas deep.

Solution and Explanation:

Since each line of type is 32 picas wide, the number of 8-point ems in it is $\dfrac{\overset{4}{\cancel{32}} \times 12}{\underset{1}{\cancel{8}}} = 48$.

Since the paragraph has a depth of 24 picas, the number of 8-point ems in this depth is $\dfrac{\overset{3}{\cancel{24}} \times 12}{\underset{1}{\cancel{8}}} = 36$.

Therefore the total number of ems of 8-point type in the paragraph $= 48 \times 36 = 1728$.

If we used Form 2 of the rule, we would have:

$$\text{No. of ems of type set solid} = \frac{\left(\dfrac{\text{Width of line in picas} \times 12}{\text{Point size of em}}\right) \times}{\left(\dfrac{\text{Depth of printed matter in picas} \times 12}{\text{Point size of em}}\right)}$$

$$= (\frac{\overset{4}{\cancel{32}} \times 12}{\underset{1}{\cancel{8}}}) \times (\frac{\overset{3}{\cancel{24}} \times 12}{\underset{1}{\cancel{8}}})$$

$$= (48) \times (36)$$

$$= 1728 \text{ ems of 8-point type}$$

■ EXAMPLE 2:

How many 10-point ems are there in a printed form 3 in. wide and 5 in. deep?

Solution and Explanation:

Here the dimensions of the printed form are given in inches. We can use Form 3 of the rule.

$$\text{No. of ems of type set solid} = \frac{\left(\dfrac{\text{Width of line in inches} \times 72}{\text{Point size of em}}\right) \times}{\left(\dfrac{\text{Depth of printed matter in inches} \times 12}{\text{Point size of em}}\right)}$$

$$= (\frac{3 \times \overset{36}{\cancel{72}}}{\underset{5}{\cancel{10}}}) \times (\frac{\overset{1}{\cancel{5}} \times \overset{36}{\cancel{72}}}{\underset{1}{\cancel{10}}})$$

$$= \frac{3 \times 36 \times 36}{5}$$

$$= 777.6 = 778 \text{ ems of 10-point type}$$

Hence the number of 10-point ems in this form is 778.

■ EXAMPLE 3:

A compositor sets eight pages 5 in. wide by 8 in. deep. How many 12-point ems does this job contain?

Solution and Explanation:

Since the size of the forms is given in inches, we can use Formula 3.

$$\text{No. of ems of type set solid} = \frac{W \times 72}{\text{Point size of em}} \times \frac{D \times 72}{\text{Point size of em}}$$

Here $\begin{aligned} W &= 5 \text{ in.} \\ D &= 8 \text{ in.} \end{aligned}$ Substituting in the formula, we have

$$\text{No. of ems of} \atop \text{type set solid} = \frac{5 \times \overset{6}{\cancel{72}} \times 8 \times \overset{6}{\cancel{72}}}{\underset{1}{\cancel{72}} \qquad \underset{1}{\cancel{72}}}$$

$$= 30 \times 48$$

$$= 1440 \text{ ems of 12-point type}$$

This value is for one page. For eight pages, the total number of ems is $8 \times 1440 = 11{,}520$. Hence the job contains 11,520 ems of 12-point type.

16.10   Problems Involving the Computation of Number of Ems of Type Set Solid

1. The size of a type page is 26 picas by 46 picas. How many ems of 10-point type set solid are there on this page?

2. A book page is 6 in. by 9 in. The type on this pages occupies an area 42 picas by 55 picas and is set solid with 10-point type. How many ems of this size type are there on this page?

3. Each of six type forms is 4 in. wide by $2\frac{1}{4}$ in. deep. It is set with 12-point type set solid. How many ems of this size type are there on each of these forms? How many are there on all six?

4. How many ems of 8-point type set solid are there in one type page 22 picas by 38 picas?

5. A paragraph is 4 in. wide and $2\frac{1}{2}$ in. deep. How many ems of 8-point type set solid does it contain?

6. A type page is $5\frac{1}{2}$ in. wide by 7 in. deep. How many ems of 14-point type set solid does it contain?

7. A column of type is 14 picas by 48 picas. How many ems of 8-point type set solid does it contain?

8. Each type page of a 12-page pamphlet is 22 picas by 38 picas. How many ems of 12-point type set solid are there in one page? in the 12 pages?

9. A type column is 12 picas wide and 20 picas deep. If it is set with 8-point type set solid, how many ems of this size type does it contain?

10. A page of type measures $3\frac{1}{4}$ in. wide by $5\frac{1}{2}$ in. deep. How many ems of 8-point type set solid are there in this page?

16.11   How the Number of Ems in a Given Width and Depth of Leaded Type Is Computed

In the composition of type, it is often found necessary to add more white or blank space between lines. This is done by means of lengths of spacing metal or slugs of various point sizes, as previously explained. Lines of type arranged this way are said to be leaded (pronounced "ledded").

Leading a line of type increases the "point size" of the type used by an amount equal to the point size of the lead. The commonly used leading is 2 points and is called single leading. Double leading is 4 points. Unless otherwise specified, 2 point is assumed.

A line of 6-point type single-leaded is thus equivalent to 8-point size; a line of 8-point type with 2-point leading equals 10-point size. The printer says, for example, "6 point on 8," "8 on 10."

Suppose that we want to find the number of lines on a printing job having a depth of 5 in., set with 8-point type, leaded. (If this were composed on a machine it would be described as 8 on 10.) We would reason as follows:

Since each line is leaded, its point size is increased 2 points and hence becomes $8 + 2$ or 10 points. In 5 in. there are 5×72 points. Dividing 5×72 by 10 we obtain $\frac{5 \times 72}{10} = 36$ lines.

This reasoning can be put into a formula reading:

1. $\text{No. of lines of leaded type} = \dfrac{\text{Depth of printed matter in inches} \times 72}{\text{Point size of type plus point size of leading}}$

2. $\text{No. of lines of leaded type} = \dfrac{\text{Depth of printed matter in picas} \times 12}{\text{Point size of type plus point size of leading}}$

The following examples illustrate the application of these formulas.

■ EXAMPLE 1:

A form is 6 in. deep. How many lines of 10-point type, leaded, are there in it?

Solution and Explanation:

Since the depth of the form is given in inches, we use Formula 1.

$$\text{No. of lines of leaded type} = \frac{\text{Depth of printed matter in inches} \times 72}{\text{Point size of type plus point size of leading}}$$

$$= \frac{6 \times 72}{10 + 2}$$

$$= \frac{6 \times \overset{6}{\cancel{72}}}{\underset{1}{\cancel{12}}}$$

$$= 36$$

Hence there are 36 lines of 10-point type, leaded, in a form 6 in. deep.

■ EXAMPLE 2:

How many lines of 6-point, leaded type are there in a form 24 picas deep?

Solution and Explanation:

When the 6-point type is leaded (single-leaded), its point size is increased to 6 + 2 or 8 points. Using Formula 2, we have:

$$\text{No. of lines of leaded type} = \frac{\text{Depth of form in picas} \times 12}{\text{Point size of type plus point size of leading}}$$

$$= \frac{24 \times 12}{6 + 2}$$

$$= \frac{\overset{3}{\cancel{24}} \times 12}{\underset{1}{\cancel{8}}}$$

$$= 36$$

Hence there are 36 lines of 6-point leaded type in a form 24 picas deep.

We have seen how the number of ems in type set solid can be computed. How does one compute the number of ems in a given form set in a particular point size type and leaded? Evidently, if we compute the number of ems in a single line, and multiply this by the number of lines, the product would give the total number of ems in the form.

This simple procedure can be put into formula form as follows:

1. $$\text{No. of ems in a form of leaded type} = \left(\begin{array}{c}\text{Ems per line}\\\text{of leaded type}\end{array}\right) \times \left(\begin{array}{c}\text{Number of lines}\\\text{of leaded type}\end{array}\right)$$

2. $$\text{No. of ems in a form of leaded type} = \left(\frac{\text{Width of line in picas} \times 12}{\text{Point size of type}}\right) \times \left(\frac{\text{Depth of form in picas} \times 12}{\text{Point size of type} + \text{point size of leading}}\right)$$

$$= \left(\frac{W \times 12}{\text{Point size of type}}\right) \times \left(\frac{D \times 12}{\text{Point size of type} + \text{point size of leading}}\right)$$

(W = Width of line in picas)
(D = Depth of form in picas)

3. $$\text{No. of ems in a form of leaded type} = \left(\frac{\text{Width of line in inches} \times 72}{\text{Point size of type}}\right) \times \left(\frac{\text{Depth of form in inches} \times 72}{\text{Point size of type} + \text{point size of leading}}\right)$$

$$= \left(\frac{W \times 72}{\text{Point size of type}}\right) \times$$

$$\left(\frac{D \times 72}{\text{Point size of type + point size of leading}}\right)$$

(W = Width of line in inches)
(D = Depth of form in inches)

The following problems will illustrate the application of these formulas.

■ EXAMPLE 1:

How many ems of 8-point leaded type are there in a job 18 picas wide by 30 picas deep?

Solution and Explanation:

Since we know the width of each line in picas and the depth of the form in picas, we can use Formula 2:

$$\begin{aligned}\text{No. of ems of} \\ \text{leaded type}\end{aligned} = \left(\frac{\text{Width of line in picas} \times 12}{\text{Point size of type}}\right) \times$$

$$\left(\frac{\text{Depth of form in picas} \times 12}{\text{Point size of type + point size of leading}}\right)$$

$$= \frac{18 \times 12}{8} \times \frac{30 \times 12}{8 + 2}$$

$$= \frac{\overset{9}{\cancel{18}} \times \overset{3}{\cancel{12}}}{\underset{1}{\underset{\cancel{2}}{\cancel{8}}}} \times \frac{\overset{3}{\cancel{30}} \times 12}{\underset{1}{\cancel{10}}}$$

$$= 27 \times 36$$

$$= 972$$

Hence there are 972 ems of 8-point type, leaded, in this job.

■ EXAMPLE 2:

A job has ten forms each 4 in. wide by 7 in. deep, set with 8-point, double-leaded type. How many ems are there in this job?

Solution and Explanation:

$$\begin{aligned}\text{No. of ems of} \\ \text{leaded type}\end{aligned} = \left(\frac{\text{Width of line in inches} \times 72}{\text{Point size of type}}\right) \times$$

$$\left(\frac{\text{Depth of form in inches} \times 72}{\text{Point size of type + point size of leading}}\right)$$

$$= \frac{4 \times 72}{8} \times \frac{7 \times 72}{8 + 4}$$

$$= \frac{4 \times \overset{9}{\cancel{18}}}{\underset{1}{\cancel{8}}} \times \frac{7 \times \overset{6}{\cancel{18}}}{\underset{1}{\cancel{18}}}$$
$$= 36 \times 42$$
$$= 1512 \text{ ems}$$

This is the number of ems in one form. Since there are ten forms, the total number of ems is 10×1512 or $15{,}120$ ems. Hence, there are $15{,}120$ ems in this job as specified.

16.12   Problems Involving Computation of Ems of Leaded Type

1. How many ems of 10-point type, 2-point leaded, are there in a type form 24 picas wide and 16 picas deep?

2. How many ems of 8-point type, 2-point leaded, are there in a type-form size 3 in. wide by 5 in. deep?

3. The printed area on a page is 24 picas wide and 33 picas deep. It is set with 14-point type, 2-point leaded. How many ems of 14-point type does it contain?

4. The printed matter on a page is 23 picas wide, $37\frac{1}{2}$ picas deep. If the page is set with 12-point type, 2-point leaded, how many ems of 12-point type does it contain?

5. A page contains printed matter $21\frac{1}{4}$ picas wide by 43 picas deep. How many ems of 8-point type does it contain if the type is 2-point leaded?

6. The type area on a 6-in. by 9-in. page is 5 in. by 8 in.
   a) How many ems of 10-point type with 2-point leading are there in the type area?
   b) How many ems of 6-point type with 1-point leading are there in the type area?

7. The size of a type page is 4 by 6 in. How many ems of 8-point type, double-leaded, does it contain?

8. The size of each of the 10-type pages of a pamphlet is 4 by 6 in. How many ems of 18-point leaded type does each page contain? How many ems of this size type are there in the ten pages?

9. A paragraph is set in 12-point leaded type and is 4 in. by $2\frac{3}{4}$ in. How many ems of this type does it contain?

10. The preface of a certain publication is $5\frac{1}{2}$ in. by 6 in. How many ems of 12-point leaded type does it contain?

CHAPTER 17

Mathematics Applied to Printing—II

17.1 Size and Weight of Paper

Although there are a great many kinds of papers, their sizes (length and width) and weights have been standardized into relatively few groups. The papers in these groups have standard sizes, and a ream (500 sheets) of these papers has a standard weight. These standard sizes are called *basis sizes* and the standard weights of 500 sheets are called *basis weights*. When paper stock is ordered, in addition to specifying the particular brand, kind of paper, and quantity, the size of the sheets and their weights per ream must be given. The weights can also be specified for 1000 sheets **(M)**.

For example, a particular kind of bond paper may be listed in the catalog of a particular paper-supply house as:

Basis	17 × 22	16	20	24

$$\frac{22 \times 34}{35 \times 45} \qquad \frac{32}{67\frac{1}{2}} \qquad \frac{40}{84} \qquad \frac{48}{101}$$

The significance of these numbers is as follows:
The numbers in the box, reading:

Basis	17 × 22	16	20	24

mean that this particular paper comes in a size 17 in. by 22 in., and in basis weights of 16, 20, and 24 lb. per ream. The underlined number, 22, denotes the dimension along which the grain of the paper runs.

The numbers 22 × 34 in the first row below the box which reads

$$22 \times 34 \qquad 32 \qquad 40 \qquad 48$$

indicate that the size of the paper is 22 × 34, and that the grain of the paper is in the direction of the 22-in. dimension. The numbers

$$32 \qquad 40 \qquad 48$$

in this row are the weights of a ream of paper of size 22 × 34, and are *twice* the weights appearing above them in the box. This is due to the fact that a size 22 × 34 sheet is twice as big as a size 17 × 22 sheet, and hence weighs twice as much. These numbers are called *substance* numbers.

In like manner, the numbers 35 × 45 in the second row below the box, which reads

$$35 \times 45 \qquad 67\tfrac{1}{2} \qquad 84 \qquad 101$$

indicate that the size of the paper is 35 × 45, and that the grain of the paper runs along the 45-in. dimension. The numbers

$$67\tfrac{1}{2} \qquad 84 \qquad 101$$

are the *substance* weights or weights of a ream of this size paper but whose basis size is 17 × 22 and whose basis weights are the numbers in the box directly above each of them.

The substance weights can be easily computed for any particular brand and size of paper, if one knows the basis size and weight of that paper.

As an illustration, let us find the weight of a ream of the same brand of bond paper discussed above, but having a size 35 × 45. We can reason out this problem in the following way. If the paper whose weight is wanted is *larger* than the basis size, it should weigh *more* than the basis weight; if it is *smaller,* it should weigh *less.* If we could find what *ratio* the new size is to the basis size, we could multiply this ratio by the basis weight and get the weight required. We can put this into a convenient and useful formula in the following manner

$$\text{Weight of specific size of paper} = \frac{\text{Basis weight}}{\text{Basis size}} \times \text{Size of specific paper}$$

The following examples will illustrate the use of this formula:

■ **EXAMPLE 1:**

If the basis size and weight of a particular kind of bond paper are 17 × 22–20, what is the weight of a ream of the same kind of paper whose size is 35 × 45?

Solution and Explanation:

Here the basis size is 17 × 22, the basis weight is 20 lb. and the size of the specific paper is 35 × 45. Substituting these values into the formula, we obtain:

$$\text{Weight of specific size of paper} = \frac{\text{Basis weight}}{\text{Basis size}} \times \text{Size of specific paper}$$

$$\text{Weight of specific size of paper} = \frac{\overset{10}{\cancel{20}}}{17 \times \underset{11}{\cancel{22}}} \times 35 \times 45$$

$$\text{Weight of specific size of paper} = \frac{15{,}750}{187}$$

$$= 84.2 \text{ lb.}$$

The answer is given as 84 lb. Hence the weight of one ream of 35 × 45 paper of 20-lb. basis weight is 84 lb. This paper can be specified as 35 × 45–84 paper.

■ EXAMPLE 2:

A certain brand of text paper is described as basis 25 × 38–70. How much does a ream of this paper weigh if the size of each sheet of the ream is $22\frac{1}{2} \times 35$?

Solution and Explanation:

Here we know that the basis size is 25 × 38, the basis weight is 70 lb., and the specific size of the paper is $22\frac{1}{2} \times 35$. Using the formula

$$\text{Weight of specific size of paper} = \frac{\text{Basis weight}}{\text{Basis size}} \times \text{Size of specific paper}$$

Substituting into this formula, we have

$$\text{Weight of specific size of paper} = \frac{70}{25 \times 38} \times 22\frac{1}{2} \times 35$$

$$= \frac{\overset{\overset{7}{\cancel{14}}}{\cancel{70}}}{\underset{\underset{1}{\cancel{5}}}{\cancel{25}} \times 38} \times \frac{\overset{9}{\cancel{45}}}{\underset{1}{\cancel{2}}} \times 35$$

$$= \frac{7 \times 9 \times 35}{38}$$

$$= \frac{2205}{38}$$

$$= 58.0 \text{ or } 58 \text{ lb.}$$

Hence the weight of a ream of the specific paper whose size is $22\frac{1}{2} \times 35$ is 58 lb. This paper would then be specified $22\frac{1}{2} \times 35$–58.

It is important to point out that there is another method of specifying and ordering paper stock; this was briefly mentioned in the first paragraph of this section.

This method uses the weight of *1000 sheets* in the specification of paper stock. It is used by the Government Printing Office and by some of the paper-supply houses and eventually is expected to supplant the ream basis of ordering. Using this method, a particular bond paper, for example, would be specified (in part) as 17 × 22–40M. Here the M is the Roman numeral for 1000; hence 17 × 22–40M tells us that the size of the paper is $17 \times \underline{22}$ and that *the weight of 1000 sheets* is 40 lb. (*One ream* of this paper would weigh 20 lb.)

Suppose that we wish to order 3000 sheets of this bond paper. A complete specification would include:

a) the number of sheets of paper,

b) the size of each sheet (dimensions are in inches),

c) the weight in pounds of 1000 sheets,

d) the color of the paper,

e) the brand name of the paper,

f) the cost in dollars and cents per 100 lb. (cwt) of the paper.

Hence we would write:

3000 sheets $17 \times \underline{22}$–40M white ——————————— bond at
(brand name)

——————————/cwt. For other papers their finish would be given also.
(cost)

A formula similar to the one used above may be given when the weight of 1000 sheets is specified. This formula is:

$$\text{Weight of 1000 sheets of specific size paper} = \frac{\text{Weight of 1000 sheets of basis size}}{\text{Basis size}} \times \text{Size of specific paper}$$

These examples will illustrate the use of this formula:

■ **EXAMPLE 1:**

A particular brand of book paper is specified (in part) as $25 \times \underline{38}$–100M. What is the weight of 1000 sheets of this paper having a size $35 \times \underline{45}$?

Solution and Explanation:

Using the formula based on 1000 sheets we have:

$$\text{Weight of 1000 sheets of specific size paper} = \frac{\text{Weight of 1000 sheets of basis size}}{\text{Basis size}} \times \text{Size of specific paper}$$

$$= \frac{\overset{\overset{2}{\cancel{4}}}{\cancel{100}}}{\underset{1}{\cancel{25}} \times \underset{19}{\cancel{38}}} \times 35 \times 45$$

$$= \frac{70 \times 45}{19}$$

$$= 165.8$$

$$= 166 \text{ lb.}$$

Hence the weight of 1000 sheets of this paper size 35 × 45 is 166 lb. It would be specified (in part) as 35 × 45–166M.

■ **EXAMPLE 2:**

A certain brand of offset paper is specified as 25 × 38–160M. What is the weight of 1000 sheets of this paper having a size of 23 × 29?

Solution and Explanation:

Using the formula based on 1000 sheets we have:

$$\begin{array}{l} \text{Weight of 1000} \\ \text{sheets of specific} \\ \text{size paper} \end{array} = \frac{\text{Weight of 1000 sheets of basis size}}{\text{Basis size}} \times \begin{array}{l} \text{Size of} \\ \text{specific} \\ \text{paper} \end{array}$$

$$= \frac{\overset{\overset{\displaystyle 16}{\cancel{32}}}{\cancel{160}}}{\underset{5}{\cancel{25}} \times \underset{19}{\cancel{38}}} \times 23 \times 29$$

$$= \frac{16 \times 23 \times 29}{5 \times 19}$$

$$= 112.3$$

$$= 112 \text{ lb.}$$

Hence the weight of 1000 sheets of this paper size 23 × 29 is 112 lb. It would be specified (in part) as 23 × 29–112M.

■ **EXAMPLE 3:**

What is the weight of 3500 sheets of 17 × 22–40M white bond paper?

Solution and Explanation:

The designation 17 × 22–40M tells us that the weight of 1000 sheets is 40 lb. Since 3500 is the same as 3.5 thousands, the weight of 3500 sheets is 40 × 3.5 = 140 lb. Hence the weight of 3500 sheets of this paper is 140 lb.

17.2 Problems Involving Computation of Weights of Paper Stock

1. If the basis size and weight of a coated book is 25 × 38–50, what is the weight of a ream of the same paper whose size is 35 × 45?

2. The basis size and weight of a duplicating paper is 17 × 22–16. What does a ream of this paper weigh if its size is 17 × 28?

3. A certain brand of safety paper for bank checks is designated basis 17 × 22–24. What does one ream of this paper weigh if its size

is 24 by 38? What is the weight of six reams of this paper?

4. The basis size and weight of a certain brand of cover paper are 20 × 26–50. Calculate the weight of a ream of the same kind of paper whose size is 23 × 35.

5. A certain brand of document paper is designated basis 24 × 36–100. What is the weight of one ream of this paper if its size is $22\frac{1}{2} \times 28\frac{1}{2}$?

6. The basis size and weight of a certain type of bond paper is 17 × 22–20. Find the weight of one and of six reams of this paper whose size is 28 × 34.

7. If a certain type of index bristol stock is designated $25\frac{1}{2} \times 30\frac{1}{2}$–140, what is the weight of 125 sheets of this stock? of 750 sheets?

8. The basis weight and size of a certain brand of uncoated printing paper is 25 × 38–70. What is the weight of 12 reams of this paper?

9. The basis size and weight of a certain brand of ledger paper is 17 × 22–36. What is the weight of three reams of this paper of size 19 × 24?

10. The basis size and weight of a certain brand of offset paper is 25 × 38–100. Find the weight of three reams of this type of paper of size 35 × 45.

11. Compute the weight of 1500 sheets of 25 × 38–120M uncoated book paper.

12. What is the weight of 1000 sheets of the same kind of paper as in Problem 11 if the size of the sheets is 38 × 50?

13. Find the weight of three cartons (12 reams) of 17 × 22–64M ledger paper.

14. What is the weight of one carton (4 reams) of 17 × 22–32M bond paper?

15. A bond paper is specified as 17 × 22–40M. What is the weight of 1000 sheets of this paper if the size of the sheets is 24 × 38?

16. A man ordered 18 reams of white duplicating paper 17 × 22–40M. What is the total weight of this paper?

17.3 Cutting Paper Stock

Paper and related stock used for printing is bought in large sheets. When orders are received by the printer for a particular job, it is usually necessary for him to cut the paper to the size specified by the customer. In doing this, he must determine the best way to cut the paper stock so as to obtain the greatest number of sheets of the required job size with the least amount of waste and with a minimum amount of time and effort.

The calculation of the number of sheets of a given size that may be cut from a given stock sheet can be done by

Method A: a simple arithmetical procedure, in which the size of the stock sheet is compared with the size of the job sheet. (The calculations using *Method A* are done in *two ways* in order to determine which way will provide the largest number of job sheets from each stock sheet.)

Method B: making a layout or diagram which will show the number of job size sheets and their arrangement on the stock size sheet and the area of the stock sheet that is left over. *This is used as a check on Method A.*

These two methods, worked together, should be used in doing this type of work.

In applying *Method A* above, we write a fraction whose numerator is the size of the *stock sheet* and whose denominator is the size of the *job sheet*. Then, by using a process similar to cancellation (which may be done in two ways), we can determine how many job sheets are obtainable from each stock sheet with the minimum waste. After this has been accomplished, a layout or diagram should also be made. This will serve as a check on the arithmetic and should keep errors to a minimum. It should be noted that the direction of the grain in the stock sheet may have to be considered.

A cut called a "Dutch cut" is sometimes obtained if one or more pieces of the required dimensions can be obtained by using the material remaining, provided the grain direction is not of essential importance.

Method A can be put into the form of a formula as follows:

$$\frac{\text{No. of job sheets cut}}{\text{from one stock sheet}} = \frac{\text{Size of stock sheet}}{\text{Size of job sheet}}$$

The following examples will illustrate the application of this formula. Dimensions in the examples and problems are in inches.

■ **EXAMPLE 1:**

A printer wishes to cut forms having a size $4\frac{1}{4} \times 11$ from stock sheets size 17×22. How many forms of this size can be cut from each stock sheet?

Solution and Explanation:

Method A (First Way). The basic formula is:

No. of job sheets cut from one stock sheet $= \dfrac{\text{Size of stock sheet}}{\text{Size of job sheet}}$

Substituting the known sizes into this formula we obtain:

No. of job sheets cut from one stock sheet $= \dfrac{17 \times 22}{4\frac{1}{4} \times 11}$

We now divide the $4\frac{1}{4}$ in the denominator and the 17 in the numerator by $4\frac{1}{4}$, writing 1 under the $4\frac{1}{4}$ and 4 above the 17. We next divide the 11 in the denominator and the 22 in the numerator by 11, writing 1 under the 11 and 2 above the 22.

The work appears thus at this stage

$$\text{No. of job sheets cut from one stock sheet} = \dfrac{\overset{4}{\cancel{17}} \times \overset{2}{\cancel{22}}}{\underset{1}{\cancel{4\frac{1}{4}}} \times \underset{1}{\cancel{11}}} = 8$$

The 8 after the equal sign to the right of the fraction is the product of the 4 by the 2 in the numerator.

It is now evident that, using this method of cutting, it will be possible to get eight forms size $4\frac{1}{4} \times 11$ from each stock sheet. This method may be called *the method of vertical division or first way.*

Method A (Second Way). We now use the *second way* of Method A, or the "cross-division" method to determine *which of the two will give more job sheets from each stock sheet.*

Starting as before, we have

No. of job sheets cut from one stock sheet $= \dfrac{17 \times 22}{4\frac{1}{4} \times 11}$

This time we divide the $4\frac{1}{4}$ in the denominator and the 22 in the numerator by $4\frac{1}{4}$. We divide the 11 in the denominator and the 17 in the numerator by 11. We write 5 above the 22 and 1 above the 17. In addition to this, we write $\frac{3}{4}$ above the 5 in the numerator and 6 above the 1 in the numerator. (These are the remainders.) The product of 1 by 5, which is 5, we write at the right of the fraction. The work appears thus at this stage:

$$\text{No. of job sheets cut from one stock sheet} = \dfrac{\overset{6}{\underset{1}{\cancel{17}}} \times \overset{\frac{3}{4}}{\underset{5}{\cancel{22}}}}{\underset{1}{\cancel{4\frac{1}{4}}} \times \underset{1}{\cancel{11}}} = 5$$

This method of division shows that the 22-in. dimension of the stock sheet can be cut into 5 equal spaces each $4\frac{1}{4}$ in. long, with $\frac{3}{4}$ in. remaining.

In addition, it shows that the 17-in. dimension of the stock sheet can be divided into one space 11 in. long with 6 in. remaining. This means that five job sheets size $4\frac{1}{4} \times 11$ can be cut from one stock sheet by the second way of Method A. The strip, 6 in. wide and 22 in. long, is left unused. A smaller strip, $\frac{3}{4}$ in. wide along part of the 17-in. dimension of the stock sheet, will also be left unused.

We have now completed the computations according to *both ways* of *Method A*. It appears that using the *first way,* we will be able to get eight job sheets from each stock sheet, with no material left over. Using the *second way* we will get five job sheets from each stock sheet, with considerable material left over. From this leftover material we can cut two more job sheets, getting a total of seven.

To verify these conclusions, and check our work at the same time, we now make use of Method B.

Method B. Using this method, we make a layout (preferably to some convenient scale) of each of the two ways of Method A.

Using the *first way* of Method A, the layout appears as shown in Figure 292.

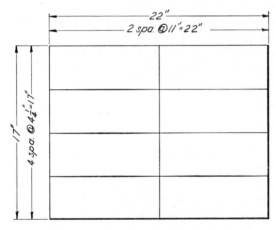

Fig. 292.

Layout Showing How 8 Forms Size
$4\frac{1}{4}" \times 11"$ Can Be Cut From 1 Stock Sheet
Size 17"×22"

This layout shows that eight pieces of the required size can be cut from each stock sheet size 17×22 with no waste. It is a check on the arithmetic and should always be made.

Using the *second way* of Method A, the layout appears as shown in Figure 293.

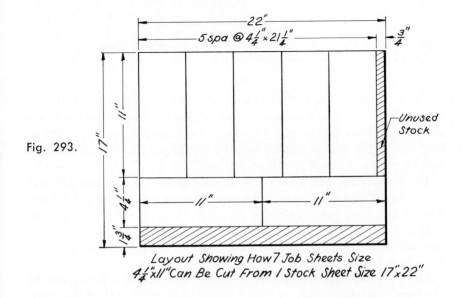

Fig. 293.

Layout Showing How 7 Job Sheets Size
4¼"x11"Can Be Cut From 1 Stock Sheet Size 17"x22"

We can see clearly that we can obtain a total of seven job sheets from each stock sheet, with some material unused. This layout verifies our computation, and, like the previous layout, should always be made.

Of these two ways of cutting the stock sheet, we select the *first* way, which gives us eight job sheets from each stock sheet.

■ EXAMPLE 2:

How many office cards 4 × 6 can be cut from an index bristol size $20\frac{1}{2} \times 24\frac{3}{4}$?

Solution and Explanation:

Since we know the size of the stock sheet and the size of the office cards (which are the "job sheets" in the formula) we can write:

$$\text{No. of job sheets cut from one stock sheet} = \frac{\text{Size of stock sheet}}{\text{Size of job sheet}}$$

$$= \frac{20\frac{1}{2} \times 24\frac{3}{4}}{4 \times 6}$$

As stated above, we can divide the numerator and the denominator of this fraction in two ways.

Method A (First Way). We divide the 4 in the denominator and the $20\frac{1}{2}$ in the numerator by 4. We also divide the 6 in the denominator and the $24\frac{3}{4}$ in the numerator by 6. The work appears as follows:

$$\text{No. of job sheets cut from one stock sheet} = \frac{\overset{\frac{1}{2}}{\overset{5}{\cancel{20\tfrac{1}{2}}}} \times \overset{\frac{3}{4}}{\overset{4}{\cancel{24\tfrac{3}{4}}}}}{\underset{1}{\cancel{4}} \times \underset{1}{\cancel{6}}} = 20$$

The 5 above the $20\tfrac{1}{2}$ is the whole number of times 4 goes into $20\tfrac{1}{2}$. The $\tfrac{1}{2}$ above this 5 is the amount left over when the $20\tfrac{1}{2}$-in. dimension was divided into five equal lengths 4 in. long. The strip $\tfrac{1}{2}$ in. wide and $24\tfrac{3}{4}$ in. long that is left over or unused may be considered as waste or scrap or may be put on the shelf for future odd jobs.

The 4 above the $24\tfrac{3}{4}$ is the whole number of times 6 goes into $24\tfrac{3}{4}$, and the $\tfrac{3}{4}$ above this 4 is the amount left over when the $24\tfrac{3}{4}$-in. dimension was divided into four equal lengths 6 in. long. (This provides a strip $\tfrac{3}{4}$ in. wide and 20 in. long running along the short side of the paper which is also not used.) Multiplying the 5 by the 4 in the numerator we obtain 20, which is written to the right of the fraction line.

The 20 represents the number of office cards size 4×6 that can be cut from one stock sheet of index bristol size $20\tfrac{1}{2} \times 24\tfrac{3}{4}$ if the cards were cut according to *this* particular method.

Method A (Second Way). In the second way of cutting the stock sheet, the formula is written as before:

$$\text{No. of job sheets cut from one stock sheet} = \frac{20\tfrac{1}{2} \times 24\tfrac{3}{4}}{4 \times 6}$$

but this time we divide the 4 in the denominator and the 24 in the numerator by 4. We also divide the 6 in the denominator and the 20 in the numerator by 6. The result appears thus:

$$\text{No. of job sheets cut from one stock sheet} = \frac{\overset{2\tfrac{1}{2}}{\overset{3}{\cancel{20\tfrac{1}{2}}}} \times \overset{\frac{3}{4}}{\overset{6}{\cancel{24\tfrac{3}{4}}}}}{\underset{1}{\cancel{4}} \times \underset{1}{\cancel{6}}} = 18$$

The 3 in the numerator above the $20\tfrac{1}{2}$ represents the whole number of times 6 goes into 20. The 6 in the numerator above the $24\tfrac{3}{4}$ represents the whole number of times 4 goes into 24.

The $2\tfrac{1}{2}$ above the 3 in the numerator represents the number of inches in the $20\tfrac{1}{2}$-in. dimension of the stock sheet that remains unused. The $\tfrac{3}{4}$ above the 6 in the numerator represents the number of inches left unused in the $24\tfrac{3}{4}$ dimension of the stock sheet.

Multiplying the 3 and the 6 in the numerator together, we obtain 18. This is the number of office cards size 4×6 that can be cut from one stock sheet of index bristol size $20\frac{1}{2} \times 24\frac{3}{4}$ if the cards were cut according to this *second way.*

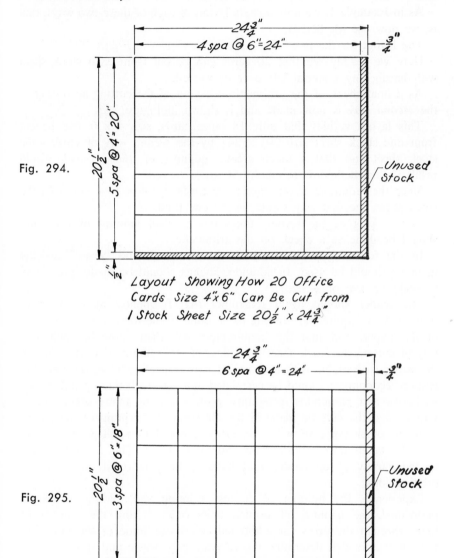

Fig. 294.

Layout Showing How 20 Office Cards Size 4″x 6″ Can Be Cut from I Stock Sheet Size $20\frac{1}{2}$″ x $24\frac{3}{4}$″

Fig. 295.

Layout Showing How 18 Office Cards 4″x 6″ Can Be Cut From I Stock Sheet Size $20\frac{1}{2}$″x $24\frac{1}{2}$″

It is apparent that there would be two more cards cut from each stock sheet if they were cut according to the *first way*.

As in Example 1, we now make a layout of each of these two ways, that is, we now use Method B.

The layout for the *first way* of cutting is shown in Figure 294.

Here we readily see that 20 cards can be cut from each stock sheet with hardly any material left over or wasted.

As a final check of the arithmetic, a layout of the cutting according to the *second way* is now made and is shown in Figure 295.

This layout verifies that only 18 office cards, size 4×6, can be cut from one stock sheet size $20\frac{1}{4} \times 24\frac{3}{4}$ by the *second way* of cutting the stock sheet and that a much greater quantity of unused stock would result if this method were employed.

Since the requirement was that office cards size 4×6 be cut from the stock sheet, the first way would be the one used.

The making of the layouts takes but a small amount of time and should be done as a check on the arithmetic.

In the following problems, both the "vertical" and "cross" division methods should be used. In addition, layouts should be made, preferably to scale ($\frac{1}{2}$ size or $\frac{1}{4}$ size).

The reader should again remember that frequently many types of printing jobs require the printing to be done in the *direction of the grain* of the paper, and that this requirement will then allow for only one way of cutting the stock sheet regardless of the amount of waste. Thus if the paper is available with a choice of two grain directions, the one that is more economical should be calculated and specified. Such printing jobs as books and pamphlets, programs, posters, among many others, often require that the cuts be made in the direction of the grain of the paper.

As in other types of work, a certain amount of spoilage and waste must be taken into consideration and allowed for. This is in part due to the variety of operations that have to be performed on particular printing jobs.

Experience, the number of cutting, printing and folding operations performed, the quantity of printed units ordered, and the number of times through the press for additional colors are some of the most important factors that determine the allowance for waste and spoilage.

17.4 Problems Involving the Cutting of Paper Stock*

1. How many sheets size $5\frac{1}{2} \times 8\frac{1}{2}$ in. can be cut from one stock sheet size $17 \times \underline{22}$? How many can be cut from a ream of stock sheets $17 \times \underline{22}$? (One ream $= 500$ sheets.)

---
* In these problems the dimensions are in inches.

2. How many cards size 3 × 5 can be cut from one sheet of bristol index size $20\frac{1}{2}$ × $24\frac{3}{4}$? How many can be cut from 1000 sheets of this size index bristol?

3. A ream of stock size 17 × 22 is to be used to cut office forms size $5\frac{1}{2}$ × $8\frac{1}{4}$. How many such forms can be cut from one sheet? From the entire ream?

4. A firm wants 1000 notices printed on 7 × $8\frac{1}{2}$ paper. If the size of the stock is 17 × 22, how many stock sheets will be needed?

5. A printer wishes to use 10,000 sheets size 7 × 17 for advertising. If the stock used to cut this has a size 28 × 34, how many stock sheets will be needed?

6. Two hundred scratch pads are to be made by cutting paper stock size $8\frac{1}{2}$ × 11 into size $4\frac{1}{4}$ × $5\frac{1}{2}$. Each pad is to have 50 sheets. How many sheets of the paper stock will be needed?

7. Ten thousand pamphlets are to be put together using 16 sheets, size 9 × 12, which will print into 32 pages. If these sheets are to be cut from stock size 38 × 50, how many stock sheets will be needed for one pamphlet? For the 10,000 pamphlets? Allow 10 percent spoilage for printing and binding.

8. A company places an order with a printer for 10,000 statements, size $5\frac{1}{2}$ in. by $8\frac{1}{2}$ in. The printer cuts these statements from stock sheets, size 35 × 45. How many statements can be cut from one stock sheet? How many stock sheets will be used for the 10,000 statements?

9. A printer received an order for 5000 announcements, size 6 × 9, to be printed on one side. If he cut these announcements from stock size 25 × 38, how many stock sheets did he need? Allow 5 percent for spoilage and waste.

10. A manufacturer orders 10,000 advertising leaflets consisting of one sheet printed on both sides and folded so as to have four pages of printed matter. If the size of the sheet before folding is $5\frac{1}{2}$ × 17, and the stock sheet has a size 17 × 22, how many stock sheets will be needed for 10,000 leaflets? Allow 10 percent for spoilage.

17.5   Wages in the Printing Trades

In finding the weekly earnings of workers in the printing trades, one would multiply the hourly wage rate by the number of hours per week. To find the annual earnings multiply the weekly earnings by 52, the number of weeks in a year. It should be remembered that the hourly rate of pay varies from one part of the country to another. Knowledge of wages is important not only in determining payrolls but also in estimating the cost of a job.

■ **EXAMPLE 1:**

A hand compositor working on the day shift of a newspaper in a city in one of the central states is paid $3.18 per hour and works $37\frac{1}{2}$ hr. per week. What are his weekly earnings? On the basis of 52 weeks, what are his annual earnings?

Solution and Explanation:

To find the weekly earnings, multiply hourly rate by the number of hours worked per week.

$$\$3.18 \times 37\frac{1}{2} = \$3.18 \times 37.5 = \$119.25$$

To find the yearly earnings, multiply this amount by 52.

$$\$119.25 \times 52 = \$6201.00$$

Hence, the weekly earnings of the compositor are $119.25 and his yearly earnings are $6201.00.

■ **EXAMPLE 2:**

A photoengraver working on the day shift of a newspaper in a metropolitan city in one of the central states is paid $4.95 per hour and works 36 hr. per week. Find his weekly and yearly earnings if he works 52 weeks per year.

Solution and Explanation:

His weekly earnings, as in Example 1, are found by multiplying his hourly rate of pay by the number of hours he works per week. This is:

$$\$4.95 \times 36 = \$178.20$$

His yearly earnings are found by multiplying this amount by 52:

$$\$178.20 \times 52 = \$9,266.40$$

The photoengraver, therefore, earns $178.20 per week and $9,266.40 per year.

17.6   Problems Involving Computation of Wages

1. While working on a job a printer received $5.60 per hour and an apprentice $2.50 per hour. If each worked 36 hr. per week for three weeks what did each earn?

2. A printing shop has five printers, each being paid $4.75 per hour. If they work 36 hr. per week what does each earn during this time? What are their combined earnings?

3. During the second half of the first year of his training, a type-setter's apprentice received 45 percent of a journeyman typesetter's wages.

If the journeyman's hourly rate was $3.60, what was the apprentice's hourly rate?

4. During the second half of the third year of his apprenticeship, the apprentice in Problem 3 received 65 percent of the journeyman's hourly wages. What were his hourly earnings then? What would he earn in a 36-hr. week? in 52 such weeks?

5. During the last six months of his six years of apprenticeship, the the apprentice in Problem 3 received 95 percent of the journeyman's hourly wages. What were his hourly earnings? How much would he earn in a 36-hr. week? in 52 such weeks?

6. A journeyman printer works 36 hr. per week at the rate of $5.20 per hour. What are his gross earnings (no deductions) per week? What are his gross earnings for 52 weeks?

7. An apprentice printer works 36 hr. per week at $3.20 per hour. What does he earn in 26 weeks?

8. A journeyman printer works 36 hr. per week at the rate of $4.50 per hour. What are his gross weekly earnings? What are his gross earnings every two weeks?

9. A printing shop uses three printers for 30 hr. to complete a job. If each printer is paid at the rate of $4.90 per hour, what is the total cost of their time?

10. What are the gross earnings for 52 weeks of a printer working 36 hr. per week at $6.00 per hour?

Unit V
SHOP FORMULAS

CHAPTER 18

Speed Formulas

18.1 Introduction

This chapter deals with the applications of mathematics to problems arising in a shop. Many such problems can be frequently solved by the use of common sense. Others require some amount of arithmetic and a knowledge of evaluating formulas. In this kind of work one should use every precaution to avoid mistakes. Answers that are wrong are worse than no answers at all. When one has performed a computation, he should always stop and make some kind of a check to see if his work is free from mistakes. The time spent in doing this will be more than worth it. The checking of every problem should become a permanent habit for all, students as well as workmen.

18.2 What a Formula Is

Formulas commonly used by workers in the various trades are called *shop formulas. A shop formula is a statement, in mathematical form, of a rule for computing the value of some quantity.* When this rule is stated in mathematical form, certain letters of the alphabet are used to represent the number values of the quantities in the formula. These letters are connected by numbers and mathematical signs which tell us what we should do with the quantities in the formulas, that is, whether we should add, subtract, multiply, divide, square, take square roots, or perform a combination of these operations.

Formulas are used in every branch of engineering, in the trades and in the shops. Among the most useful abilities a student can acquire in his mathematical work is the ability to evaluate formulas without making mistakes.

We may liken a formula to a recipe. A recipe not only tells us the kind and amount of ingredients to use, but also what to do with the ingredients. A recipe would be worthless unless it met these two requirements. In the same way, unless the quantities appearing in a formula are connected by mathematical signs, and unless we know the values of all the quantities *except one,* the formulas could not be *evaluated* and would be almost useless. By evaluating a formula, we mean finding the numerical value of *one* of the quantities represented by a letter in the formula when *all* the others are known.

Consider the following illustration. We know from geometry that the circumference of a circle is approximately 3.1416 times its diameter. Using the letter D to represent the length of the diameter and the letter

C to represent the length of the circumference, we can state this rule in the form of a formula as follows

$$C = 3.1416D.$$

It will be noticed that, in writing this formula, the multiplication sign has been omitted between the numerical value 3.1416 and the letter D. Multiplication signs are usually omitted in formulas where a number and a letter or two or more letters are *multiplied* together. Thus $2ab$ means 2 times a times b. If there is any possibility of misunderstanding, however, the multiplication signs should be shown.

The number 3.1416 appears in many formulas and is represented by the Greek letter π, pronounced "pie." Standardized symbols are used to represent values which appear frequently in mathematical formulas. Technical words or terms are often abbreviated when they are used in formulas. When the abbreviations consist of two or more letters, the letters should be written close to each other. For example, the abbreviation for the expression "revolutions per minute" is written *rpm* with no period after the *m*. Here it should be pointed out that *rpm,* as used here, does *not* mean r times p times m, since *this* particular abbreviation is known to stand for "revolutions per minute." Similarly, "horsepower" is abbreviated *hp* and the writing of the letters h and p next to each other does *not* mean h times p. Usually familiarity with the symbols and formulas used will prevent any misunderstandings that might arise.

In mechanical engineering, a formula that enables one to compute the number of horsepower developed by a given force, $F,$ moving uniformly through a distance d in a time $t,$ is

$$hp = \frac{Fd}{550t}$$

Here, hp = the number of horsepower developed

$\quad\quad F$ = force in pounds

$\quad\quad d$ = distance in feet through which the force F moves

$\quad\quad t$ = time in seconds

The person evaluating this formula would clearly understand that hp did not mean h times p but stood, instead, for the abbreviation for "horsepower." The formulas that we are dealing with in this book can all be evaluated if we know the numerical values of all the quantities represented by the letters except one, as already stated above.

In the formulas $C = 3.1416D$ and $hp = \dfrac{Fd}{550t}$, C and hp are called the *subject* of each formula respectively. In evaluating a formula, we *usually* wish to find the numerical value of the *subject* of the formula.

It is possible to change the subject of a formula, and obtain a new formula from the original one. Thus, if we take the formula $C = 3.1416D$ and divide both sides of it by 3.1416, we get:

$$\frac{C}{3.1416} = \frac{\overset{1}{\cancel{3.1416}D}}{\underset{1}{\cancel{3.1416}}}$$

$$\frac{C}{3.1416} = D$$

or
$$\boxed{D = \frac{C}{3.1416}}$$

If we had used the form $C = \pi D$ and divided both sides by π, we would have:

$$\frac{C}{\pi} = \frac{\overset{1}{\cancel{\pi}D}}{\underset{1}{\cancel{\pi}}}$$

or
$$\boxed{D = \frac{C}{\pi}}$$

We have now changed the subject of the original formula. It is now D, the diameter. If we know the numerical value of C, we can use this new formula directly to find the numerical value of D.

The following examples will illustrate the use of these formulas.

■ **EXAMPLE 1:**

The diameter of a pulley is 30 in. What is its circumference?

Solution and Explanation:

Since we know how big the diameter is, we can find the circumference by using the formula $C = 3.1416D$. Replacing D by its numerical value, 30, we have:

$$C = 3.1416 \times 30$$
$$C = 94.248 \text{ in. or}$$
$$C = 94\tfrac{1}{4} \text{ in.}$$

Hence the circumference of a pulley 30 in. in diameter is $94\tfrac{1}{4}$ in.

■ **EXAMPLE 2:**

What is the diameter of one of the cables used to support a bridge if its circumference is $73\tfrac{3}{4}$ in.?

Solution and Explanation:

Here, since the circumference is known, and we wish to find the diameter D, we use the formula:

$$D = \frac{C}{3.1416}$$

Substituting $73\frac{3}{4}$ or 73.75 for C, we have:

$$D = \frac{73.75}{3.1416}$$

$$D = 23.475 \text{ in.}$$

$$\text{or} \quad D = 23\frac{15}{32} \text{ in.}$$

In the design, production, and manufacture of machine parts dimensions are usually given to at least three decimal places. This means that the computations must be carried out to four decimal places and then rounded off to three decimal places. For certain machine operations such as grinding, dimensions are given to four decimal places. Computations involving such operations would then have to be carried out to five decimal places and rounded off to four decimal places. Measuring tools and gauges are available by means of which measurements can be made to 0.001 of an inch or 0.0001 of an inch or to even higher degrees of precision.

18.3 Surface Speeds and Cutting Speeds

The formula for the length of the circumference of a circle can be used in computing the *surface* or *peripheral speeds* of pulleys and drills. It can also be used in the computation of the *cutting speeds* of lathe tools, milling cutters, circular saws, grinding wheels and other revolving tools.

Surface or peripheral speed is usually expressed in *feet per minute* (fpm), and is equal to the distance in feet through which a point on the circumference moves in one minute. This distance is equal to the *length of the circumference* in feet *multiplied* by the number of *revolutions per minute*.

If we use the letter S to represent *surface speed* in *feet per minute*, and "rpm" to represent the *number of revolutions per minute*, then the *shop formula* connecting these quantities is:

$$S = \text{Circumference in feet} \times \text{rpm}$$

$$\text{or} \quad S = 3.1416 \times \text{diameter in feet} \times \text{rpm}$$

However, the diameters of drills, pulleys, and stock are given in inches. It is a simple matter to change the formula to give the surface speed directly when the diameter is given in inches. Since there are 12 in. in 1 ft., we can write the formula as:

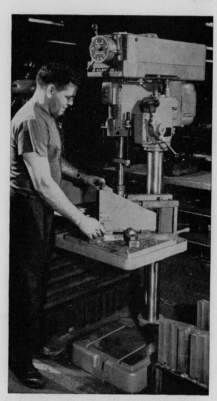

A drill press.

Clausing

$$S = \frac{3.1416 \times \text{diameter in inches} \times \text{rpm}}{12}$$

Now $\dfrac{3.1416}{12} = 0.2618$, hence we can write the formula in the convenient form:

$$\boxed{S = 0.2618 \times D \times \text{rpm}}$$

In this formula, S = surface speed in feet per minute
D = diameter in inches
rpm = revolutions per minute

In computations involving the surface speeds of saws, revolving cutting tools or of metal stock revolving against a cutting tool, the surface speed is referred to as *cutting speed*. In computations involving belts, gear and pulley speeds, it is referred to as *surface speed*.

The following problems will illustrate the use of this formula.

A grinder attachment used in a lathe.

Clausing

■ EXAMPLE 1:

A grinding wheel 8 in. in diameter turns at 1750 rpm. What is its surface speed?

Solution and Explanation:

The formula for surface speed is $S = 0.2618 \times D \times \text{rpm}$. In our problem

$$D = 8 \text{ in.}$$
$$\text{rpm} = 1750$$

Therefore: $S = 0.2618 \times 8 \times 1750$

or $S = 3665 \text{ fpm}$

Therefore, the surface speed of this wheel is 3665 fpm.

This same shop formula can be used to find the diameter in inches when the surface speed in feet per minute and the number of rpm is known. If we divide both sides of the original formula $S = 0.2618 \times D \times \text{rpm}$ by $0.2618 \times \text{rpm}$ we obtain

$$\frac{S}{0.2618 \times \text{rpm}} = \frac{\overset{1}{\cancel{0.2618}} \times D \times \overset{1}{\cancel{\text{rpm}}}}{\underset{1}{\cancel{0.2618}} \times \underset{1}{\cancel{\text{rpm}}}}$$

or $\dfrac{S}{0.2618 \times \text{rpm}} = D$, which, when we write it in the more customary manner, becomes:

$$D = \frac{S}{0.2618 \times \text{rpm}}$$

The following example illustrates how this formula may be used.

■ **EXAMPLE 2:**

What is the diameter of a line shaft pulley which has a surface speed of 1885 fpm when running at 600 rpm?

Solution and Explanation:

In this problem $S = 1885$ fpm
  and rpm $= 600$

Substituting these numbers into the formula, we obtain the following:

$$D = \frac{S}{0.2618 \times \text{rpm}}$$

$$D = \frac{1885}{0.2618 \times 600}$$

$$D = \frac{1885}{157.08} = 12 \text{ in.}$$

That is, the diameter of the pulley is 12 in. If we divide both sides of the formula $S = 0.2618 \times D \times$ rpm by $0.2618 \times D$, we obtain:

$$\frac{S}{0.2618 \times D} = \frac{\overset{1}{\cancel{0.2618}} \times \overset{}{\cancel{D}} \times \text{rpm}}{\underset{1}{\cancel{0.2618}} \times \underset{1}{\cancel{D}}}$$

or $\dfrac{S}{0.2618 \times D} = $ rpm, which, when rewritten becomes:

$$\text{rpm} = \frac{S}{0.2618 \times D}$$

This is another useful form of the original formula. The following example illustrates a typical application of this formula.

■ **EXAMPLE 3:**

What is the rpm of a flywheel 36 in. in diameter that has a surface speed of 4712 fpm.

Solution and Explanation:

In this problem we know that $D = 36$ in., and $S = 4712$ fpm. Substituting these values into the formula:

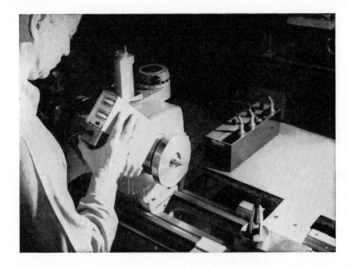

An instrument
for checking
the rpm and
smoothness of
operation of a
lathe.

Clausing

$$\text{rpm} = \frac{S}{0.2618 \times D}$$

$$\text{we have: rpm} = \frac{4712}{0.2618 \times 36}$$

$$\text{rpm} = 499.96$$

That is, the rpm of the flywheel is 500, for all practical purposes.

18.4 Problems Involving Computation of Surface Speeds, RPM, and the Circle Formula

1. The shaft of a 2-hp motor is 1 in. in diameter. If the motor turns at 1800 rpm, what is the surface speed of the shaft?

2. What is the surface speed of a 10-in. pulley turning at 300 rpm?

3. The grinding wheel on a grinder is 8 in. in diameter and turns at 1750 rpm. What is its cutting speed?

4. What is the diameter of a pulley which has a surface speed of 942 fpm when running at 900 rpm?

5. A 15-in. pulley is attached to a line shaft turning at 180 rpm. What is its surface speed?

6. What is the cutting speed of a radial saw 12 in. in diameter rotating at 3450 rpm?

7. An electric hand saw blade is $7\frac{1}{2}$ in. in diameter. If it is rotating at 4500 rpm, what is its cutting speed?

8. The circular saw blade on a swing saw is 10 in. in diameter. If it is rotating at 3450 rpm, what is its cutting speed?

9. An average recommended cutting speed for brass is 120 fpm.

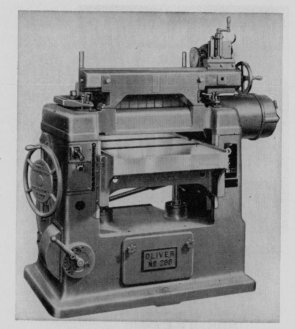

Fig. 302.
A surface planer.

Oliver Machinery Co.

If the work is 2 in. in diameter, at how many rpm should the lathe be set?

10. Compare the rim speeds of two pulleys — one 12 in. in diameter, the other 20 in. in diameter, running on the same shaft at 180 rpm.

11. What should be the rpm of a $2\frac{1}{2}$-in. milling cutter in order to obtain a cutting speed of 100 fpm?

12. The rotor of a large alternating-current generator is 40 in. in diameter. If it turns at 3600 rpm, what is its surface speed?

13. If the diameter (tip-to-tip length) of the propeller of a turboprop passenger plane is 10 ft. and turns at 1400 rpm, what is its surface speed?

14. The flywheel on a steam engine driving a large ventilator fan is 5 ft. in diameter and turns at 100 rpm. What is its surface speed?

15. The blades of the main motor of a helicopter are 56 ft. in diameter and turn at 258 rpm. What is their surface speed?

16. The effective cutting diameter of the blades on the surface planer in Figure 302 is $4\frac{1}{4}$ in. This machine is listed as making 3600 rpm. According to this, what is the cutting speed of the blades?

17. At a spindle speed of 550 rpm what is the cutting speed in fpm of the piece of wood 4 in. in diameter that is being turned in the wood lathe shown in Figure 303?

Fig. 303.

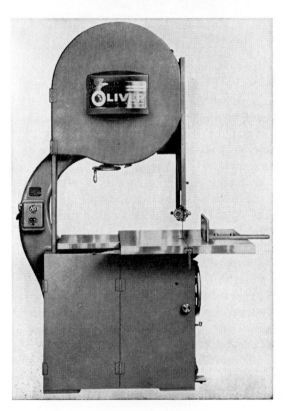

Fig. 304.   A band saw.

Oliver Machinery Co.

18. The 36-in. band saw in Figure 304 is listed as making 720 rpm. What is the cutting speed of the band saw for this number of rpm?

19. With the allowable cutting speed of 75 fpm, what is the rpm of a piece of steel $3\frac{1}{2}$ in. in diameter that is being turned in an engine lathe?

20. Calculate the belt speeds of the pulleys arranged on the shafting illustrated in Figure 305.

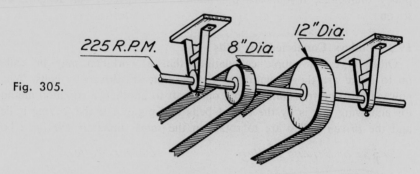

225 R.P.M.   8" Dia.   12" Dia.

Fig. 305.

21. A pulley is attached to the spindle of an induction motor turning at 860 rpm. If the pulley diameter is 8 in. what is its surface speed?

22. The diameter (tip to tip) of the propellers of a passenger airplane is 13 ft. 6 in. If these propellers turn at 2900 rpm, what is their tip surface speed?

23. If the recommended cutting speed of a high-speed steel drill $\frac{1}{2}$ in. in diameter is 70 fpm, at how many rpm must it be run?

24. A pulley is fastened to a motor running at 1200 rpm. If this pulley is to have a surface speed of 1950 ft. per second, what must be its diameter?

25. An artificial satellite had an orbital speed of 18,000 mph, and made a complete trip around the earth in 90 min., or 1.5 hr. Find the diameter in miles of its orbit, assuming the orbit was circular.

26. A satellite weighing about 8800 lb. was launched into space by the Advanced Projects Agency of the Defense Department of the United States. The orbit time of this satellite, which was actually an Atlas missile, was about 100 min. or $1\frac{2}{3}$ hr. The orbital velocity (similar to what we have called surface speed) was about 17,000 mph. Assuming that this satellite moved in a circular path, find the diameter of its orbit.

27. The American artificial satellite Explorer I had an estimated orbital velocity of about 18,400 mph and an orbit time of about 1.91 hr. If this satellite were assumed to move in a circle, what would be the diameter of its orbit?

NOTE: The orbits of these satellites were assumed to be circular for purposes of computation. Actually they traveled in elliptical orbits.

CHAPTER 19

Pulleys Connected By Belts

19.1 Introduction
The application of mathematics to pulley systems is important because many shop operations involve the use of pulleys and the calculation of pulley diameters, revolutions per minute, belt speeds, belt lengths, and so on.

19.2 Pulleys Connected by Belts
Other types of simple calculations that a workman may be called on to make are those relating to pulleys that are driven by belts. When power has to be transmitted from one shaft to another, a common method for achieving this is by the use of belts and pulleys. If the *driving* pulley and the *driven* pulley are to rotate in the *same* direction, the *open* belt

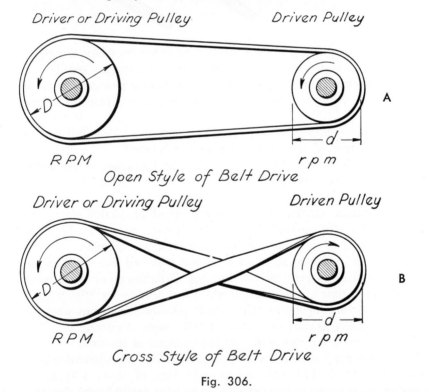

Fig. 306.

drive is used (Fig. 306A). If the driving pulley and the driven pulley rotate in *opposite* directions, the "cross" belt drive is used (Fig. 306B). To help distinguish between the diameters and speeds of the driving

Link-Belt Co.

Using V-belts to transmit power from a gasoline engine to a large compressor.

and driven pulleys we shall use *capital* letters for the driving pulley and *small* or *lower case* letters for the driven pulleys. Thus, the diameter of the driving pulley will be indicated by the capital letter *D,* while the diameter of the driven pulley will be indicated by the small letter *d.* Likewise, the number of revolutions per minute of the driving pulley will be indicated by the *capital* letters "RPM," and those of the driven pulley by the *small* letters "rpm." In the computations discussed here, the assumption will be made that the belt-driven pulleys will have the *same* surface speeds. This means that the amount of creep and slip is considered to be negligible. With this assumption, the surface speed of the *driven* pulley will equal the surface speed of the *driving* pulley.

Expressed in still another form this becomes *Surface speed of driving pulley = Surface speed of driven pulley.* We can also say that

$$\pi \times D \times RPM = \pi \times d \times rpm$$

Dividing both sides of this equation by π, we get:

$$\boxed{D \times RPM = d \times rpm}$$

This relation, stated in words as follows: *If the diameter of the driving pulley is multiplied by the number of revolutions per minute of the driving pulley, the product will equal the diameter of the driven pulley multiplied by the revolutions per minute of the driven pulley.*

There are four quantities in this fundamental relation, namely, D, RPM, d, and rpm. We can hence obtain four other useful formulas from this relation which will enable us to determine any one of the four quantities when the other three are known. These shop formulas are:

$$1.\ D = \frac{d \times \text{rpm}}{\text{RPM}}$$

$$2.\ \text{RPM} = \frac{d \times \text{rpm}}{D}$$

$$3.\ d = \frac{D \times \text{RPM}}{\text{rpm}}$$

$$4.\ \text{rpm} = \frac{D \times \text{RPM}}{d}$$

The following problems will illustrate the use of these formulas.

■ **EXAMPLE 1:**

A motor running at 1750 RPM is to drive a 20-in. pulley on a shaft that runs at 350 rpm. What size pulley should be used on the motor?

Solution and Explanation:

In this problem we know that:
   a) the diameter of the driven pulley = 20 in.
   b) the rpm of the driven pulley = 350
   c) the RPM of the driving pulley = 1750
To find D, the diameter of the driving pulley, we use Formula 1 above:

$$D = \frac{d \times \text{rpm}}{\text{RPM}}$$

Substituting the known values, we obtain:

$$D = \frac{\overset{4}{\cancel{20}} \times \overset{1}{\cancel{350}}}{\underset{\underset{1}{\cancel{5}}}{\cancel{1750}}} = 4 \text{ in.}$$

Hence the diameter of the driving pulley is 4 in.

■ **EXAMPLE 2:**

At what RPM is a 4-in. pulley running if it drives a 20-in. pulley at 170 rpm?

Solution and Explanation:

Here we know that $D = 4$ in.; $d = 20$ in.; rpm $= 170$, and we wish to find the RPM of the driving pulley. Using Formula 2, we have:

$$RPM = \frac{d \times rpm}{D}$$

$$RPM = \frac{\overset{5}{\cancel{20}} \times 170}{\underset{1}{\cancel{4}}} = 850$$

Therefore, the driving pulley runs at 850 RPM.

■ **EXAMPLE 3:**

What is the diameter of a pulley on a shaft running at 225 rpm if it is driven by a 6-in. pulley running at 900 RPM?

Solution and Explanation:

In this problem we know that rpm $= 225$; $D = 6$ in.; RPM $= 900$, and we are to find the diameter of the driven pulley, d. Using Formula 3, we have:

$$d = \frac{D \times RPM}{rpm}$$

$$d = \frac{6 \times \overset{4}{\cancel{900}}}{\underset{1}{\cancel{225}}} = 24 \text{ in.}$$

The diameter of the driven pulley is 24 in.

■ **EXAMPLE 4:**

If an 18-in. pulley making 250 RPM drives a 12-in. pulley by means of a belt, how many revolutions per minute does the 12-in. pulley make?

Solution and Explanation:

Here we are given $D = 18$ in.; RPM $= 250$; $d = 12$ in.; and we wish to determine the revolutions per minute of the driven pulley. We use the formula

$$\text{rpm} = \frac{D \times \text{RPM}}{d}$$

Substituting the known values into this formula we find that:

$$\text{rpm} = \frac{\overset{3}{\cancel{18}} \times \overset{125}{\cancel{250}}}{\underset{\underset{1}{\cancel{2}}}{\cancel{12}}}$$

$$\text{rpm} = 375$$

Hence the smaller (driven) pulley makes 375 revolutions per minute.

It is interesting to consider the belt speed in connection with the above problems. Since we have based all our work on the assumption that the amount of slippage was negligible, the belt speed must be the same as the surface speed of either pulley.

Hence the belt speed is equal to the surface speed of either the driving pulley or the driven pulley. Hence we have

---

Belt speed = 0.2618 × D × RPM
or Belt speed = 0.2618 × d × rpm

Where D = diameter of the driving pulley in inches.
  RPM = number of revolutions per minute of the driving pulley.
   d = diameter of the driven pulley in inches.
  rpm = number of revolutions per minute of the driven pulley, and belt speed is in feet per minute.

19.3 Belting

Length of Open Belt. Fairly simple formulas are available for the length of a belt for the open-belt type of pulley drive. Referring to the drawing (Fig. 307), the length of the open belt, to a very good degree of approximation, is given by Formula A.

$$L = 2C + \frac{\pi}{2}(D + d) + \frac{(D - d)^2}{4C}$$

In this formula:
   C = distance between pulley centers in inches,
   D = diameter of larger pulley in inches,
   d = diameter of smaller pulley in inches,
   L = total length of belt in inches.

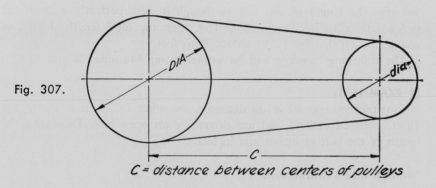

Fig. 307.

C = distance between centers of pulleys

If we use 3.1416 for π, then $\frac{\pi}{2} = 1.5708 = 1.57$ approximately and we can write this as Formula B:

$$L = 2C + 1.57 \ (D + d) + \frac{(D - d)^2}{4C}$$

In words, this says that, to find the length of the belt:

1. *Multiply the center-to-center distance by 2.*
2. *Multiply the sum of the pulley diameters by 1.57.*
3. *Subtract the smaller pulley diameter from the larger. Square this difference. Divide this result by 4 times the center-to-center distance.*
4. *Add the results of steps 1, 2, and 3 together.*

If the driven and driving pulleys are of approximately the same diameter, this formula can be simplified still further into Formula C:

$$L = 2C + 1.57 \ (D + d)$$

In words, this says that, to find the length of the belt when the driven and driving pulleys have approximately the same diameter,

1. *Multiply the center-to-center distance by 2.*
2. *Multiply the sum of the pulley diameters by 1.57.*
3. *Add the results of Steps 1 and 2 together.*

It should be noted that these formulas do not allow for the thickness of the belt, slack in the belt, and joining the ends of the belt together, but give the length of the belt as though it were perfectly tight. If the belt length is to be computed in feet, then the total length should, of course, be divided by 12 to reduce it to feet.

The following example will be worked using Formulas B and C.

■ EXAMPLE 1:

Two pulleys, one 20 in. in diameter, the other 18 in. in diameter, are 10 ft. between centers and are driven by an open belt. Determine the length of the belt in inches and in feet.

Solution and Explanation:

USING FORMULA B

Step 1: First we list all the known data:

D = 20 in., the diameter of the larger pulley,

d = 18 in., the diameter of the smaller pulley,

C = 120 in., the distance between the centers of the pulleys. (The distance between the centers of the pulleys was given as 10 ft. This is 10 × 12 or 120 in.)

Step 2: The formula we use is Formula B:

$$L = 2C + 1.57(D + d) + \frac{(D - d)^2}{4C}$$

Substituting the known data, we have:

$$L = 2 \times 120 + 1.57(20 + 18) + \frac{(20 - 18)^2}{4 \times 120}$$

To evaluate this formula, that is, to determine L, we simplify each of the parts on the right-hand side. We have 2 × 120 or 240; also 1.57 × (20 + 18) becomes 1.57(38) or 59.66, and

$$\frac{(20 - 18)^2}{4 \times 120} \text{ becomes } \frac{(2)^2}{4 \times 120} \text{ or } \frac{4}{4 \times 120} \text{ or } \frac{1}{120} \text{ or } 0.0083.$$

Step 3: We can now write:

L = 240 + 59.66 + 0.0083, or

L = 299.67 in.

Hence the total length of the belt is 299.67 in. or 300 in. in round numbers.

Changing 299.67 in. to feet by dividing it by 12, we have

$$L = \frac{299.67}{12} = 24.97 \text{ ft.} = 25 \text{ ft.}$$

(Since 0.97 ft. = 0.97 × 12 = 11.64 in. or $11\frac{41}{64}$ in., L = 25 ft. in round numbers.)

This, it is pointed out again, makes no allowance for the joint or for the slack in the belt or for the belt thickness.

Using Formula C

Step 1: Formula C is: $L = 2C + 1.57(D + d)$

Substituting 120 for C, 20 for D, and 18 for d, we have:

$$L = 2 \times 120 + 1.57(20 + 18)$$
$$L = 240 + 1.57(38)$$
$$L = 240 + 59.66$$
$$L = 299.66 \text{ in. or } 300 \text{ in. in round numbers.}$$

Hence, the total length of the belt is 300 in.

Changing 299.66 in. to feet by dividing by 12, we have

$$L = \frac{299.66}{12} = 24.97 \text{ ft.}$$

Since 0.97 ft. = $0.97 \times 12 = 11.64$ in. or $11\frac{41}{64}$ in., the total length of the belt is 24 ft. $11\frac{41}{64}$ in. or 25 ft. in round numbers.

In this particular problem, the term $\dfrac{(D - d)^2}{4C}$ in Formula B was so small (0.0083 in.) as to be negligible. However, it may happen that, in other cases, it may be large enough to be included. This can occur if the pulley diameters differ from each other considerably, and if the distance C is rather small. This is the reason for including the more accurate Formula B and the approximate Formula C.

Length of Crossed Belt: The formula for determining the length of a crossed belt in terms of the pulley diameters and the center-to-center distance of the pulleys can be written in several forms (Fig. 308).

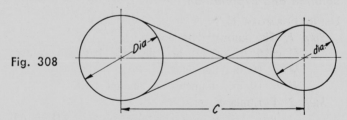

Fig. 308

A formula accurate for all ordinary purposes is Formula D:

$$L = 2C + \frac{\pi}{2}(D + d) + \frac{(D + d)^2}{4C}$$

In this formula, as in the formula for the length of an open-style belt:

C = distance between pulley centers in inches,
D = diameter of larger pulley in inches,
d = diameter of smaller pulley in inches,
L = total length of belt in inches,
π = 3.14 approximately.

This can be written as Formula E:

$$L = 2C + 1.57(D + d) + \frac{(D + d)^2}{4C}$$

In this formula, if the pulley diameters are small compared to their center-to-center distance, the numerical value of the term $\frac{(D + d)^2}{4C}$ will be small also. In such cases, the term $\frac{(D + d)^2}{4C}$ could be neglected. Thus we could simplify Formula E to read as Formula F:

$$L = 2C + 1.57(D + d)$$

This formula would be used when the pulley diameters are about $\frac{1}{10}$ of their center-to-center distance. In all these formulas, the various letters represent the same quantities as listed above.

The use of these formulas is illustrated in the following problems:

■ EXAMPLE 2:

Determine the length of crossed belt needed in connecting two pulleys 16 in. and 10 in. in diameter and 5 ft. apart.

Solution and Explanation:

USING FORMULA E

Step 1: The known data are:

     $C = 5$ ft. or 60 in., distance between centers of pulleys
     $D = 16$ in., diameter of larger pulley
     $d = 10$ in., diameter of smaller pulley

Step 2: Formula E is:

$$L = 2C + 1.57(D + d) + \frac{(D + d)^2}{4C}$$

Substituting the known data in this formula, we have:

$$L = 2 \times 60 + 1.57(16 + 10) + \frac{(16 + 10)^2}{4 \times 60}$$

$$L = 120 + 1.57(26) + \frac{(26)^2}{240}$$

$$L = 120 + 40.82 + \frac{676}{240}$$

$$L = 160.82 + 2.82$$

$$L = 163.64 \text{ in.}$$

Converting this length to feet, we have:

$$L = \frac{163.64}{12} = 13.64 \text{ ft.} = 13 \text{ ft. } 7\tfrac{11}{16} \text{ in.}$$

Thus the length of the belt is 13 ft. $7\tfrac{11}{16}$ in.

If we used the approximate Formula F, then the term $\dfrac{(D + d)^2}{4C}$ used in Formula E would have been omitted. Since this term amounts to 2.82 in., the length of the belt using Formula F would be 2.82 in. less than that obtained by using the more accurate Formula E.

In the calculations involving the length of open and crossed belts, one should again remember that the formulas make no allowance for slack, thickness of belt or for joining the ends of the belt together.

Length of Belting in a Coil. If belting is rolled into a coil, a shop formula is available for finding the approximate length of the belt. Assume the following data are known:

N = number of laps or turns in the coil

D = outside diameter of the coil *in inches*

d = inside diameter of the coil *in inches*

We want to find:

L = length of belt in the coil *in feet*

We can think of the coil as having an *average* diameter. This will be $\dfrac{1}{2}\left(\dfrac{D}{12} + \dfrac{d}{12}\right)$ or $\dfrac{D + d}{24}$ ft. The length of *one* lap of such a diameter would be $3.1416 \times \dfrac{(D + d)}{24}$ or $0.131 (D + d)$ ft. Since there are N laps or turns, the total approximate length will be:

$$L = 0.131 \times (D + d) \times N$$

In evaluating this formula for any particular values of D, d, and N, we first add D and d, then multiply this sum by N. Last, we multiply this product by 0.131 to obtain the value of L. This avoids carrying decimal values along in the multiplication.

An example illustrates the application of this formula.

■ **EXAMPLE 3:**

A length of belting is in a coil whose outside diameter is 15 in. The inside diameter of the coil is 5 in., and there are 20 laps or turns in the coil. How many feet of belting are there in this coil?

Solution and Explanation:

Listing the known data, we have:

$$D = 15 \text{ in., outside diameter}$$
$$d = 5 \text{ in. inside diameter}$$
$$N = 20 \text{ laps or turns}$$

Substituting these data into the formula, we obtain:

$$L = 0.131 \times (D + d) \times N, \text{ we have}$$
$$L = 0.131 \times (15 + 5) \times 20$$
$$L = 0.131 \times (20) \times 20$$
$$L = 52.4 \text{ ft.}$$

Changing 0.4 ft. to inches, we find that it is equal to $4\frac{13}{16}$ in. Hence the *approximate* length of the belting in this coil is 52 ft. $4\frac{13}{16}$ in. or 52 ft. to the nearest foot.

19.4   Problems Involving the Calculation of Belt Lengths:

1. Calculate the approximate length of belt needed to connect two pulleys in open drive, if their diameters are 18 in. and 12 in. and their centers are 5 ft. apart.

2. Two pulleys whose diameters are 28 in. and 32 in. are 18 ft. on centers. If a crossed-belt drive were used on these pulleys, what would be the approximate length of belt needed? If an open-belt drive were used, approximately how long would the belt be?

3. Calculate the length of belt needed for each type of drive shown in the drawing (Fig. 309).

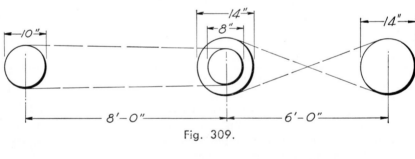

Fig. 309.

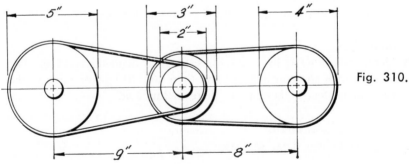

Fig. 310.

4. Calculate the length of each belt for the pulley arrangement shown in Figure 310.

5. Find the length of the belt connecting the pulleys shown in Figure 311.

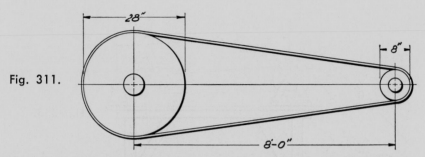

Fig. 311.

6. Two pulleys measuring 24 in. and 22 in. have their centers 14 ft. apart, and are connected by a crossed belt. Compute the approximate length of the belt.

7. In checking over the shop inventory, an apprentice listed the following rolls of belting:

Roll Number	No. of Laps	Outside Diameter	Inside Diameter
1	9	8″	$3\frac{1}{2}$″
2	12	$12\frac{1}{2}$″	5″
3	10	14″	8″
4	24	$19\frac{1}{2}$″	6″

Compute the length of each roll in feet.

8. Compute the approximate length of belting needed for the arrangement of pulleys in Figure 312.

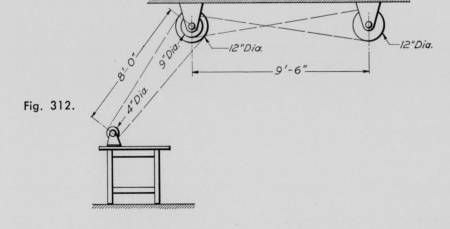

Fig. 312.

9. A coil of belting measuring 16 in. in outside diameter and 6 in. in inside diameter has 12 laps. Calculate the length of the belt in this coil in feet.

10. Find the approximate length of each belt shown in Figure 313.

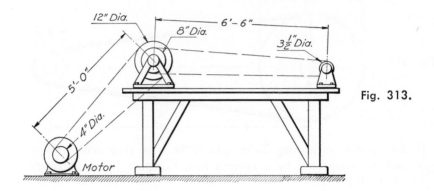

Fig. 313.

CHAPTER 20

Gear Drives

20.1 Introduction

Mechanical power can be transmitted by means of belts, rotating cylinders, and other devices depending on friction. These methods have the disadvantage that when slippage occurs, the speed ratio will not remain constant. When mechanical power is to be transmitted with a constant ratio, chain drives are used. If, in addition to the requirement of a constant-speed ratio, the center distances are short, then gear drives can be used because of their positive action and lack of slippage.

Among the most commonly used types of gears are those known as *spur gears, helical gears,* and *bevel gears.* Spur gears are used to transmit power when the shafts are parallel (Fig. 314). Helical gears are also

Fig. 314. Spur gears (left); bevel gear (right).

Link-Belt Co.

Link-Belt Co.

Link-Belt Co.

Fig. 315. Helical gears.　　　Fig. 316. Herringbone gears.

used for the transmission of power when the shafts are parallel, and have the advantages of a more uniform rotation under intermittent loads, longer life, and less noisy operation (Fig. 315). The herringbone gear is one type of gear based on the helical form of teeth (Fig. 316). Bevel gears are used to transmit power between shafts that would intersect if extended, or when the drive shaft and the driven shafts are at an angle to each other (Fig. 314, right).

In an arrangement of gears, the gear that does the driving is called the *driving gear,* or *driver.* The gear that is driven is called the *driven gear* or *follower gear.*

Gears and arrangements of gears are widely used in many types of machines and equipment. Among these are washing machines, lathes, clocks, automobiles, farm machinery, gun turrets, ship-propulsion systems, turboprop airplanes, winches, and capstans. Where direct contact of gears is impractical chain drive may be employed. Unlike belt drive, a chain provides positive drive with no loss to slippage (Fig. 317). See Chapter 21.

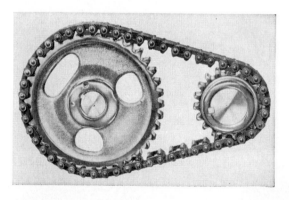

Fig. 317. A chain drive.

Link-Belt Co.

20.2 Gear-Drive Calculations

Computations relating to gear drives are fundamentally similar to those relating to pulley drives. In the case of pulley drives, the fundamental equation was:

Diameter of driving pulley **× RPM of driving pulley**	**Diameter of driven pulley** **× rpm of driven pulley**

Let us consider the case of two gears. Let the driving gear have 24 teeth and the driven gear have 48 teeth.

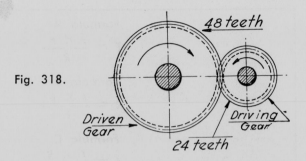

Fig. 318.

The diagram (Fig. 318) illustrates, in very simplified form, the two gears in question.

The outermost circle indicates the circle of the tops of the gear teeth. The next circle, shown by the long and short dashes, is the pitch circle, which is the most important diameter for making gear tooth calculations. The third circle, shown by the short dashes, is the root circle, the circle of the bottom of the gear spaces. This method of illustrating gear arrangements saves time and avoids making complicated drawings in which the individual gear teeth might be shown.

Since the gear teeth are in mesh, when the driver gear makes one complete revolution, it has engaged only 24 teeth in the driven gear. When the driver gear makes two complete turns, the driven gear will have turned completely only once.

Hence we can say, in this case, that $24 \times 2 = 48 \times 1$, or in general,

Number of teeth on driving gear × number of revolutions of driving gear	**=**	**Number of teeth on driven gear × number of revolutions of driven gear**

If we let

T = number of teeth on driving gear
R = number of revolutions of driving gear
t = number of teeth on driven gear
r = number of revolutions of driven gear

Then the above rule can be written in the form:

$$T \times R = t \times r$$

If we know any three of the four quantities appearing in this formula, we can solve for the fourth quantity. We thus can write:

Formula A

$$T = \frac{t \times r}{R}$$

Formula B

$$R = \frac{t \times r}{T}$$

Formula C

$$t = \frac{T \times R}{r}$$

Formula D

$$r = \frac{T \times R}{t}$$

In working problems on gear drives and gear arrangements or gear trains as they are called, one should always make a simple drawing or sketch representing the individual gears by circles. The known data should be shown near the circles showing the respective gears.

The following problems will illustrate how these formulas are used.

■ EXAMPLE 1:

Determine the number of teeth on a driving gear which revolves 10 times while turning a 114 tooth gear $1\frac{2}{3}$ times.

Solution and Explanation:

Making a simple diagram (Fig. 319) of these gears and labeling it, we have:

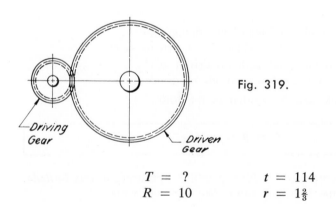

Fig. 319.

Driving Gear

Driven Gear

$$T = ? \qquad\qquad t = 114$$
$$R = 10 \qquad\qquad r = 1\tfrac{2}{3}$$

Using Formula A, we have:

$$T = \frac{t \times r}{R} \qquad\qquad \begin{aligned} t &= 114 \\ r &= 1\tfrac{2}{3} \\ R &= 10 \end{aligned}$$

Substituting what is known into this formula, we obtain:

$$T = \frac{114 \times 1\tfrac{2}{3}}{10}$$

$$T = \frac{114 \times \tfrac{5}{3}}{10} = \frac{114}{10} \times \frac{5}{3}$$

$$T = 19$$

Hence there are 19 teeth in the driving gear. As a check, we substitute the four quantities into the basic rule:

$$T \times R = t \times r$$

$$19 \times 10 \overset{?}{=} 114 \times 1\tfrac{2}{3}$$

$$190 \overset{?}{=} 114 \times \tfrac{5}{3}$$

$$190 = 190 \qquad \text{(check)}$$

We conclude that our solution is correct.

■ EXAMPLE 2:

If a gear having 12 teeth drives a gear having 30 teeth, how many turns must the driving gear make for each complete revolution of the driven gear?

Solution and Explanation:

As in Example 1, we make a simple diagram (Fig. 320) showing the two gears and label it.

In this problem, we must find R, the number of revolutions of the driving gear. Using Formula B we have:

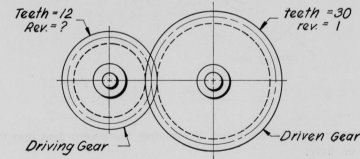

Fig. 320.

$$R = \frac{t \times r}{T} \qquad\qquad \begin{aligned} t &= 30 \\ r &= 1 \\ T &= 12 \end{aligned}$$

Substituting the known data into the formula, we obtain:

$$R = \frac{30 \times 1}{12} = 2\tfrac{1}{2}$$

Hence the driving gear makes $2\tfrac{1}{2}$ revolutions in order for the driven gear to make one complete revolution.

As a check on our work, we use the basic rule

$$T \times R = t \times r$$

Substituting the known data, we obtain

$$12 \times 2\tfrac{1}{2} \overset{?}{=} 30 \times 1$$
$$30 = 30 \qquad \text{(check)}$$

Hence our answer is correct.

■ **EXAMPLE 3:**

How many teeth should a gear have if it makes $3\tfrac{1}{2}$ revolutions while the driving gear makes 2 revolutions? The driving gear has 28 teeth.

Solution and Explanation:

As in the other problems, we make and label a diagram (Fig. 321) of the gears considered.

Using Formula C, we have:

$$\begin{aligned} T &= 28 & t &= ? \\ R &= 2 & r &= 3\tfrac{1}{2} \end{aligned}$$

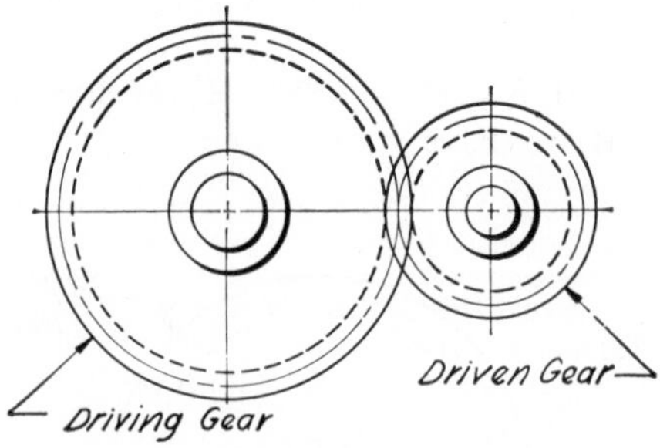

Fig. 321.

Driving Gear

Driven Gear

$$t = \frac{T \times R}{r} \qquad\qquad \begin{aligned} T &= 28 \\ r &= 3\tfrac{1}{2} \\ R &= 2 \end{aligned}$$

and t is to be computed. Substituting the known data into the formula, we have:

Link-Belt Co.
A carload of coal is emptied on a rotating cylinder.

$$t = \frac{28 \times 2}{3\frac{1}{2}}$$

$$t = \frac{28 \times 2}{\frac{7}{2}} = \overset{4}{\cancel{28}} \times 2 \times \frac{2}{\cancel{7}_1}$$

$$t = 16$$

Hence the driven gear must have 16 teeth. As a check on our work, we again substitute into the basic formula.

$$T \times R = t \times r$$

$$28 \times 2 \overset{?}{=} 3\frac{1}{2} \times 16$$

$$56 \overset{?}{=} \tfrac{7}{2} \times 16$$

$$56 = 56 \quad \text{(check)}$$

and we feel confident that our answer is correct.

■ EXAMPLE 4:

How many revolutions will a driven gear having 108 teeth make while the driving gear having 60 teeth makes 9 revolutions?

$$T = 60 \qquad\qquad t = 108$$
$$R = 9 \qquad\qquad r = \ ?$$

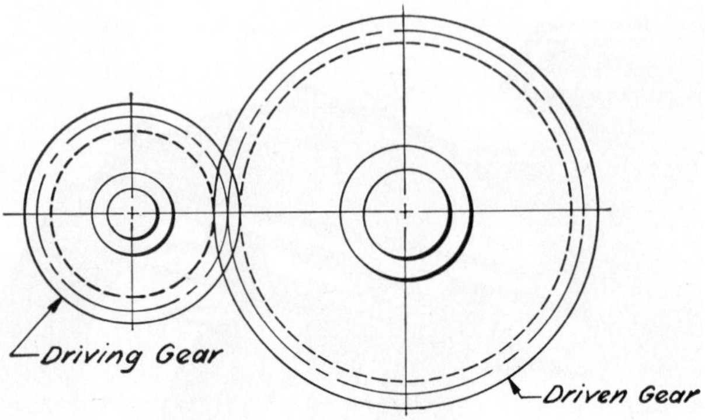

Fig. 322.

Driving Gear

Driven Gear

Solution and Explanation:

Figure 322 is a diagram of the gears.

Using Formula D we have:

$$r = \frac{T \times R}{t} \qquad\qquad \begin{aligned} T &= 60 \\ R &= 9 \\ t &= 108 \end{aligned}$$

and r is to be computed. Substituting the known data into this formula, we have:

$$r = \frac{60 \times 9}{108}$$

$$r = \frac{540}{108}$$

$$r = 5$$

Hence the drive gear will make 5 revolutions.

To check our work, we again make use of the basic formula

$$T \times R = t \times r$$

Substituting the four quantities now known, we obtain:

$$60 \times 9 = 108 \times 5$$
$$540 = 540 \qquad \text{(check)}$$

We conclude that our answer is correct.

20.3 Simple Gear Trains

A *simple* gear train is an arrangement of two or more gears in mesh, each on a separate shaft, used for transmitting power from one shaft to another. In gear trains using three or more such gears, one or more of the gears may serve both as driven and driving gears, and are called idler gears.

Idler gears are used principally for two reasons:

1. When the driving and driven gears intermesh, they will rotate in

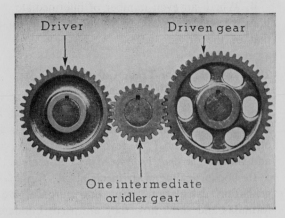

Fig. 323.

opposite directions. When *both* are to rotate in the *same* direction, an idler gear must be placed between.

2. When the center distance of the driving and driven shafts is such that unusually large gears would be required to connect them, one or more idler gears can be used between the driving and driven gears. This reduces the driving and driven gears to more convenient sizes.

Gear trains of this type are shown in Figures 323 and 324.

From inspection of these illustrations, it should be clear that:

1. When only *one* intermediate gear, or one idler gear, is used, the driven gear rotates in the *same* direction as the driving gear.

2. Where *two* intermediate gears, or two idler gears, are used, the driven gear rotates in the *opposite* direction to the driving gear.

3. Where the gear train is larger, and an *odd* number of intermediate, or idler gears is used, such as 3 or 5, the *direction* of rotation of the driven gear will be the *same* as that of the driving gear.

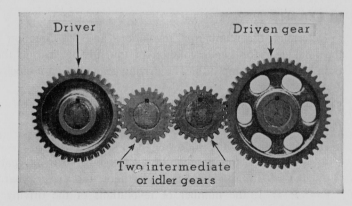

Fig. 324.

4. Where an even number of intermediate gears, as 2, 4, or 6, is used, however, the *direction* of rotation of the final gear will be *opposite* to that of the driving gear.

20.4 Simple Gear-Train Calculations

In *simple* gear-train calculations involving only the *first driving gear* and the *last* or *final driven gear,* neither the intermediate gears nor the idler gears enter into the calculations, unless it is desired to know their direction or number of revolutions. Instead, only the *first driving gear* and the *final driven gear need be considered.*

In books dealing with mechanisms, formulas are derived for handling gear-train calculations. For our purpose, we will state the necessary formulas and show how they are used. Fundamentally these formulas are derived from the fact that when two gears are in mesh and turning, their surface speeds must be the same. Also, as stated above, the intermediate or idler gears do not appear in the formulas.

Hence, in order to determine the number of revolutions that the *final driven gear* makes for *one revolution* of the *driving gear,* the *same* formula as that used for gear-drive calculations would be used. That is, we would use Formula D:

$$r = \frac{T \times R}{t}, \qquad \text{where}$$

T = number of teeth on driving gear,
t = number of teeth on final driven gear,
R = number of revolutions of driving gear,
r = number of revolutions of final driven gear.

The following problem is typical of those involving gear trains and illustrates the application of this formula.

■ EXAMPLE 1:

Determine the number of revolutions and the direction of rotation of the final gear for *one* revolution of the driving gear in the simple gear train shown in Figure 325. The driving gear turns in a clockwise direction.

Solution and Explanation:

Part 1

In this problem, the following data are known:
   T = 45, the number of teeth on the driving gear,
   t = 30, the number of teeth on the driven gear,
   R = 1, the number of revolutions of the driving gear.

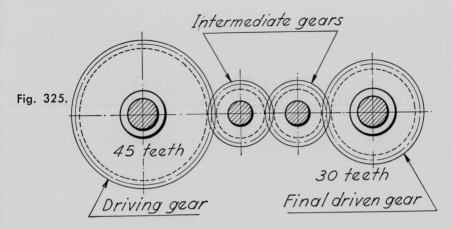

Fig. 325.

Intermediate gears

45 teeth

Driving gear

30 teeth

Final driven gear

We are to find r, the number of revolutions of the driven gear, and the direction of rotation of the driven gear.

Using Formula D, we obtain:

$$r = \frac{T \times R}{t}$$

$$r = \frac{45 \times 1}{30} = 1\tfrac{1}{2}$$

That is, the driven gear makes $1\tfrac{1}{2}$ revolutions for each revolution of the driving gear.

Part 2

To find the direction of rotation of the driven gear, we draw *two* small arrows on each of the gears, starting with the driving gear, which we were told turns in a clockwise direction.

At *each point of contact,* the arrows point in the *same* direction. By drawing these arrows on each of the gears, we find that the *final* or driven gear turns in a *counterclockwise* direction.

We have hence found that the driven gear makes $1\tfrac{1}{2}$ revolutions for 1 revolution of the driving gear and that the driven gear turns in a counterclockwise direction, or *opposite* to the driving gear.

■ **EXAMPLE 2:**

Calculate the number of revolutions of the driving gear in the simple gear train shown in Figure 326. If the driven gear turns in a clockwise direction, in what direction does the driving gear turn?

Solution and Explanation:

Here, the known data are:

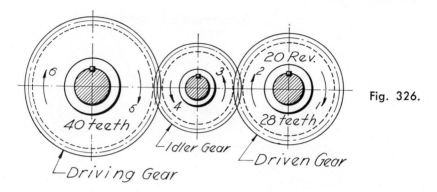

Fig. 326.

$T = 40$, number of teeth on driving gear,
$t = 28$, number of teeth on driven gear,
$r = 20$, number of revolutions of driven gear.

We are to find R, the number of revolutions of the driving gear and the direction of rotation of the driven gear.

Using Formula B:

$$R = \frac{t \times r}{T}, \text{ we have,}$$

$$R = \frac{28 \times 20}{40} = 14.$$

Hence the driving gear makes 14 revolutions while the driven gear makes 20 revolutions.

To find the direction of rotation of the driving gear, we show two arrows on the driven gear, one on its right, the other on its left, where it makes contact with the idler gear. These are the arrows marked *1* and *2*. We next show two arrows on the idler gear. These are numbered *3* and *4*, with *3* pointing upward as does arrow *2*. Arrow *4* is on the left side of the idler gear, pointing in a downward direction. Arrow *5* is next drawn on the right side of the driving gear, pointing in a downward direction as arrow *4* does. Finally, we draw arrow *6*, on the left side of the driving gear, pointing upward. This direction is clockwise, and is the direction in which the driving gear turns.

A somewhat more difficult example, combining pulleys and gears, is the following:

■ EXAMPLE 3:

The diagram (Fig. 327) illustrates a combination belt-and-gear drive on a small printing press. One printing impression is made each time gear *A* revolves. How many impressions are made per minute on this

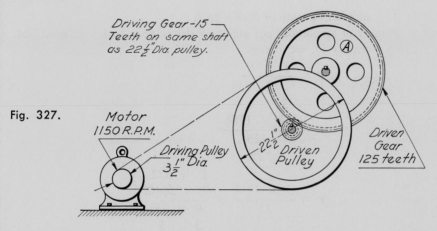

Fig. 327.

Driving Gear-15 Teeth on same shaft as $22\frac{1}{2}$" Dia. pulley.

Motor 1150 R.P.M.

Driving Pulley $3\frac{1}{2}$" Dia.

$22\frac{1}{2}$" Driven Pulley

Driven Gear 125 teeth

press if the motor runs at 1150 RPM? How many impressions would be made in 15 minutes?

Solution and Explanation:

We first consider the driving and driven pulleys. Using the same formula and symbols as we did in computing the surface speed of belts, we have:

$D = 3\frac{1}{2}$ in., diameter of driving pulley

RPM $= 1150$, number of revolutions of driving pulley per minute

$d = 22\frac{1}{2}$, diameter of driven pulley

rpm $=$ revolutions per minute of driven pulley, which is to be found.

Substituting in the formula, we obtain:

$$\text{rpm} = \frac{D \times \text{RPM}}{d}$$

$$\text{rpm} = \frac{3\frac{1}{2} \times 1150}{22\frac{1}{2}}$$

$$\text{rpm} = \frac{\frac{7}{2} \times 1150}{\frac{45}{2}} = \frac{7}{\frac{2}{1}} \times \overset{230}{\cancel{1150}} \times \frac{\frac{1}{2}}{\frac{\cancel{45}}{9}}$$

$$\text{rpm} = \frac{1610}{9} = 178\frac{8}{9}$$

This is the rpm of the driven pulley.

Since the 15-tooth gear is on the same shaft as the driven pulley, it makes the same number of revolutions as the driven pulley.

We next consider the 15-tooth gear as the driving gear and the 125-tooth gear as the driven gear.

We now have

$R = 178\frac{8}{9}$, number of revolutions per minute of driving gear,

$T = 15$, number of teeth of driving gear,

$t = 125$, number of teeth of driven gear,

$r =$ number of revolutions per minute of driven gear, which we must find.

Using Formula D, we obtain:

$$r = \frac{T \times R}{t}$$

$$r = \frac{\overset{3}{\cancel{15}} \times 178\tfrac{8}{9}}{\cancel{125}}$$
$$25$$

$$r = \frac{3 \times \frac{\overset{1610}{1610}}{9}}{25} = \frac{\overset{1}{\cancel{3}} \times \overset{322}{\cancel{1610}}}{\underset{3}{\cancel{9}} \times \underset{5}{\cancel{25}}}$$

$$r = \tfrac{322}{75} = 21\tfrac{7}{15}$$

We have thus found that gear A will make $21\tfrac{7}{15}$ revolutions per minute, and, consequently, $21\tfrac{7}{15}$ impressions per minute. In 15 minutes the number of impressions would be $21\tfrac{7}{15} \times 15$ or $\frac{322}{\underset{1}{\cancel{15}}} \times \overset{1}{\cancel{15}}$ or 322.

20.5   Problems Relating to Calculations in Simple Gearing

1. How many teeth must a gear have to run at 126 rpm, when driven by a gear having 84 teeth and running at 30 RPM?

2. How many turns will a 64-tooth spur gear make for eight turns of a 48-tooth spur gear that meshes with it?

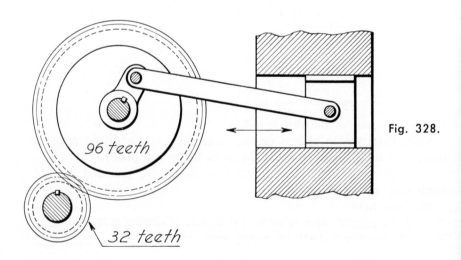

Fig. 328.

96 teeth

32 teeth

3. How many revolutions will a 16-tooth gear make in 2 min. if it drives a 96-tooth gear 14 revolutions in 30 sec.

4. The setup in Figure 328 shows the gear drive on a special cutting machine. The small gear makes 120 RPM. Each time the larger gear makes one revolution one complete cutting stroke is made. At this rate how many cutting strokes are made per minute?

5. The machine illustrated in Figure 329 is used for slitting sheet

Fig. 329.

metal. It is operated by a handle which is attached to the driving-gear shaft. The driving gear has 16 teeth and the larger gear has 60 teeth. How many turns of the driving gear are necessary for one turn of the driven gear?

6. The gearing on a standard carpenter's hand drill is arranged as in the sketch (Fig. 330). If the spindle gear turns $4\frac{1}{2}$ times for one turn

Fig. 330.

of the handle, how many teeth are there on the larger gear to which the handle is attached?

7. The ordinary home lawn mower is geared as shown in Figure 331. How many revolutions will the cutting blades make for one revolution

Fig. 331.

of the larger gear? It is to be noted in this that the smaller gear is a spur gear in which the teeth are on the *outer* rim of the gear and *extend out* from the center. On the larger gear, however, the teeth are on the *inside* of the gear and *extend inward*. This latter type of a gear is known as an *internal* gear.

8. How many teeth should gear *A* have in the gear train shown in Figure 332 in order to make 12 revolutions per minute?

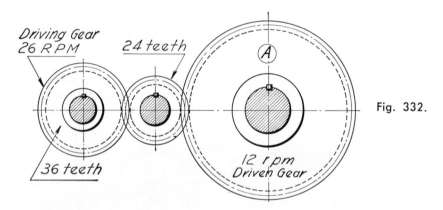

Fig. 332.

9. Find the direction of rotation and the number of rpm for the gear marked *B* in Figure 333.

10. How many revolutions per minute does the 32-tooth gear shown in this simple gear train (Fig. 334) make? What is its direction of rotation?

11. For this simple gear train (Fig. 335), find the number of revolutions made by the 24-tooth gear and its direction of rotation.

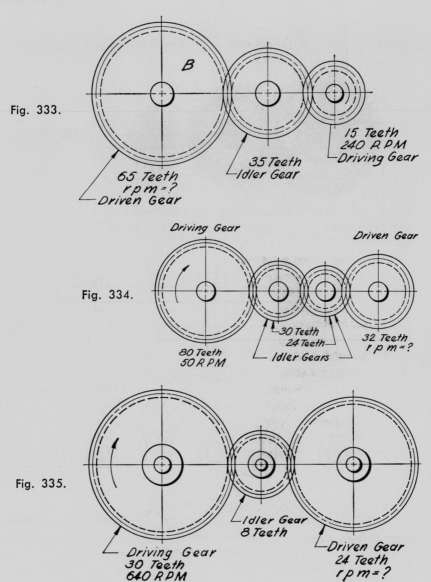

Fig. 333.

65 Teeth
rpm = ?
Driven Gear

35 Teeth
Idler Gear

15 Teeth
240 RPM
Driving Gear

B

Fig. 334.

Driving Gear

Driven Gear

80 Teeth
50 RPM

30 Teeth
24 Teeth
Idler Gears

32 Teeth
rpm = ?

Fig. 335.

Driving Gear
30 Teeth
640 RPM

Idler Gear
8 Teeth

Driven Gear
24 Teeth
rpm = ?

20.6 Compound Gear Trains

In our work on simple gear trains we found that each shaft of such a train carried one gear. In a compound-gear train, however, each axle except the first and last carries two gears. Figure 336 clearly illustrates one such type of compound gear train.

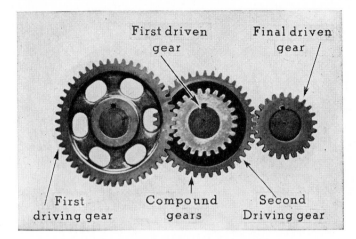

First driven gear

Final driven gear

Fig. 336.

First driving gear

Compound gears

Second Driving gear

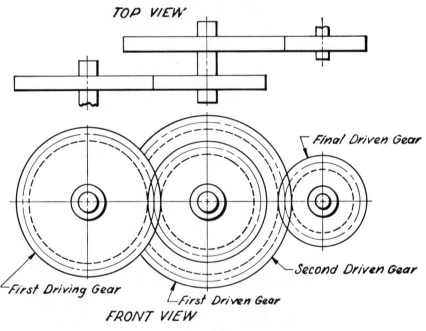

TOP VIEW

Final Driven Gear

Second Driven Gear

First Driving Gear

First Driven Gear

FRONT VIEW

Fig. 337.

The same gear train can be represented diagramatically as in Figure 337.

Compound-gear trains are used where high-speed ratios are required, and where it is necessary to transmit power and motion to a shaft which is not parallel to the driving shaft. Compound-gear trains can be made using spur gears only, or bevel gears only, or a combination of spur and bevel gears. Gear trains of this kind find many uses in connection with the transmission and speed-changing systems of automobiles, trucks, tractors, diesel locomotives, ships, and aircraft. They also find use in hoists, clocks, and machine lathes.

20.7 Compound-Gear-Train Calculations

The types of calculations we shall be concerned with in connection with our work on compound-gear trains will involve each of the gears in the trains. These calculations can be performed by considering the respective gears in pairs, as one would do in simple gearing problems.

The following problem will illustrate this procedure.

■ EXAMPLE 1:

In the compound-gear train shown in Figure 338, determine the number of revolutions made by the final driven gear for one revolution of the first driving gear.

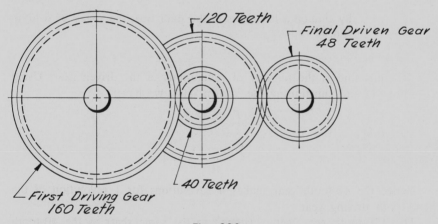

Fig. 338.

Solution and Explanation:

Following our previous work in simple gearing we consider the 160-tooth gear and the 40-tooth gear as driving and driven gears respectively. For these two gears:

$$T = 160, \text{ number of teeth on driving gear,}$$
$$R = 1, \text{ number of revolutions of driving gear,}$$
$$t = 40, \text{ number of teeth on driven gear.}$$

Clausing

By changing the gears in the gear box, the speed of a lathe can be varied.

We must find *r,* the number of revolutions of the driven gear. Using Formula D and substituting the known data, we have:

$$r = \frac{T \times R}{t}$$

$$r = \frac{160 \times 1}{40} = 4$$

Hence the 40-tooth gear makes 4 revolutions for 1 revolution of the 160-tooth driving gear.

The 120-tooth gear being fastened to the same shaft as the 40-tooth gear must turn at the same speed, and consequently makes 4 revolutions for 1 revolution of the 160-tooth driving gear.

We now consider the 120-tooth gear as a second driving gear, and the 48-tooth gear as a second driven gear. For this pair, we know that:

$T = 120$, number of teeth of second driving gear,

$R = 4$, number of revolutions of second driving gear,

$t = 48$, number of teeth of second driving gear,

and we must calculate the value of *r,* the number of revolutions of the second driven gear.

We again use Formula D and substitute the above values in it. We obtain:

$$r = \frac{120 \times 4}{48}$$

$$r = 10$$

This is the number of revolutions that the final driven gear makes for 4 revolutions of the second driving gear. However, while the second driving gear was making 4 revolutions, the first driving gear made 1 revolution. Consequently, the final driven gear makes 10 revolutions for 1 revolution of the first driving gear.

If we divided 10 by 1, we would get the ratio $\frac{10}{1}$, which is called the *train value*. This is the ratio $\frac{r}{R}$, where r is the number of revolutions of the *final driven gear* and R is the number of revolutions of the *first driving gear*.

This method may be greatly shortened however. *If we multiply the product of the number of teeth on the driving gears by the number of revolutions of the first driving gear, and then divide this result by the product of the number of teeth on the driven gears, we shall obtain the number of revolutions of the final driven gear.*

This basic statement is derived in books dealing with mechanisms and the relative motion between the parts of machines. Here we will give the various useful forms of this statement, treating them as shop formulas.

Let

T_1, T_2, T_3, etc. = the number of teeth on the respective driving gears,

t_1, t_2, t_3, etc. = the number of teeth on the respective driven gears,

R = the number of revolutions of the first driving gear,

r = the number of revolutions of the final driven gear,

t_f = the number of teeth on the final driven gear.

The letters T_1, T_2, T_3, etc., are pronounced "capital T sub one, capital T sub two, capital T sub three," etc.

The letters t_1, t_2, t_3, etc., are pronounced "little t sub one, little t sub two, little t sub three," etc.

We can then write the following important shop formula in connection with compound-gear trains.

Formula E

$$\frac{r}{R} = \frac{T_1 \times T_2 \times T_3, \text{ etc.}}{t_1 \times t_2 \times t_3, \text{ etc.}}$$

The ratio $\dfrac{r}{R}$ is called the *train value,* while the ratio $\dfrac{R}{r}$ is called the *speed ratio.*

In words, we can state this formula as:

$$\text{Train value} = \frac{\text{Product of number of teeth on driving gears}}{\text{Product of number of teeth on driven gears}}$$

The following useful formulas can now be stated:

1. To find the number of teeth on the first driving gear, use:

Formula E1

$$T_1 = \frac{\text{Product of number of teeth on all driven gears} \times \text{number of revolutions of final driven gear}}{\text{Number of revolutions of first driving gear} \times \text{product of number of teeth on all other driving gears}}$$

---

2. To find the number of revolutions of the first driving gear, use:

Formula E2

$$R = \frac{\text{Product of number of teeth on all driven gears} \times \text{number of revolutions of final driven gear}}{\text{Product of number of teeth on all driving gears}}$$

---

3. To find the number of teeth on the final driven gear, use:

Formula E3

$$t_f = \frac{\text{Product of number of teeth on all driving gears} \times \text{number of revolutions of first driving gear}}{\text{Product of number of teeth on all other driven gears} \times \text{number of revolutions of final driven gear}}$$

---

4. To find the number of revolutions of the final driven gear, use:

Formula E4

$$r = \frac{\text{Product of number of teeth on all driving gears} \times \text{number of revolutions of first driving gear}}{\text{Product of number of teeth on all driven gears}}$$

How these formulas are applied is explained in the following examples:

■ **EXAMPLE 2:**

For the gear train shown in Figure 339, how many revolutions per

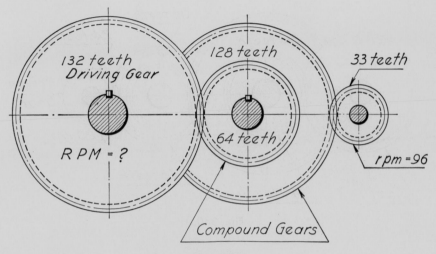

Fig. 339.

minute must the first driving gear make in order for the final driven gear to turn at 96 revolutions per minute?

Solution and Explanation:

In this problem:

T_1 = 132, number of teeth on first driving gear,

T_2 = 128, number of teeth on second driving gear,

t_1 = 64, number of teeth on first driven gear,

t_2 = 33, number of teeth on second (final) driven gear,

r = 96, number of revolutions of second driven gear.

Since we are to find R, the number of revolutions of the first driving gear, we use Formula E2.

$$R = \frac{t_1 \times t_2 \times r}{T_1 \times T_2}$$

$$R = \frac{64 \times 33 \times 96}{132 \times 128} = 12$$

Therefore, the first driving gear makes 12 revolutions per minute.

■ **EXAMPLE 3:**

Determine the number of teeth on the first driving gear in the gear train in Figure 340.

Solution and Explanation:

In this problem, the following data are known:

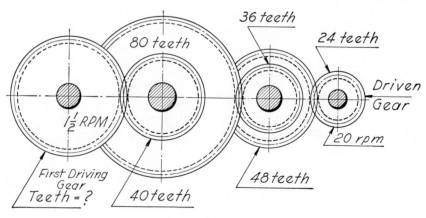

Fig. 340.

For the driving gears, $R = 1\frac{1}{2}$; $T_2 = 80$; $T_3 = 48$.

For the driven gears, $r = 20$; $t_1 = 40$; $t_2 = 36$; $t_3 = 24$.

To find T_1, the number of teeth on the first driving gear, we use Formula E1,

$$T_1 = \frac{t_1 \times t_2 \times t_3 \times r}{R \times T_2 \times T_3}$$

Substituting the known values, we have:

$$T_1 = \frac{\overset{1}{\cancel{40}} \times 36 \times \overset{1}{\cancel{24}} \times \overset{\overset{5}{\cancel{10}}}{\cancel{20}}}{1\frac{1}{2} \times \underset{\underset{1}{\cancel{2}}}{\cancel{80}} \times \underset{\underset{1}{\cancel{2}}}{\cancel{48}}}$$

$$T_1 = \frac{36 \times 5}{1\frac{1}{2}} = \frac{180}{\frac{3}{2}} = \frac{360}{3} = 120$$

Hence the number of teeth on the first driving gear is 120.

■ **EXAMPLE 4:**

What is the number of teeth on the last driven gear in this gear train (Fig. 341)? What is the train value? What is the speed ratio?

Solution and Explanation:

In this problem we know the following data:

For the driving gears, $T_1 = 90$; $T_2 = 60$; $T_3 = 48$; $R = 72$.

For the driven gears, $t_1 = 192$; $t_2 = 150$; $r = 12$.

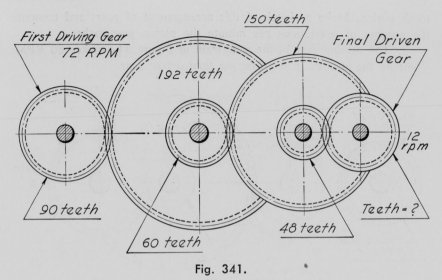

Fig. 341.

To find t_f, the number of teeth on the final driven gear we use Formula E3.

$$t_f = \frac{T_1 \times T_2 \times T_3 \times R}{t_1 \times t_2 \times r}$$

Substituting the known values we obtain:

$$t_f = \frac{\overset{9}{\cancel{90}} \times \overset{\overset{1}{\cancel{15}}}{\cancel{60}} \times \overset{1}{\cancel{48}} \times \overset{\overset{1}{\cancel{6}}}{\cancel{72}}}{\underset{1}{\cancel{192}} \times \underset{1}{\cancel{150}} \times \underset{1}{\cancel{12}}}$$

$$t_f = 54$$

Therefore, the number of teeth on the final driven gear is 54.

The train value equals $\dfrac{r}{R}$ or $\dfrac{12}{72} = \dfrac{1}{6}$. The speed ratio equals $\dfrac{R}{r}$ or $\dfrac{72}{12} = \dfrac{6}{1}$.

20.8 Problems Involving Compound-Gear-Train Calculations

1. A bevel gear having 48 teeth and running at 42 RPM drives a 36-tooth bevel gear. On one end of the shaft on which this 36-tooth gear is fastened there is also a 75-tooth gear which meshes with a 30-

tooth pinion. Make a sketch of this arrangement of gears and compute the number of revolutions per minute the pinion gear makes.

2. The driving gear in the gear train in Figure 342 makes 80 RPM. Compute the number of teeth on the final driven gear.

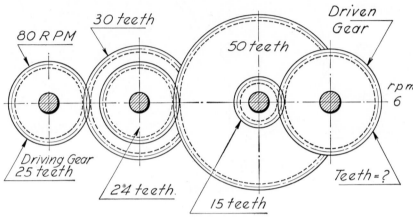

Fig. 342.

3. A familiar style of automobile jack is operated as shown in the gear train illustrated in Figure 343. Each time gear *A* makes one revolution in the direction indicated the screw moves up ⅛ in. How many revolutions of gear *B* are needed to move the screw up ¼ in.?

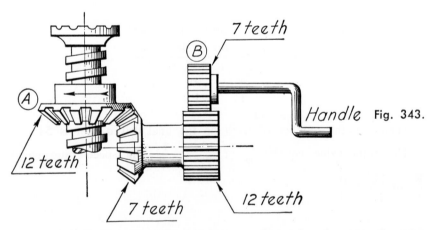

Fig. 343.

4. For the gear train shown in Figure 344, compute the number of revolutions per minute made by the gear having 32 teeth.

5. Compute the number of RPM of the driving gear in the reducing gear train shown in Figure 345.

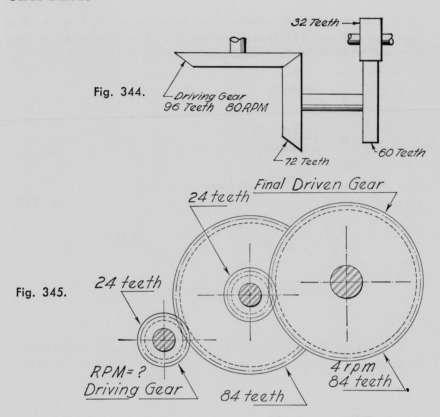

Fig. 344.

32 Teeth

Driving Gear
96 Teeth 80 RPM

72 Teeth

60 Teeth

Fig. 345.

Final Driven Gear

24 teeth

24 teeth

RPM=?
Driving Gear

84 teeth

4 rpm
84 teeth

6. Determine the number of revolutions per minute made by the 90-tooth bevel gear in the gear drive shown in Figure 346.

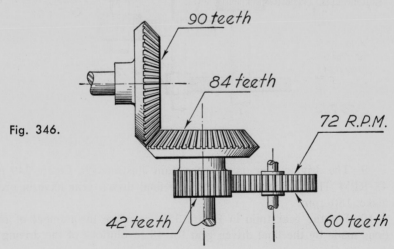

Fig. 346.

90 teeth

84 teeth

72 R.P.M.

42 teeth

60 teeth

7. The gear train on a lathe set up for screw cutting is arranged as diagramed in Figure 347. During one turn of the lead screw gear how many turns will be made by the spindle gear?

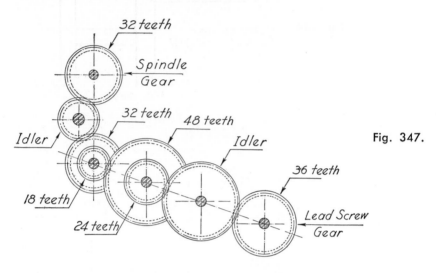

Fig. 347.

8. From the sketch (Fig. 348) of a compound-gear train, determine the number of revolutions per minute made by the final driven gear.

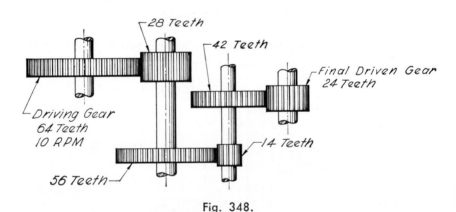

Fig. 348.

9. The driving gear on the gear train illustrated in Figure 349 makes 48 RPM. How many teeth should the final driven gear have in order to make 180 rpm?

10. For the gear train in Figure 350, calculate the number of revolutions made by the final driven gear for 48 revolutions of the driving gear.

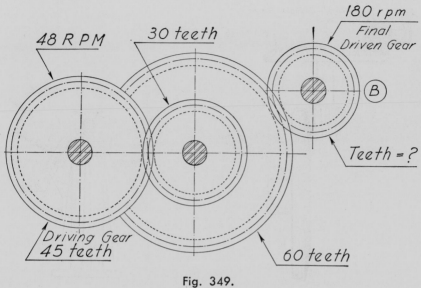

Fig. 349.

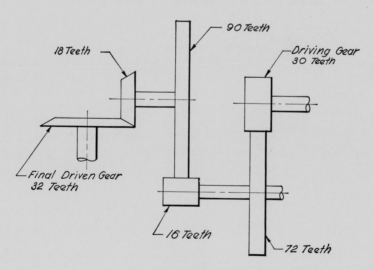

Fig. 350.

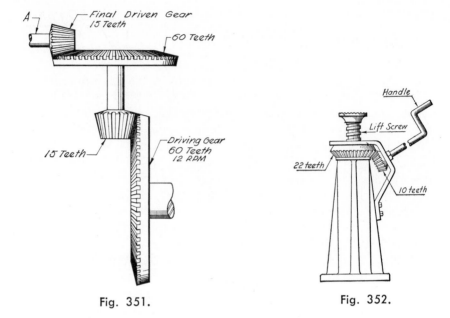

Fig. 351.   Fig. 352.

11. Determine the number of revolutions per minute of the shaft A in the gear train shown in the sketch (Fig. 351).

12. In the automobile jack shown in the sketch (Fig. 352), the lifting screw moves $\frac{1}{8}$ in. for each turn of the larger gear. How many turns of the handle are needed to raise the screw $\frac{5}{8}$ in.?

CHAPTER 21

Chain Drives

21.1 Introduction

In certain installations where power must be transmitted between parallel shafts, the use of gears or belt drives may not be feasible. In those cases, power may be transmitted by the use of chains and sprocket wheels or sprockets, as they are commonly called. (A sprocket wheel or sprocket is a wheel with teeth on its circumference, over which the chain passes.)

One type of chain used for this purpose is called the *combination chain*. This type is used in installations where small amounts of power are transmitted at low speeds. It finds wide use in conveyor applications.

Another type of chain drive used for power transmission is the *roller-chain drive*. Roller chains have considerable versatility. They can be used at either high or low speeds and for transmitting either large or small amounts of power. They operate at very high levels of mechanical efficiency and do so without slipping. The usual type of roller-chain drive consists of two sprockets mounted on parallel shafts and connected by a suitable length of roller chain. For many applications, however, quite intricate arrangements of sprockets and chains can be devised. The size, design, and horsepower rating of roller chains and sprockets have been standardized and complete information appears in the American Standards

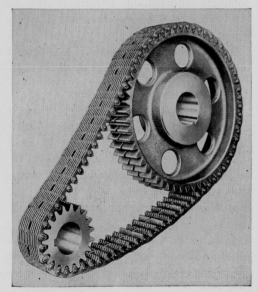

Silent chain drive.

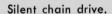

Link-Belt Co.

A roller chain drive.

Association ASA B29.1 — 1963. — *Transmission Roller Chains and Sprocket Teeth* (SAE SP–69).*

A third type of chain drive is the *silent-chain* or inverted-tooth drive. This type of drive is used where a minimum of noise is an important consideration and where large amounts of power are to be transmitted. Chains of this type are made up of links of special shape which engage the sprocket teeth without the use of rollers.

As in the case of the roller-chain drives, the size, design, and horsepower ratings of the silent-chain drives have been standardized and complete information appears in the American Standards Association ASA B29.2 — 1957 — *Inverted Tooth (Silent) Chains and Sprocket Teeth* (SAE SP–68).*

Two familiar applications of chain drives are found in the bicycle and in connection with the timing mechanism of an automobile engine.

21.2 Chain-Drive Calculations

The rigorous design of chain drives is a long and complicated procedure. However, handbooks, manufacturers' catalogs, and design tables can expedite the design considerably. Here we will not be concerned with the problems of the mechanical design of chain drives. Our interest will be limited to problems of the same sort as were discussed in connection with simple gear trains.

It will be recalled that the basic formula used in simple gear trains was:

$$T \times R = t \times r$$

This formula, and the other forms derived from it can be used in the solution of our problems. When used with chain drives, we will let

* Published by the Society of Automotive Engineers, Inc., 485 Lexington Ave., New York, N. Y. 10017.

T = number of teeth on driving sprocket,
R = number of revolutions per minute of driving sprocket,
t = number of teeth on driven sprocket,
r = number of revolutions per minute of driven sprocket.

The following examples illustrate how two forms of this basic formula are applied to chain drives.

■ **EXAMPLE 1:**

The driving sprocket of a silent-chain drive has 21 teeth and runs at 1725 RPM. (*a*) Find the rpm of the driven sprocket if it has 38 teeth. (*b*) What is the speed ratio?

Solution and Explanation:

a) In this problem all the factors that appear in the basic formula except r are known. The appropriate form of the basic formula to use is:

$$r = \frac{T \times R}{t} \qquad \begin{aligned} T &= 21 \\ R &= 1725 \\ t &= 38 \end{aligned}$$

Substituting into the formula, we have:

$$r = \frac{21 \times 1725}{38}$$

$$r = \frac{36225}{38}$$

$$r = 953\tfrac{11}{38}$$

or $r = 953$, neglecting the fractional part of an rpm.

Hence the number of revolutions per minute made by the driven sprocket is 953.

b) The speed ratio is defined as the ratio of R to r, hence the speed ratio is

$$\frac{R}{r} = \frac{1725}{953} = \frac{1.81}{1}$$

Therefore the speed ratio is 1.81 to 1. In words this means that the driving gear makes 1.81 revolutions for 1 revolution of the driven gear.

As a check on our work for part *a*) we substitute the known and the computed quantities into the basic formula:

$$T \times R = t \times r$$

$$21 \times 1725 \overset{?}{=} 38 \times 953\tfrac{11}{38}$$

$$36225 = 36225$$

Hence the computed value of r is correct.

Link-Belt Co.

Using a silent chain drive at an engine test stand during dynamometer testing.

■ **EXAMPLE 2:**

A roller-chain drive installation uses a driven sprocket having 36 teeth. If the driving sprocket turns at 300 RPM and the driven sprocket at 200 rpm, how many teeth are there on the driving sprocket?

Solution and Explanation:

Since we wish to find the number of teeth in the driving sprocket, we use the form of the formula reading:

$$T = \frac{t \times r}{R} \qquad\qquad \begin{aligned} R &= 300 \\ t &= 36 \\ r &= 200 \end{aligned}$$

Substituting into the formula, we obtain:

$$T = \frac{36 \times 200}{300}$$
$$T = 24$$

Hence the driving sprocket has 24 teeth. As a check on our work, we make use of the basic formula:

$$T \times R = t \times r$$

Substituting the known and the computed quantities into the formula, we obtain:

$$24 \times 300 \stackrel{?}{=} 36 \times 200$$
$$7200 = 7200$$

Hence the computed value of T is correct.

21.3   Problems Involving Chain-Drive Calculations

1. A motor runs at 1725 RPM and carries a driving sprocket with 19 teeth. A chain drive transmits power from the motor to a large wheel having 57 teeth. Compute the number of revolutions per minute made by the large wheel.

2. A large wheel having 76 teeth turns at 530 revolutions per minute. A chain drive connects this wheel with a driving sprocket having 23 teeth. The driving sprocket is fastened to the shaft of a motor. What is the speed of the motor?

3. A belt-driven machine is to be changed over to a silent chain drive as illustrated in Figure 358. The speed of the motor is 1140 RPM. How many teeth must the sprocket on the motor have?

4. The timing gears on a popular priced automobile are arranged as in Figure 359. How many revolutions of the small gear are made for 4 revolutions of the larger gear?

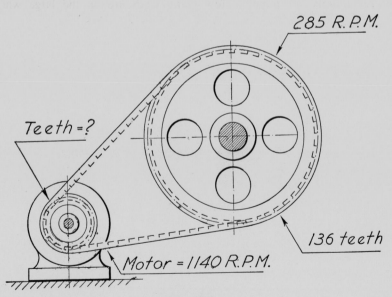

Fig. 358.

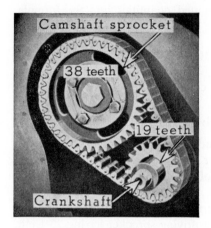

Fig. 359.

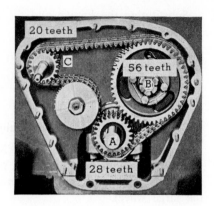

Fig. 360.

5. The timing-gear drive in Figure 360 is typical of that on many automobile engines. When the crankshaft *A* is turning at 1200 RPM what is the rpm of the camshaft sprocket *B*, also the rpm of the sprocket *C* on the generator shaft?

6. A motor running at 1160 RPM carries a sprocket having 19 teeth. A chain drive transmits power from the motor to a large wheel making 290 revolutions per minute. How many teeth are on the large wheel?

CHAPTER 22

Screw Threads

22.1 Introduction

The various types of machines and structures that we make use of in our daily lives are held together in many ways. For wood and brick structures — nails, wood screws, bolts, mortar, and glue may be used. Steel structures are usually riveted, welded, or bolted together. Machines and machine parts may be held together by welds, rivets, pins, keys, and various kinds of metal threaded fasteners.

Although for ordinary work these fasteners are available in standard sizes, frequently machinists or toolmakers may be called on to make

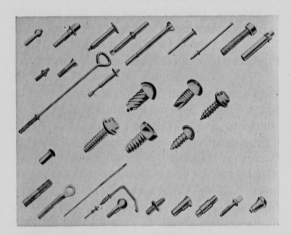

Types of screw thread fasteners.

Townsend Company

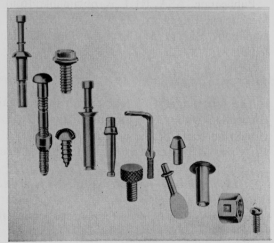

special threaded fasteners. A person working in a shop or engineering office will find it to his advantage to have a working knowledge of the various types of machine screws, bolts, cap screws, and other such types of threaded fasteners. He should also be familiar with the kinds and designations of the standard threads, because he may have occasion to read shop drawings and specifications, or to order fasteners of various kinds.

Standardization of Screw Threads. The basic work leading to the establishment of the American Screw Thread System was done by William Sellers about the time of the Civil War. By careful examination of the existing thread forms and diameter-pitch combinations and the use of good engineering practice he developed the Sellers Standard thread. In 1868 this became the United States Standard thread, and was adopted by industry, railroad companies, and government services.

In the intervening years, committees under the sponsorship of the Society of Automotive Engineers and the American Society of Mechanical Engineers have taken part in the improvement of the existing standards. In 1948, standardization committees of the United States, Great Britain, and Canada reached final agreement, establishing the Unified and American Screw Thread System. Publication ASA B1.1–1960 entitled *Unified and American Screw Threads* contains data on this system including thread forms, dimensions, and tables. In addition to this, the U. S. Dept. of Commerce National Bureau of Standards Handbook H28 (1957) — Part I, Part II, entitled *Screw-Thread Standards for Federal Services* also contains much data on Unified and American, American National and National Miniature Threads. These publications contain complete and detailed information and should be consulted by the interested reader.

Publication ASA B1.1 is obtainable from the American Society of Mechanical Engineers, 29 W. 39th St., New York, N. Y. 10018, and Handbook H28 (1957) from the Superintendent of Documents, Washington, D. C. 20025.

22.2　Definitions

The following list of terms, with their definitions, will prove useful in connection with screw threads. Figures 361 and 362 will be useful in visualizing some of these ideas:

1. *Crest* — The crest is the outermost surface of a thread which joins the flanks of a thread.
2. *Double thread* — A double thread is a thread whose lead is twice its pitch.
3. *Flank* — The flank is the surface joining the crest with the root of a thread.

4. *Height (or Depth)* — The height (or depth) of a thread is the distance between the crest and the root of a thread, measured perpendicular to the thread axis.

5. *Lead* — The lead is the distance a thread travels in the direction of its axis in one complete rotation in reference to a fixed threaded part with which it meshes.

6. *Left-hand thread* — A left-hand thread is a thread which, when viewed in the direction of its axis, appears to move away from the observer as it turns in a counterclockwise direction.

7. *Major diameter* — The major diameter is the diameter of a thread measured at its crest.

8. *Minor diameter* — The minor diameter is the diameter of a thread measured to its root.

9. *Pitch diameter* — The pitch diameter (on a straight thread) is the diameter of an imaginary cylinder having the same axis as the thread and whose surface would pass through the profiles of the thread at such points as to make the width of the thread groove one half of the basic pitch.

10. *Right-hand thread* — A right-hand thread is a thread which, when observed in the direction of its axis, appears to move away from the observer as it turns in a clockwise direction.

11. *Root* — The root of a thread is the bottom surface that joins the sides of two adjacent threads.

12. *Single thread* — A single thread is a thread whose pitch equals its lead.

13. *Straight thread* — A straight thread is a thread (internal or external) cut on a cylindrical surface.

14. *Thread angle* — The thread angle is the angle between the flanks of a thread, measured in a plane through the thread axis.

15. *Triple thread* — A triple thread is a thread whose lead is three times its pitch.

Pitch. One of the most important ideas in connection with threads is that of *pitch*. By the pitch of a screw thread is meant the distance, measured parallel to the axis, from any point on one thread to the corresponding point on the adjacent thread.

Threads per Inch. This is the number of complete threads per inch of axial length, and is specified in the ASA Standards tables.

We can express the above definitions in the form of two simple shop formulas. In words, these may be stated thus:

$$\text{Pitch (in inches)} = \frac{1}{\text{Number of threads per inch}}$$

$$\text{Number of threads per inch} = \frac{1}{\text{Pitch}}$$

In the language of algebra these become:

$$p = \frac{1}{n}$$

$$n = \frac{1}{p}$$

In these formulas, p represents the *pitch* of the threads and n represents the number of threads per inch. The use of these formulas is explained in the following problems.

■ **EXAMPLE 1:**

What is the pitch of the threads on a bolt having 16 threads per inch?

Solution and Explanation:

Since the pitch is equal to 1 divided by the number of threads per inch, we have:

$$p = \frac{1}{n}$$

$$p = \frac{1}{16} = 0.0625 \text{ in.}$$

Hence the pitch of the threads is $\frac{1}{16}$ in. or 0.0625 in. expressed as a decimal.

■ **EXAMPLE 2:**

How many threads per inch are there on a screw having a pitch of 0.125 in.?

Solution and Explanation:

Since the number of threads per inch is equal to 1 divided by the pitch, we have

$$n = \frac{1}{p}$$

$$n = \frac{1}{0.125} = 8$$

Therefore, there are 8 threads per inch on a screw having a pitch of 0.125 in.

Kinds of Threads. So far as their use is concerned, threads can be divided into two classes, namely, those used for screw fasteners and those

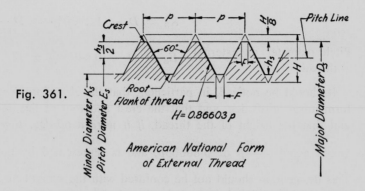

Fig. 361.

American National Form
of External Thread

used for the transmission of motion as in lathes, jacks, valves, presses, and similar machinery or equipment.

There are two systems of threads in use in the United States. The first and older of these, formerly known as the United States Standard or Sellers thread, is now called the *American National* form of thread.

A cross section of the *American National* thread form, with most of the important proportions, is shown in Figure 361.

The term *external thread* refers to a thread on the external surface of a cylinder. Threads on machine screws or bolts are called *external threads*.

The term *internal thread* refers to a thread on the internal surface of a hollow cylinder. Threads on nuts and in tapped holes are called *internal threads*.

The following facts should be noted regarding the *American National* external screw-thread form:

Angle of thread   60 deg.

Number of threads per inch $n = \dfrac{1}{p}$

Pitch of thread (in inches) $p = \dfrac{1}{n}$

Depth of American National thread form $h_8 = \dfrac{3}{4}H = 0.64952p = \dfrac{0.64952}{n}$

Depth of sharp V thread $H = 0.86603p$

Width of flat at crest and root of thread $F = \dfrac{p}{8} = 0.12500p$

Minor diameter of external thread $K_8 = $ outside diameter $-$ twice depth of thread

$K_8 = $ outside diameter $- \dfrac{3}{2}H$

$$K_s = D - 1.29904p = D - \frac{1.29904}{n}$$

Pitch diameter of external thread
$$E_s = D - 0.64952p = D - \frac{0.64952}{n}$$

It should be noticed, in particular, that the *American National* thread form angle is 60 deg. and that the crest and root of the thread are flat, and that the height of the thread, *if it were a 60-deg. sharp V thread,* would equal $\frac{\sqrt{3}}{2}p$ or 0.86603p, and is represented by the symbol *H*. This designation should not be confused with the symbol h_s which represents the height (or depth) of the thread with a flat crest and root.

Bolts, nuts, and screws are still being manufactured in the United States using this American National thread form. Eventually, however, this thread form will be superseded by the Unified series form.

The Unified and American threads, as stated above, are a result of the 1948 standardization agreement between the United States, Great Britain, and Canada. These make up the second system of thread forms and constitute the present American standards.

Certain diameters and pitches in this second system, considered as standard in the three countries mentioned, are called *Unified.* Certain others, used in the *United States* only, are called *American.* Both *Unified* and *American* have the same thread profile. Eventually, all thread forms used in this country will be replaced by the *Unified thread* form, as previously stated.

A cross section of the *Unified* external screw-thread form, with most of its important proportions, is shown in Figure 362.

The following important proportions and data apply to the *Unified* external screw-thread form:

Thread angle	60 deg.
Number of threads per inch	$n = \dfrac{1}{p}$
Pitch of thread (in inches)	$p = \dfrac{1}{n}$
Height of sharp V thread	$H = 0.86603p = \dfrac{0.86603}{n}$
Height of external thread	$h_s = \dfrac{17H}{24} = 0.61343p = \dfrac{0.61343}{n}$
Flat at crest of thread	$F = \dfrac{p}{8} = 0.125p = \dfrac{0.125}{n}$

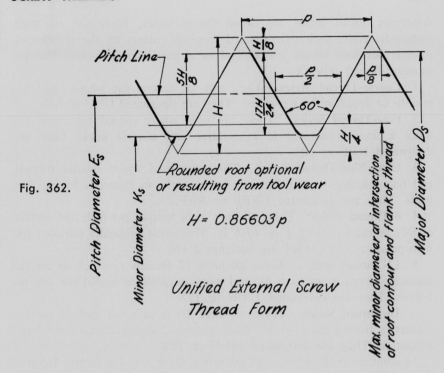

Fig. 362.

Pitch Line

H/8

p/2

p/8

5H/8

H

17H/24

60°

H/4

Pitch Diameter *E*s

Minor Diameter *K*s

Major Diameter *D*s

Max. minor diameter at intersection of root contour and flank of thread

Rounded root optional or resulting from tool wear

H = 0.86603 p

Unified External Screw Thread Form

Pitch diameter of external thread $E_S = D_S - 0.64952p$

Minor diameter of external thread K_S = outside diameter — twice depth of thread

$$K_S = D_S - 2 \times 0.61343p$$

$$K_S = D_S - 1.22687p$$

$$K_S = D_S - \frac{1.22687}{n}$$

It should be noticed, in particular, that the *Unified* thread form angle is also 60 deg.; that the root may be flat or rounded; and that the height (or depth) of the thread, *if it were a 60-deg. sharp V thread,* would also equal $\frac{\sqrt{3}}{2}p$ or 0.86603p, and is represented by the symbol *H*. This designation should not be confused with the symbol h_S which represents the height (or depth) of the thread.

Metal fasteners, such as screws, bolts, and nuts are manufactured in various sizes (diameters) and pitches.

Certain groups of diameter-pitch combinations of the Unified and

American thread forms are called thread series. There are six such standards series, each differentiated from the others by the number of threads per inch which are applied to a particular diameter. The six standard-thread series are:

1. **Coarse-Thread Series.** These are for general use where rapid assembly or disassembly is required. They are designated UNC or NC.

2. **Fine-Thread Series.** These are used where special conditions require a fine thread and in automotive and aircraft work. They are designated UNF or NF.

3. **Extra-Fine-Thread Series.** These are used where smaller threads and finer pitches are required, as, for example, in materials having thin walls. They are designated UNEF or NEF.

4. **8-Thread Series.** These all have eight threads per inch and certain diameters running from 1 in. to 6 in. They were originally intended for high-pressure joints. They are designated 8N.

5. **12-Thread Series.** These all have 12 threads per inch in certain diameters from $\frac{1}{2}$ in. to 6 in. and were originally intended for use on boilers. They are designated 12UN or 12N.

6. **16-Thread Series.** These all have 16 threads per inch in certain diameters from $\frac{3}{4}$ in. to 6 in. These provide fine-pitch threads for large diameters. They are designated 16UN or 16N.

In addition to these six standard series, there are also certain *Selected Special Combinations* of diameter and pitch. These are designated UNS, NS, or UN.

In the publications ASA B1.1 and *Handbook H28* the *Unified* thread data are shown in **bold** type. These thread sizes are also marked by using the letter U in the thread symbol. This letter indicates that the thread sizes so marked are standard threads in the United States, Great Britain, and Canada.

The American National thread form also has six diameter-pitch combinations or thread series. In *Handbook H28* (1957) — Part I, pp. 122–124, these are listed as American National:

1. **Coarse-Thread Series,** designated NC
2. **Fine-Thread Series,** designated NF
3. **Extra-Fine-Thread Series,** designated ENF
4. **8-Thread Series,** designated 8N
5. **12-Thread Series,** designated 12N
6. **16-Thread Series,** designated 16N

The comments made for each thread series of the Unified and American thread form (except the designations) can be applied to the respective American National thread series.

The reader will find it to his advantage to consult and become familiar with the many handbooks that are available and the standards which have been referred to. There he will find complete information on thread forms, classes of threads, sizes, tolerances, and other very important and useful data which cannot well be included here.

22.3 Tolerances and Thread Classes

One of the chief reasons why we enjoy the world's highest standard of living is that we are able to produce economically and in large quantities nearly all of the machinery, machine parts, tools, appliances, and other equipment we use in our homes and places of work. When a particular piece of equipment breaks down or becomes defective we are able to replace the defective part with little difficulty and restore the equipment to working order in a relatively short time and without serious delay.

The reason we are able to do this is due to the fact that various parts are manufactured to certain specifications and dimensions. To manufacture a particular part to *exact* dimensions would be extremely costly. The designer, consequently, specifies that if the dimensions of a particular part fall within certain given values, the part will be accepted and will prove satisfactory no matter by whom it was manufactured.

The total permissible variation of a size is called its *tolerance*. Tolerance is also defined as the difference between the limits of a size. Suppose, for example, that certain parts were specified to have a diameter of .475 in. To produce these parts to this dimension might be so costly as to make their use limited or prohibitive. However, by allowing a variation in size of say .002 in., that is, by allowing the production of these parts with dimensions anywhere from .476 in. to .474 in., their production could be carried out with substantially less cost. On a drawing, this information would be shown as .475±.001 (dimensions in inches), and would indicate that any diameter from .476 in. to .474 in. would be acceptable. The dimensions .476 and .474 are called *limits*. Now, according to the definition of tolerance, it should be the difference between the limits, or .476–.474 or .002 in. Hence, in this example, the tolerance is .002 in. Tolerances may also be used in specifying the location of centers of holes, the sizes of reamed holes, and so on.

When parts are fitted into each other, a clearance must be allowed, depending on the type of fit desired. This is called an *allowance,* and is defined as an intentional difference between the maximum limits of the parts that fit into each other, and may be positive or negative depending on whether it is a clearance or an interference fit. It may also be thought of as being the closest allowable fit, or the smallest diameter of a hole minus the largest diameter of the part fitting into it. Thus in the drawing

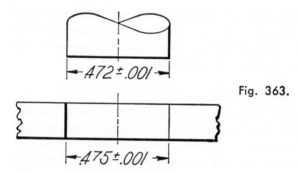

Fig. 363.

(Fig. 363), the hole diameter can vary from .476 to .474 in., while the shaft diameter can vary from .473 to .471 in. The allowance is the difference between the smallest hole and the largest shaft, or .474–.473 or + .001 in. (which, in this example, would be considered a clearance fit). For complete details on general types of fits between parts the reader should consult the American Society of Mechanical Engineers publication B4.1 — 1955, *Preferred Limits and Fits for Cylindrical Parts.*

Threads are separated into classes depending on the tolerances and allowances assigned to each class. The reason for establishing these classes is to insure that screw-thread parts made by various manufacturers will be interchangeable.

For the Unified and American threads the tolerance classes are 1A, 2A, 3A, for external threads and 1B, 2B, and 3B for internal threads. These classes may be briefly described as follows:

Classes 1A and 1B — For threaded components where rapid and easy assembly is necessary and where a liberal allowance is required to permit this.

Classes 2A and 2B — For screws, nuts, bolts, and similar threaded fasteners used for general applications. In these classes belong most of the threaded fasteners commercially manufactured.

Classes 3A and 3B — For those applications where closeness of fit and high accuracy are required.

Tolerances and allowances may be computed from rather complicated formulas but are more easily obtainable from tables.

The American National thread series is grouped into four tolerance classes.

Class 1 — This class includes screw-thread work that must be assembled quickly and easily.

Class 2 — This class includes the largest portion of threaded work in interchangeable manufacture.

Class 3 — This class includes interchangeable screw-thread work of the highest grade.

Class 4 — This class includes screw-thread work which requires a fine snug fit.

Screw-Thread Designations. Threads on screws or bolts are cut or rolled on stock that has what is called a *nominal* diameter. This is the diameter on which the grooves forming the threads are formed. Sizes less than ¼ in. in diameter are referred to by numbers. These run from 0 for the smallest diameter to 12 for the largest. These numbers are 0, 1, 2, 3, 4, 5, 6, 8, 10, and 12. The decimal equivalent diameters of each of these number sizes are given in the Standards and various handbooks.

Screws whose nominal diameter is ¼ in. or larger are specified by giving the diameter in inches or fractions of an inch.

The standard method of designating screw threads consists in listing, in order, the following data:

1. *The nominal size* (as a number from 0 to 12 as explained above or as a diameter in inches or fractions of an inch),
2. *The number of threads per inch,*
3. *The thread-series designation,*
4. *The thread-class designation.*

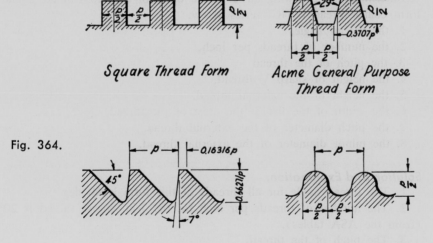

Square Thread Form   Acme General Purpose Thread Form

Fig. 364.

Buttress Thread Form (American Standard)   Knuckle Thread Form

External Threads

Thus an external screw thread marked 8 (0.1640)–32 NC–2A refers to a number 8 (0.1640 in. diameter) screw having 32 threads per inch, thread series NC (American National Coarse), thread class 2A. Right-hand threads carry no further designation.

The designation ⅜–24 UNF–1A–LH refers to a thread on a ⅜-in.-diameter screw, thread series UNF (Unified fine-thread series), thread class 1A, left-hand thread.

Other Thread Forms. The Unified and American screw-thread form is used chiefly for fasteners, that is, for screws, nuts, and bolts. Other thread shapes are available for the transmission of power and motion. Among these are the *square thread,* the *Acme thread,* the *buttress thread,* and the *knuckle thread.*

Some of these threads, with their proportions, are illustrated in Figure 364.

22.4   Calculations Pertaining to Screw Threads

In connection with the Unified and American thread form there are at least 20 formulas listed in the ASA B1.1, *Unified and American Screw Threads* standards. Some of the most important of these will be considered here.

■ **EXAMPLE 1:**

Determine the following basic thread data for a ¼–20 Unified thread form coarse-thread (UNC) series screw:

1. the thread angle,
2. the number of threads per inch,
3. the pitch of the thread,
4. the height of sharp V thread,
5. the height of the external thread,
6. the width of the flat at the crest of the thread,
7. the pitch diameter of the external thread,
8. the minor diameter of the external thread.

Solution and Explanation:

1. The thread angle for all threads of this form is 60 deg.
2. The number of threads per inch for the ¼-in. coarse thread is 20 (from the ASA tables).
3. The pitch of the thread:

$$p = \frac{1}{n}$$

$$p = \frac{1}{20} = 0.0500 \text{ in.}$$

4. The height of sharp V thread:

$$H = 0.86603p$$
$$H = 0.86603 \times 0.0500 = 0.04330 \text{ in.}$$

5. The height of the external thread:

$$h_S = 0.61343p$$
$$h_S = 0.61343 \times 0.0500$$
$$h_S = 0.03067 \text{ in.}$$

6. The width of the flat at the crest of the thread:

$$F = \frac{p}{8}$$
$$F = \frac{0.0500}{8} = 0.00625 \text{ in.}$$

7. The pitch diameter of the external thread:

$$\begin{aligned} E_S &= D_S - 0.64952p \\ &= \tfrac{1}{4} - 0.64952 \times 0.0500 \\ &= \tfrac{1}{4} - 0.032476 \\ &= 0.2175 \text{ in.} \end{aligned}$$

8. The minor diameter of the external thread:

$$\begin{aligned} K_S &= D_S - 1.22687p \\ &= \tfrac{1}{4} - 1.22687 \times 0.0500 \\ &= \tfrac{1}{4} - 0.0613435 \\ &= 0.1887 \text{ in.} \end{aligned}$$

A second example will illustrate the determination of the corresponding basic thread data for an American National form coarse thread series screw.

■ EXAMPLE 2:

Determine the following basic thread data for a $\tfrac{1}{4}$–20 American National form coarse-thread series screw:

1. the thread angle,
2. the number of threads per inch,
3. the pitch of the thread,
4. the height of sharp V thread,
5. the depth of the external thread,
6. the width of the flat at the crest of the thread,
7. the pitch diameter of the external thread,
8. the minor diameter of the external thread.

Solution and Explanation:

1. The thread angle for the American National thread form is 60 deg.
2. The number of threads per inch for the $\frac{1}{4}$-in. coarse series threads is 20 (from the tables).
3. The pitch of the thread:

$$p = \frac{1}{n} = \frac{1}{20} = 0.0500 \text{ in.}$$

4. The height of sharp V thread:
$H = 0.86603p$
$H = 0.86603 \times 0.0500 = 0.04330$ in.
5. The height of the external thread:
$h_S = 0.64952p$
$h_S = 0.64952 \times 0.0500 = 0.03248$ in.
6. The width of the flat at the crest of the thread:

$$F = \frac{p}{8} = \frac{0.05000}{8} = 0.00625 \text{ in.}$$

7. The pitch diameter of the external thread:
E_S = Basic major diameter − height of thread
E_S = Nominal size (outside diameter) − $0.64952p$
$E_S = \frac{1}{4} - 0.03248$
$E_S = 0.2175$ in.
8. The minor diameter of the external thread:
K_S = Basic major diameter − twice height of thread
K_S = Nominal size − $1.2990p$
$K_S = \frac{1}{4} - 0.06495$
$K_S = 0.1850$ in.

It can be seen that the only differences in these eight items computed are in the height (also called the depth) of the threads and the minor diameter of the external thread.

■ **EXAMPLE 3:**

How deep a cut must be made in cutting a Unified coarse thread on a bolt having eight threads to the inch?

Solution and Explanation:

The height (or depth) of the Unified thread:

$$h_S = 0.61343p$$
$$\text{or } h_S = \frac{0.61343}{n}$$

now $n = 8$, hence

$$h_\mathrm{s} = \frac{0.61343}{8}$$

$$h_\mathrm{s} = 0.0767 \text{ in.}$$

Therefore, the depth of the cut is 0.0767 in.

■ EXAMPLE 4:

A square threaded screw on a bench vise has four threads to the inch. What is the pitch of the thread? What is the depth of the thread?

Solution and Explanation:

Since the pitch $p = \dfrac{1}{n}$, we have $p = \dfrac{1}{4} = 0.2500$ in. The depth of the square thread equals one half of the pitch. Therefore, the depth =

$$\frac{p}{2} = \frac{0.2500}{2} = 0.1250 \text{ in.}$$

■ EXAMPLE 5:

The Unified fine-thread series shows 16 threads per inch for a $\frac{3}{4}$-in. diameter bolt. Find:
1. the height (or depth) of the external thread,
2. the double height (or depth) of the external thread,
3. the minor diameter of this bolt.

Solution and Explanation:

Using the formulas already given, we find that:
1. The height (or depth) of the external thread:

$$h_\mathrm{s} = 0.61343p = \frac{0.61343}{n}$$

$$\text{or } h_\mathrm{s} = \frac{0.61343}{16} = 0.03834 \text{ in.}$$

Hence the height of the external thread is 0.03834 in.
2. The double height (or depth) of the external thread is $2h_\mathrm{s}$.

$$\text{Hence } 2h_\mathrm{s} = 1.22687p = \frac{1.22687}{n}$$

$$2h_\mathrm{s} = \frac{1.22687}{16} = 0.07668 \text{ in.}$$

Therefore the double height (or depth) of the external thread is 0.07668 in.
3. The minor diameter of this bolt is

$$K_\mathrm{s} = D_\mathrm{s} - 2h_\mathrm{s}$$

$$K_S = 0.7500 - 0.07668$$
$$\text{or } K_S = 0.6733 \text{ in.}$$

Hence the minor diameter of this bolt is 0.6733 in.

22.5   Problems Involving Screw-Thread Calculations

For the following problems involving the *Unified and American* thread form, find the value of p, the pitch; H, the height of the sharp V thread; h_S, the height of the external thread; and K_S, the minor diameter. Carry the computations out to five decimal places and round them off to four decimal places.

1. Screw threads described as 1 (.073)–64 UNC–3A.
2. Screw threads described as $\frac{1}{2}$–13 NC–3A.
3. Screw threads described as $2\frac{1}{2}$–4 UNC–2A.
4. Screw threads described as $\frac{1}{4}$–28 UNF–2A.
5. Screw threads described as 12 (.216)–24 NC–2A. (The dimension .216 is the nominal size or diameter in inches.)

For Problems 6 through 9, involving the *American National* thread form, find the value of p, the pitch; H, the height of the sharp V thread; h_S, the height of the external thread; and K_S, the minor diameter. Round off the computations to four decimal places.

6. Screw threads described as $\frac{3}{8}$–24 NF–2A.
7. Screw threads described as 2–8 N–2A.
8. A roundhead machine screw with threads described as 10 (.190)–24 NC–2A.
9. A flathead machine screw with threads described as 8 (.164)–32 NC–2A.
10. Compute the pitch and the depth of a square thread cut on a stock 1 in. in diameter if there are five threads per inch.
11. Compute the pitch and depth of a general-purpose Acme thread cut on stock having a diameter of 1 in. and five threads per inch.
12. What is the width of the lathe tool required to cut $2\frac{1}{2}$ square threads to the inch? How deep is the cut?
13. What is the area at the minor diameter of the thread in Problem 2?
14. Compute the area at the minor diameter of the thread in Problem 3. If each square inch of this area sustains a load of 2500 lb., what is the total load sustained?
15. The bolt whose threads are specified in Problem 1 carries a load of 7000 lb. Compute the area at the minor diameter of the thread. Divide the load by this area. This quotient is called the *stress*. How many pounds per square inch is it?
16. For the roundhead cap screw shown in Figure 365 compute the same data as for Problem 1 above.

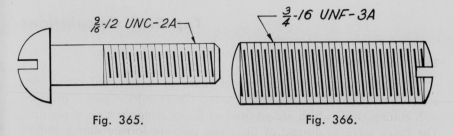

Fig. 365.   Fig. 366.

17. For the oval point slotted headless setscrew shown in Figure 366 compute the same data as for Problem 1 above.

18. For the tie rod shown (Fig. 367), compute the pitch and minor diameter of each of the threaded ends.

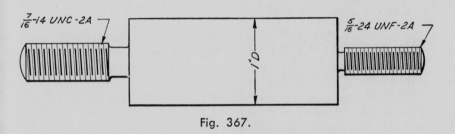

Fig. 367.

19. What is the area at the minor diameter of the threads in each end of the tie rod in Problem 18?

20. Compute the pitch and minor diameter of the setscrew shown in Figure 368.

Fig. 368.

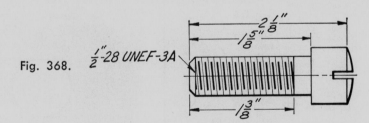

CHAPTER 23

Tap-Drill Calculations

23.1 Drills and Taps

The drills used in the drilling of holes in metals and other hard materials are cylindrical end-cutting tools. The cylindrical part is provided with cutting edges which are grooved or fluted along the axis of the drill. The flutes serve to dispose of the chips that are formed during drilling

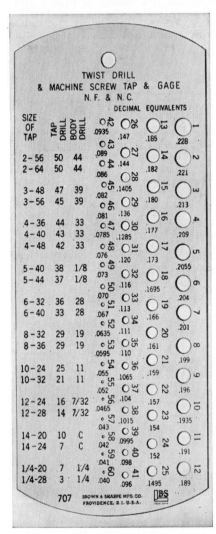

Tap drill sizes.

Brown & Sharpe Mfg. Co.

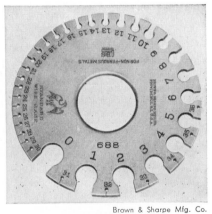

Brown & Sharpe Mfg. Co.

Wire gauge sizes.

Cleveland Twist Drill Co.

A straight shank twist drill.

Cleveland Twist Drill Co.

A carbon drill.

Cleveland Twist Drill Co.

A taper-shank twist drill.

and also to allow a cutting lubricant to come in contact with the cutting edges.

With respect to their sizes (diameters), twist drills are arranged in:

a) A *number* series, running from No. 80, having a decimal equivalent diameter of 0.0135 in., up to No. 1, having a decimal equivalent diameter of 0.2280 in. (80 sizes in all, referred to as the wire gauge sizes).

b) A *letter* series, running from *A*, having a decimal equivalent diameter of 0.2340 in., to *Z*, having a decimal equivalent diameter of 0.4130 in. (26 sizes).

c) A *fractional* series, running from $\frac{1}{64}$, having a decimal equivalent diameter of 0.0156 in., to $\frac{1}{2}$, having a decimal equivalent of 0.5000 in.

These three series all have *straight* shanks.

Tables listing *taper* shank drills in sizes from $\frac{1}{8}$ in. to $3\frac{1}{2}$ in. as well as other tables and data on twist drills will be found in *American Standard Twist Drills* (ASA B5.12 — 1958), published by the American Society of Mechanical Engineers, 29 West 39th Street, New York, N. Y. 10018, which the reader is encouraged to read and consult.

23.2   Tap-Drill Calculations

When screws or bolts are inserted into holes in metal parts to fasten them together, these holes must be drilled in the metal and then threaded to accommodate the fasteners. The drills used in drilling these holes are called tap drills, and the threads are called tapped threads. Reference to Figure 369 should make these terms clear.

The tool used to form the internal threads after the holes are drilled is called a tap. The process of forming the internal threads is called tapping.

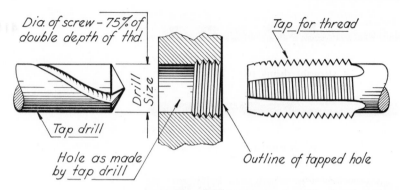

Fig. 369.

Although some tapping must be done by hand, most internal threads are tapped by using special machines and fixtures.

The choice of the proper tap-drill size, although reducible to a fairly good rule-of-thumb procedure, may be complicated by many factors. Among these are:

1. the kind of material to be drilled,
2. the condition of the drills,
3. the speed of the drills,

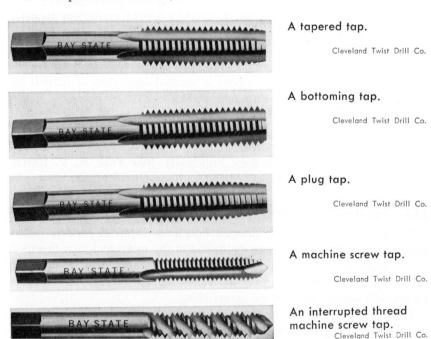

A tapered tap.

Cleveland Twist Drill Co.

A bottoming tap.

Cleveland Twist Drill Co.

A plug tap.

Cleveland Twist Drill Co.

A machine screw tap.

Cleveland Twist Drill Co.

An interrupted thread machine screw tap.

Cleveland Twist Drill Co.

4. the variations in standard drill sizes,

5. the kind of lubricant used,

6. the types of holes to be drilled (such as through holes which go clear through the material, or blind holes which do not).

Other important factors are the thread pitch, the percent of full thread to be tapped, and the ratio of the depth of the tapped hole to the tap diameter.

When tap drills that are too small in diameter are used, tapping becomes difficult and may result in the breaking of the taps, the removal of which is both time-consuming and costly. Too large a tap drill, on the other hand, may result in the tapping of too small a percentage of the full thread. In the Appendix will be found Tables of Straight Shank Twist Drills and Tap Drills (see pp. 484–489).

To begin with, it is easy to see that if we drilled a hole with a diameter equal to the major (or nominal) diameter of the screw, that the screw would not be able to engage the metal. If we drilled a hole with a diameter equal to the minor diameter of the screw (the diameter at the base of the thread) it would be necessary to tap full threads in the metal. This would be difficult to do, and is unnecessary from the point of view of strength.

Experience has led to the use of a tap-drill diameter such that 75 percent of the full thread may be tapped, although for deep holes this may be reduced to 50 percent. On the basis of 75 percent full thread, a simple working formula for the tap-drill size may be derived. We recall that, for the American National thread form, the basic depth of the thread is:

$$h_S = 0.64952p$$

or $h_S = \dfrac{0.64952}{n}$ where p = pitch in inches and

n = number of threads per inch.

If we multiplied this value by 2, we would obtain the "double" height of the thread. We get, then:

$$2h_S = \dfrac{1.29904}{n}$$

If we then agree that 75 percent of the full thread is satisfactory, we would multiply $2h_S$ by $\dfrac{75}{100}$, and get:

$$0.75 \times 2hs = \dfrac{0.75 \times 1.29904}{n}$$

or $1.50h_S = \dfrac{0.9743}{n}$

Deducting this from D, the major external thread diameter of the screw in inches, we obtain a formula for the tap-drill diameter in inches.

Formula A

$$T = D - \frac{0.9743}{n}$$

If we had used 77 percent of full thread, we would have obtained $\frac{1.00}{n}$ instead of $\frac{0.9743}{n}$ and the above formula could be written as:

Formula B

$$T = D - \frac{1}{n}$$

These two formulas are based on the American National thread form. If they are used for Unified and American thread forms, Formula A would allow about 79.5 percent of full thread and Formula B about 81.5 percent of full thread.

For developing a thread depth of a given percent, a more general formula is:

Formula C

$$T = D - (\text{percent of full thread}) \times 2 \times h_s$$

---

where D has the same meaning as before and $h_s = \frac{0.64952}{n}$ for the American National thread form and $h_s = \frac{0.61343}{n}$ for the Unified and American thread form.

Stated in words, Formula A reads

Tap-drill diameter in inches equals outside (nominal) diameter of the tap (or screw) in inches, minus 0.9743 divided by the number of threads per inch.

Similarly, Formula B reads:

Tap-drill diameter in inches equals the outside (nominal) diameter of the tap (or screw) in inches, minus 1 divided by the number of threads per inch.

The commercial drill size in 64ths of an inch may be found by determining how many *full* 64ths there are in the calculated size. This is determined by multiplying the *decimal* portion of the calculated size by 64. The whole number in this result indicates the number of full 64ths in this decimal.

This number of 64ths, combined with original whole number if any, in the calculated size, will give the commercial tap-drill size, to the nearest 64th of an inch, that should be used.

It should be remembered that these are working rules, and that they are based on 75 to 77 percent of full thread depth. This may be reduced to 55 percent or even 50 percent depending on the particular job requirements.

It should also be remembered that the particular commercial-size drill selected after the calculation has been made may not necessarily provide for a 75 percent thread depth.

The formulas

$$T = D - \frac{0.9743}{n}$$

and $$T = D - \frac{1}{n}$$

may be used for the Unified and American thread form as well as for the American National thread form, provided one keeps in mind the resulting percent of thread depth obtained.

The student should be able to recognize the various types of tapped holes as shown in shop drawings.

Two types are met with in practice. Those drilled entirely through the material are called *through holes,* while those going partly into the material are called *blind holes.* Figure 370 shows the simplified drafting method of representing each.

The following problems illustrate how these formulas are used:

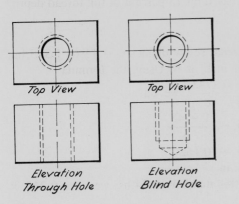

Top View

Top View

Fig. 370.

Elevation
Through Hole

Elevation
Blind Hole

■ **EXAMPLE 1:**

What is the calculated tap-drill size for drilling a hole to be tapped for a $\frac{1}{2}$–20NC bolt using the American National thread form?

Solution and Explanation:

Here the number of threads per inch n is 20. Using the formula

$$T = D - \frac{1}{n}, \text{ we get}$$

$$T = \frac{1}{2} - \frac{1}{20}$$

or $T = 0.500 - 0.050$

or $T = 0.450$ in.

Therefore the tap-drill diameter is 0.450 in. To determine the commercial drill size, this decimal number is multiplied by 64, giving $0.450 \times 64 = 28.80$ or 29. Hence the commercial drill size is $\frac{29}{64}$ in.

If we had used the formula $T = D - \dfrac{0.9743}{n}$ we would have obtained

$$T = 0.500 - \frac{0.9743}{20}$$

or $T = 0.500 - 0.0487$

$T = 0.4513$ in.

Changing this to 64ths of an inch, we obtain $0.4513 \times 64 = 28.88$ or 29. Thus the commercial drill size is $\frac{29}{64}$ in., as before. Referring to the table of tap-drill sizes, we see that this size tap drill would develop 65 percent of the full thread.

■ **EXAMPLE 2:**

What commercial tap-drill size is needed to drill a hole for a $1\frac{3}{8}$–6 UNC (Unified screw-thread form) bolt based on 75 percent of full thread depth?

Solution and Explanation:

Here we know that D, the nominal screw diameter, is $1\frac{3}{8}$ or 1.375 in., and n, the number of threads per inch, is 6. Using the formula

$$T = D - \frac{0.9743}{n}, \text{ we have}$$

$$T = 1.375 - \frac{0.9743}{6}$$

$T = 1.375 - 0.162$

$T = 1.213$ in.

Changing the decimal part of this number to 64ths, we have $0.213 \times$

$64 = 13.632$ or 14 full 64ths. The commercial tap-drill diameter is consequently $1\frac{14}{64}$ or $1\frac{7}{32}$ in.

Hence the commercial tap-drill size needed is $1\frac{7}{32}$ in. If we had used the simpler formula

$$T = D - \frac{1}{n}, \text{ we would have obtained}$$

$$T = 1.375 - \frac{1}{6}$$

or $T = 1.375 - 0.167$

or $T = 1.208$ in.

Converting 0.208 to 64ths, we find that it equals $0.208 \times 64 = 13.312$ or 13 full 64ths, and the commercial tap-drill size would be $1\frac{13}{64}$ in.

This, however, would be for a thread depth of slightly more than 75 percent.

■ EXAMPLE 3:

What commercial size tap drill is needed to drill a hole for a $\frac{5}{16}$–24 UNF–2A (Unified fine thread series) screw, based on 75 percent of full thread depth?

Solution and Explanation:

Here we know that the nominal screw diameter is $\frac{5}{16}$ in., and the number of threads per inch is 24.

Hence in the formula:

$$T = D - \frac{0.9743}{n}$$

$D = \frac{5}{16}$ in. and $n = 24$.

Substituting these in the formula we find that

$$T = \frac{5}{16} - \frac{0.9743}{24}$$

$$T = 0.3125 - 0.0406$$

$$T = 0.2719 \text{ in.}$$

If we now refer to a table of stock or commercial drill sizes, we find that a tap drill bearing the letter I has a diameter which is the nearest to this value. This particular tap drill will allow 75 percent of the full thread depth to be developed by the tap.

If we converted the above diameter to 64ths of an inch, we would find that

$$0.2719 \times 64 = 17.4 \text{ or } \frac{17}{64} \text{ in.}$$

Hence we could also use a tap drill of this diameter if one were avail-

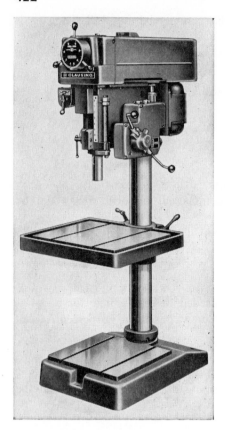

A drill press.

Clausing

able. However, the decimal equivalent of $\frac{17}{64}$ in. is 0.2656 in., and this would allow nearly 87 percent of the full thread depth to be developed by the tap. This would be considered quite high, and tapping would be difficult.

The reason for this difficulty is that no commercial *fractional-size* drills are available to allow tapping the threads to accommodate a $\frac{5}{16}$–24 UNF screw. For this particular screw thread there are *three* letter sizes available, namely *H, I,* and *J*. Of these, *H* has a diameter of 0.2660 in., *I* has a diameter of 0.2720 in., and *J* has a diameter of 0.2770 in.

This example reveals that a good procedure would be both to make the computation and to check the findings with a table of tap-drill sizes. This method would minimize the possible errors and also indicate what number or letter-size drills may be suitable if fractional sizes were not available for a particular size thread form.

In the manufacture of ring thread gauges used in testing the accuracy of external threads, 100 percent of the full thread depth is used. This percentage is used for reasons of strength and total root diameter clearance. For this value of thread depth, a formula for tap-drill size (for the American National thread form) can be obtained.

Inserting 100 percent in Formula C, we obtain:

$$T = D - 100 \text{ percent} \times 2 \times \frac{.64952}{n}$$

Since 100 percent = 1.00 the formula becomes:

$$T = D - \frac{1.29904}{n}$$

Rounding off to their decimal places for reasons of practicality, we have Formula D for finding the tap-drill size for 100 percent thread in the American National series:

$$\boxed{T = D - \frac{1.299}{n}}$$

For the Unified and American thread form, the corresponding formula is:

$$T = D - \frac{1.227}{n}$$

Finally, it should again be emphasized that the selection of the proper size of tap drill depends on many factors. The formulas given here serve more or less as starting points or guides. Experience is the best criterion in any particular case; moreover, men with many years of practice and mature judgment recommend that trial holes be drilled and tapped before the final selection of a tap-drill size is made. In the long run this will be found to be the most satisfactory and least expensive procedure.

23.3 Problems Involving Tap-Drill Calculations

1. What commercial size tap drill should be used in drilling a hole to be tapped for a $\frac{1}{4}$–20 NC–2A bolt?

2. A hole is to be drilled and tapped for a $1\frac{1}{2}$–12 NF–2A bolt. What size tap drill should be used?

3. A hole is to be drilled and tapped for a 10–32 NF–2A screw. The nominal diameter of this screw is 0.190 in. What is the decimal equivalent diameter of the tap drill to be used? What number drill should be used?

4. What is the decimal equivalent diameter of the tap drill to be used for drilling a hole to be tapped for a $\frac{3}{8}$–16 NC–2A bolt? What is the fractional size tap drill that can be used?

5. Holes are to be drilled in a steel plate and then tapped for $\frac{3}{8}$–24

UNF–2A screws. What is the decimal equivalent of the tap drill that you would recommend? What number drill is this?

6. The nominal diameter of the 6–32 NC–2A screws is 0.138 in. If holes are to be drilled and tapped for such screws, what is the diameter of the tap drill in 64ths of an inch that should be used?

7. What size tap drill should be used for the holes in the plate shown in Figure 371?

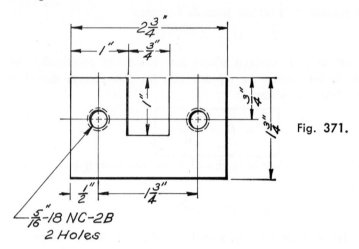

Fig. 371.

8. On a shop drawing, a tapped hole is shown and marked "$\frac{7}{8}$–9 UNC–2B." What commercial size drill should be used by the man in the shop to drill the hole?

9. Calculate the diameter of the tap drill used in drilling a hole to be tapped for a 1–8 UNC–2A screw. What is the corresponding commercial drill size?

10. A shop drawing shows a tapped hole marked as shown in Figure 372. What is the corresponding commercial tap-drill size?

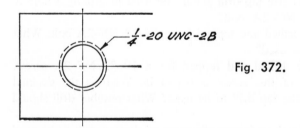

Fig. 372.

11. A casting is to be provided with four holes which are to be drilled and tapped for $\frac{9}{16}$–12 UNC–2A screws. What is the decimal equivalent of the tap-drill diameter? What commercial size drill should be used?

12. Calculate the decimal equivalent of the tap-drill diameter for a $\frac{5}{8}$–18 UNF–2A screw and for a $\frac{5}{8}$–11 UNC–1A screw. Convert each of these diameters to 64ths. Which has the larger diameter and by how many 64ths?

13. Compare the calculated decimal tap-drill sizes and also the commercial tap-drill sizes (to the nearest 64th of an inch) for a $\frac{9}{16}$–18 UNF–2A setscrew and a $\frac{9}{16}$–12 UNC–2A setscrew.

14. An apprentice was given the V block shown in the sketch (Fig. 373) and was asked to drill and tap the holes shown. What commercial-size tap drill should be used in drilling the holes?

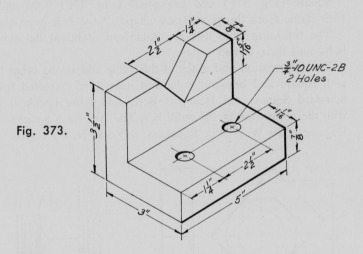

Fig. 373.

15. If $\frac{7}{16}$–20 UNF–2A screws are to be used to attach a bracket to a machine frame, what commercial-size tap drill should be used for drilling the holes in the bracket?

16. In the shop drawing of a small C clamp (Fig. 374), what size tap drill should be used in drilling the hole for the screw indicated?

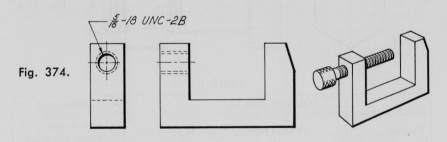

Fig. 374.

CHAPTER 24

Square and Hexagon Bolts and Nuts

24.1 Introduction

Bolts and nuts constitute another class of metal fasteners which are manufactured and used in great quantities. In contrast to screws, which fit into threaded holes in one or more of the parts they fasten together, bolts pass entirely through the parts they hold together and are tightened by a nut which engages the threaded portion of the bolt.

Square (Fig. 375) and hexagonal (Fig. 376) bolts and nuts derive their name from the geometrical shape of the bolt head and of the nut.

The following table lists the American Standard hexagon and square bolts and their thread series.

The information and notes in this table and in the other tables dealing with square and hexagon bolts and nuts were extracted from American Standard Square and Hexagon Bolts and Nuts (ASA B18.2 — 1960) with the permission of the publisher, The American Society of Mechanical Engineers, 29 West 39th Street, New York, N. Y. 10018.

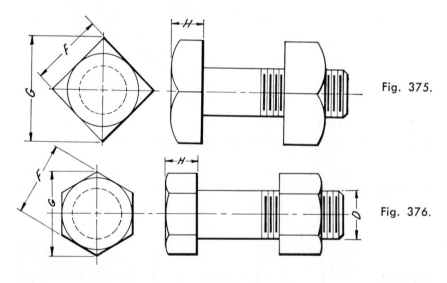

Fig. 375.

Fig. 376.

TABLE I

SQUARE BOLTS		THREADS
Regular[1]	14 sizes from ¼-in. dia. to 1⅝-in. dia.	Coarse-thread series, Class 2A

[1] Bolt is not finished on any surface.

HEXAGON BOLTS		THREADS
Regular[1]	23 sizes from $\frac{1}{4}$-in. dia. to 4-in. dia.	Coarse-thread series, Class 2A
Regular semifinished[2]	Same as for Regular	
Heavy[1]	17 sizes from $\frac{1}{2}$-in. dia. to 3-in. dia.	
Heavy semifinished[2]	15 sizes from $\frac{1}{2}$-in. dia. to 3-in. dia.	
Heavy finished[3]	Same as for heavy semifinished	Coarse-, fine-, or 8-thread series, Class 2A for plain (unplated) bolts
Finished[3]	20 sizes from $\frac{1}{4}$-in. dia. to 3-in. dia.	Same as for heavy finished bolts

[2] Semifinished bolt is processed to produce a flat bearing surface under head only.

[3] "Finished" in the title refers to the quality of manufacture and the closeness of tolerance and does not indicate that surfaces are completely machined.

24.2 Formulas for Hexagon and Square Bolt Heads

Formulas for the dimensions of square and hexagon bolt heads are found in the Standards referred to above. However, instead of listing the various formulas, it is better to arrange them in tabular form for ready reference. This arrangement is shown in the table called *Formulas for Bolt Heads*.

TABLE II
FORMULAS FOR BOLT HEADS

All dimensions in inches.

PRODUCT (Type of Bolt)	WIDTH ACROSS FLATS		HEIGHT OF HEAD	
	BASIC[1]		NOMINAL[2]	
	Size (Dia.)	Width	Size (Dia.)	Height
Regular Hexagon Bolt	$\frac{1}{4}$	$1\frac{1}{2}D* + \frac{1}{16}$	$\frac{1}{4}$ to $\frac{7}{16}$	$\frac{2}{3}D + \frac{3}{64}$
	$\frac{5}{16}$ to 4	$1\frac{1}{2}D$	$\frac{1}{2}$ to $\frac{7}{8}$	$\frac{2}{3}D + \frac{1}{32}$
			1 to $1\frac{7}{8}$	$\frac{2}{3}D + \frac{1}{16}$
			2 to $3\frac{3}{4}$	$\frac{2}{3}D + \frac{1}{8}$
			4	$\frac{2}{3}D + \frac{3}{16}$

* D = Nominal bolt size.

[1] Adjusted to 16ths. (The dimension is also called "maximum" in some tables.)

[2] $\frac{1}{4}$ in. to 1 in. sizes adjusted to 64ths.

$1\frac{1}{8}$ in. to $2\frac{1}{2}$ in. sizes adjusted upward to 32nds.

$2\frac{3}{4}$ in. to 4 in. sizes adjusted upward to 16ths.

PRODUCT (Type of Bolt)	WIDTH ACROSS FLATS		HEIGHT OF HEAD	
	BASIC[1]		NOMINAL[2]	
	Size (Dia.)	Width	Size (Dia.)	Height
	$\frac{1}{4}$	$1\frac{1}{2}D + \frac{1}{16}$	$\frac{1}{4}$ to $\frac{7}{8}$	$\frac{5}{8}D$
Regular Semifinished Hexagon Bolt	$\frac{5}{16}$ to 4	$1\frac{1}{2}D$	1 to $1\frac{1}{8}$	$\frac{5}{8}D - \frac{1}{64}$
			2 to $2\frac{3}{4}$	$\frac{5}{8}D - \frac{1}{32}$
			3	$\frac{5}{8}D$
			$3\frac{1}{4}$ to $3\frac{3}{4}$	$\frac{5}{8}D - \frac{1}{16}$
			4	$\frac{5}{8}D$
Finished Hexagon Bolt	$\frac{1}{4}$	$1\frac{1}{2}D + \frac{1}{16}$	Same as for Regular Semifinished Hexagon Bolt	
	$\frac{5}{16}$ to 3	$1\frac{1}{2}D$		
Heavy Hexagon Bolt	$1\frac{1}{2}D + \frac{1}{8}$		$\frac{3}{4}D + \frac{1}{16}$	
Heavy Semifinished Hexagon Bolt Finished Heavy Hexagon Bolt	$1\frac{1}{2}D + \frac{1}{8}$		$\frac{1}{2}$ to $\frac{7}{8}$	$\frac{3}{4}D + \frac{1}{32}$
			1 to $1\frac{7}{8}$	$\frac{3}{4}D$
			2 to 3	$\frac{3}{4}D - \frac{1}{16}$
Regular Square Bolt	$1\frac{1}{2}D$		$\frac{3}{4}D$	

For both hexagon and square bolts, the letters F, G, and H represent the following (see Figs. 375 and 376):

F represents the width across the flats of the bolt head.

G represents the width across the corners of the bolt head.

H represents the height of the bolt head.

The same letters are used to represent the corresponding dimensions of the nut. For the hexagon bolts, the *maximum* width across the corners equals $\frac{2}{3} \times \sqrt{3} \times$ the width across the flats, or $\frac{2\sqrt{3}}{3}F$. Since $\frac{2\sqrt{3}}{3}F =$ 1.1547F, a formula can be written for G in terms of F. This formula becomes:

Formula A

$G = 1.1547F$

Maximum width across the corners of hexagon bolt heads in terms of width across flats.

In words, this formula tells us that *the maximum width across the corners of the head of a hexagon bolt is 1.1547 times its width across the flats.* Another formula can be obtained for this maximum width in terms of the nominal bolt diameter. Since $F = 1\frac{1}{2}D$, then:

$$G = 1.1547 \times 1\frac{1}{2}D \text{ or}$$

Formula B

G = 1.7321D

Maximum width across corners of hexagon bolt heads in terms of bolt diameter.

Thus, to find the maximum width across the corners of the head of a hexagon bolt, multiply 1.7321 by the nominal bolt diameter.

These two formulas hold only for those bolts whose basic width across the flats is $1\frac{1}{2}D$. For the other bolts (see table and Examples 2 and 3 following), $\frac{1}{16}$ in. or $\frac{1}{8}$ in. must be added to $1\frac{1}{2}D$ to obtain F, the width across the flats, to be used in Formula B. For these cases, Formula B would become:

Formula C1

$$G = 1.1547(1\frac{1}{2}D + \frac{1}{16}) = 1.7321D + 0.0722$$

or

Formula C2

$$G = 1.1547(1\frac{1}{2}D + \frac{1}{8}) = 1.7321D + 0.1443$$

For a square bolt, the maximum width across the corners equals $\sqrt{2} \times F$, or $1.4142 \times F$. Hence the formula for the maximum width across the corners is:

Formula D

G = 1.4142F

Maximum width across the corners for square bolt heads in terms of width across flats.

Thus, to compute the maximum width across the corners of the head of a square bolt, multiply 1.4142 by width of the bolt head across the flats.

Another formula can be obtained for the maximum width in terms of the nominal square-head bolt diameter. Since $F = 1\frac{1}{2}D$, then

$$G = \sqrt{2} \times 1\frac{1}{2}D = 1.4142 \times 1\frac{1}{2}D, \text{ or:}$$

Formula E
$G = 2.1213D$
Maximum width across corners of square bolt heads in terms of bolt diameter.

Thus, to find the maximum width across the corners of the head of a square bolt, multiply 2.1213 by the nominal bolt diameter.

The nominal height or thickness of the bolt heads is represented by the letter H. This thickness varies according to the bolt diameters. The table shows that the nominal height of the bolt heads varies from $\frac{5}{8}D$

TABLE III
FORMULAS FOR NUTS*

All dimensions in inches.

Width Across Corners

For all square nuts, maximum width across corners equals 1.4142 × max. width across flats. For all hexagon nuts, maximum width across corners equals 1.1547 × maximum width across flats.

Type of Nut	Width Across Flats		Thickness of Nuts	
	Basic[1]		Nominal[2]	
	Size	Width	Size	Thickness
Regular Square } Regular Hexagon }	$\frac{1}{4}$ to $\frac{5}{8}$ $\frac{3}{4}$ to 3	$1\frac{1}{2}D$** $+ \frac{1}{16}$ $1\frac{1}{2}D$	All sizes	$\frac{7}{8}D$
Regular Semifinished Hexagon	$\frac{1}{4}$ to $\frac{5}{8}$ $\frac{3}{4}$ to 3	$1\frac{1}{2}D + \frac{1}{16}$ $1\frac{1}{2}D$	$\frac{1}{4}$ to $1\frac{1}{8}$ $1\frac{1}{4}$ to 2 $2\frac{1}{4}$ to 3	$\frac{7}{8}D - \frac{1}{64}$ $\frac{7}{8}D - \frac{1}{32}$ $\frac{7}{8}D - \frac{3}{64}$
Finished Hexagon	$\frac{1}{4}$ $\frac{5}{16}$ to 3	$1\frac{1}{2}D + \frac{1}{16}$ $1\frac{1}{2}D$	$\frac{1}{4}$ to $\frac{5}{8}$ $\frac{3}{4}$ to $1\frac{1}{8}$ $1\frac{1}{4}$ to 2 $2\frac{1}{4}$ to 3	$\frac{7}{8}D$ $\frac{7}{8}D - \frac{1}{64}$ $\frac{7}{8}D - \frac{1}{32}$ $\frac{7}{8}D - \frac{3}{64}$
Heavy Hexagon } Heavy Square }	$\frac{1}{4}$ to 4	$1\frac{1}{2}D + \frac{1}{8}$	All sizes	D
Heavy Semifinished Hexagon	$\frac{1}{4}$ to 4	$1\frac{1}{2}D + \frac{1}{8}$	$\frac{1}{4}$ to $1\frac{1}{8}$ $1\frac{1}{4}$ to 2 $2\frac{1}{4}$ to 3 $3\frac{1}{4}$ to 4	$D - \frac{1}{64}$ $D - \frac{1}{32}$ $D - \frac{3}{64}$ $D - \frac{1}{16}$

* Data extracted from *American Standard Square and Hexagon Bolts and Nuts* (ASA B18.2 — 1960) with the permission of the publisher, The American Society of Mechanical Engineers, 29 W. 39th S., New York, N. Y. 10018.

** D = Nominal nut size.

[1] Adjusted to 16ths. (This dimension is also called "maximum" in some tables.)

[2] Adjusted to fractions.

to $\frac{3}{4}D$ plus or minus a small fraction of an inch for the hexagon bolts. It is $\frac{2}{3}D$ for the regular square-head bolts. For any particular diameter bolt, the nominal thickness of the bolt head may be computed by referring to Table II for the proper formula.

The thread series used for each type of bolt is shown in Table I. They are either the coarse thread series or the coarse-, fine-, or 8-thread series. All of these are Class 2A threads. The particular number of threads per inch is found by referring to a table of Unified and American threads. Knowing the bolt diameter, the thread series and that the threads are Class 2A, one easily finds the number of threads per inch for a particular bolt.

24.3 Formulas for Square and Hexagon Nuts

For our purposes, the most important formulas for the width across the flats, the maximum width across the corners and the thickness of square and hexagon nuts are shown in Table III.

As can be seen from this table, the maximum (basic) width across the flats is either $1\frac{1}{2}D$, $1\frac{1}{2}D + \frac{1}{16}$ or $1\frac{1}{2}D + \frac{1}{8}$, according to the type and nominal nut size. This is represented by the letter F.

Thus we can say that:

$$F = 1\frac{1}{2}D$$

$$\text{or} \quad F = 1\frac{1}{2}D + \frac{1}{16}$$

$$\text{or} \quad F = 1\frac{1}{2}D + \frac{1}{8}$$

Formulas for maximum (basic) width across the flats of square or hexagon nuts, according to their type and nominal size.

The nut thickness depends on the type of nut and its nominal size. It is equal to $\frac{7}{8}D$ or D, or to $\frac{7}{8}D$ or D with either $\frac{1}{64}$, $\frac{1}{32}$, $\frac{3}{64}$, $\frac{1}{16}$ subtracted from these dimensions as shown in the table.

In determining the width across the flats of a particular nut, one finds the proper type of nut in the first column of the table, then goes across the table to find the nominal nut size and the formula for the width across the flats.

In determining the thickness of a particular nut, one finds the proper type in column 1, then the proper nominal size in column 4, and then the formula for the nut thickness in column 5.

It should be noticed that in the table the width across the flats and the thickness are given in terms of the nominal nut size, represented by the letter D.

The width across the corners for both hexagon nuts and square nuts is called G. From elementary geometry it can be shown that for hexagon nuts:

$$G = 1.1547F = 1.7321D$$
Formula for width across corners of hexagon nuts when
$$F = 1\frac{1}{2}D.$$

For the square nuts, we find that:

$$G = 1.4142F = 2.1213D$$
Formula for width across corners of square nuts.

The following examples illustrate the application of these formulas.

■ **EXAMPLE 1:**

A regular hexagon bolt has a diameter of 1 in. What is the width across the flats and the width across the corners of the head of this bolt?

Solution and Explanation:

From the table or formulas for bolt heads, we find that the width across the flats is:
$$F = 1\tfrac{1}{2}D$$
Hence: $F = 1\tfrac{1}{2} \times 1 = 1\tfrac{1}{2}$ in.
The width across the corners is
$$G = 1.1547F = 1.7321D$$
Hence: $G = 1.7321 \times 1 = 1.732$ in. (to three decimal places)
Therefore the width across the flats is $1\tfrac{1}{2}$ in. and the width across the corners is 1.732 in. or $1\tfrac{47}{64}$ in. to the nearest 64th of an inch.

■ **EXAMPLE 2:**

The columns supporting an elevated passenger station are anchored to their base plates by heavy hexagon bolts which are $1\tfrac{1}{2}$ in. in diameter. For bolts of this diameter, find:
  a) the width across the flats of the bolt head,
  b) the width across the corners of the bolt head,
  c) the thickness of the bolt head.

Solution and Explanation:

a) Referring to the table of formulas for bolt heads, we find, for heavy hexagon bolts, that the width across the flats is $1\frac{1}{2}D + \frac{1}{8}$. Hence:

$$F = 1\frac{1}{2}D + \frac{1}{8}$$

or

$$F = 1\frac{1}{2} \times 1\frac{1}{2} + \frac{1}{8}$$

$$F = 2\frac{1}{4} + \frac{1}{8} = 2\frac{3}{8} \text{ in.}$$

Hence the width across the flats for this bolt head is $2\frac{3}{8}$ in.

b) The width across the corners is found by using the formula

$$G = 1.1547F$$

Since $F = 2\frac{3}{8}$, or 2.375, we have:

$$G = 1.1547 \times 2.375$$

$$G = 2.742 \text{ in. or practically } 2\frac{3}{4} \text{ in.}$$

c) To obtain the nominal thickness of the bolt head, we refer again to the table of formulas for bolt heads. For heavy hexagon bolts we find that the nominal thickness of the head is $\frac{3}{4}D + \frac{1}{16}$. Hence for a $1\frac{1}{2}$-in. diameter bolt:

$$H = \frac{3}{4}D + \frac{1}{16}.$$

Since $D = 1\frac{1}{2}$ in., we have:

$$H = \frac{3}{4} \times 1\frac{1}{2} + \frac{1}{16}$$

or

$$H = \frac{9}{8} + \frac{1}{16} = \frac{19}{16} = 1\frac{3}{16} \text{ in.}$$

Hence the nominal thickness of the bolt head is $1\frac{3}{16}$ in.

■ EXAMPLE 3:

For the $1\frac{1}{2}$-in.-diameter heavy hexagon bolt of Example 2, determine

a) the width across the flats of the nut,

b) the width across the corners of the nut,

c) the thickness of the nut.

Solution and Explanation:

a) Referring to the table of formulas for nuts, we find, for the heavy hexagon type of nut, that the maximum width across the flats is $1\frac{1}{2}D + \frac{1}{8}$, the same as for the bolt head. Therefore $F = 2\frac{3}{8}$ in.

b) The maximum width across the corners is $G = 1.1547F$, and is the same as for the bolt head. Hence $G = 1.1547 \times 2\frac{3}{8} = 2.742$ in. or practically $2\frac{3}{4}$ in.

c) For this type of bolt, the table shows that the nominal thickness of the nut is equal to D. Therefore $H = D = 1\frac{1}{2}$ in. Hence the thickness of the nut is $1\frac{1}{2}$ in.

■ EXAMPLE 4:

For a square nut with a basic major thread diameter of $1\frac{1}{2}$ in., find

a) the width across the flats of the nut,
b) the width across the corners of the nut,
c) the thickness of the nut.

Solution and Explanation:

a) Referring to the table of formulas for nuts, we find, for the heavy square type of nut, the maximum width across the flats is $1\frac{1}{2}D + \frac{1}{8}$. Therefore $F = 1\frac{1}{2} \times 1\frac{1}{2} + \frac{1}{8} = \frac{3}{2} \times \frac{3}{2} + \frac{1}{8} = \frac{9}{4} + \frac{1}{8} = 2\frac{3}{8}$ in. Hence $F = 2\frac{3}{8}$ in.

b) The maximum width across the corners is $G = 1.4142F$. Hence $G = 1.4142 \times 2\frac{3}{8} = 1.4142 \times 2.375 = 3.359$ in.

c) For this type of bolt, the table shows that the nominal thickness of the nut is equal to D. Therefore $H = D = 1\frac{1}{2}$ in. Hence the thickness of the nut is $1\frac{1}{2}$ in.

24.4   Problems Involving Applications of Formulas for Hexagon and Square Bolts and Nuts

In these problems, the dimensions of the bolt head or nut refer to their thickness, their maximum width across the flats and their maximum width across the corners.

1. Determine the dimensions of the bolt head of a heavy hexagon bolt whose diameter is $\frac{7}{8}$ in.

2. Determine the dimensions of the nut for the bolt of Problem 1.

3. A regular square bolt has a diameter of $\frac{1}{2}$ in. Determine the dimensions of the head of this bolt.

4. A hole is to be drilled and counterbored in a casting so that the top of the head of a regular $\frac{5}{8}$-in. hexagon bolt which fits into it will be flush with the surface of the casting. How deep should this hole be counterbored?

5. A regular square bolt has a diameter of $1\frac{5}{8}$ in. What are the dimensions of the nut for this bolt?

6. Calculate the dimensions of the head of a regular and a heavy hexagon bolt whose diameter is $\frac{3}{4}$ in. How do the similar dimensions compare?

7. A heavy semifinished hexagon bolt has a diameter of 4 in. Calculate the dimensions of the nut for this size bolt.

8. The diameter of a regular square bolt is $1\frac{1}{4}$ in. Calculate the dimensions of the head of this bolt.

9. A finished hexagon bolt has a diameter of 2 in. Calculate the dimensions of the nut for this bolt.

10. A heavy finished hexagon bolt has a diameter $2\frac{1}{2}$ in. Calculate the dimensions of the head of this bolt.

11. A heavy semifinished hexagon bolt has a diameter of $2\frac{1}{2}$ in. Calculate the dimensions of the head of this bolt.

12. Compare the width across the flats, the width across the corners and the thickness of the two types of bolts in Problems 10 and 11. Which type of bolt has the larger dimensions?

25.1 Introduction

In this chapter we discuss the most important ideas regarding tapers. A knowledge of tapers is of importance to the machinist, the pattern-maker, and the woodworker. Men doing work in the shop, drafting room, or engineering office also should be familiar with the types of tapers and the computations involved in taper work.

25.2 Definition of Taper

If a length of round stock has the same diameter along its length we say that it is uniform in diameter. If the same length of stock is turned, however, so that its diameter is reduced uniformly along its length, we say that the stock has a *taper* (Fig. 380).

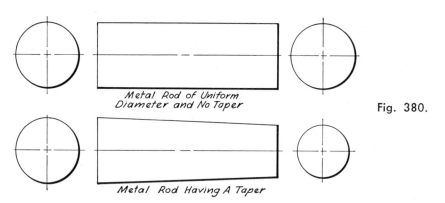

Metal Rod of Uniform
Diameter and No Taper

Fig. 380.

Metal Rod Having A Taper

We can say that *taper* is the uniform decrease of diameter of a piece of material from one end to the other, and is defined as large diameter minus small diameter. Taper per unit length depends on:

  a) the diameter of the larger end,
  b) the diameter of the smaller end,
  c) the length of the part that is tapered.

Taper is commonly expressed in inches per foot. Taper may also be expressed by the angle of taper given in degrees, minutes, and seconds.

There are many applications of tapers. Many small tools and machine parts are tapered throughout their length or have tapers on parts of them. For example, twist drills, lathe centers, arbors, pins, reamers, plugs, gauges and collets have tapers which enable them to fit into sockets having similar tapers. This insures the precise alignment of the tools or machine parts before work with them is begun.

Center-drilled holes should be left in all tapered machined objects unless otherwise specified. For instance, the occasion may arise when the taper per inch or taper per foot may have to be checked or the taper duplicated. It may be expensive, time-consuming, and inaccurate to drill center holes on an object already tapered and cut to length.

If a tapered object would require regrinding or remachining by metallizing, plating, or other such processes, it would be necessary to use adapter sleeves as drivers.

TABLE IV

SELF-HOLDING TAPERS

Taper Series — Basic Dimensions*
All dimensions in inches.

No. of Taper	Taper Per Foot (Basic)	Diameter at Gauge Line*	Origin of Series
0.239	0.50200	0.23922	Brown and Sharpe Taper Series
0.299	0.50200	0.29968	
0.375	0.50200	0.37525	
1	0.59858	0.47500	Morse Taper Series
2	0.59941	0.70000	
3	0.60235	0.93800	
4	0.62326	1.23100	
4½	0.62400	1.50000	
5	0.63151	1.74800	
6	0.62565	2.49400	
7	0.62400	3.27000	
200	0.750	2.000	¾ in. Per foot Taper Series
250	0.750	2.500	
300	0.750	3.000	
350	0.750	3.500	
400	0.750	4.000	
450	0.750	4.500	
500	0.750	5.000	
600	0.750	6.000	
800	0.750	8.000	
1000	0.750	10.000	
1200	0.750	12.000	

* The information in this table was extracted from *American Standard Machine Tapers* (ASA B5.10 — 1963) with the permission of the publisher, the American Society of Mechanical Engineers, 29 West 39th Street, New York, N. Y. 10018.

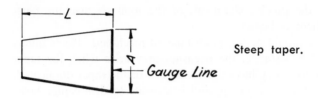

Steep taper.

TABLE V
DIMENSIONS OF STEEP MACHINE TAPERS*
All dimensions in inches.

No. of Taper	Taper Per Foot**	Diameter at Gauge Line A		Length Along Axis L	
5	3.500	$\frac{1}{2}$	0.500	$\frac{11}{16}$	0.6875
10†	3.500	$\frac{5}{8}$	0.625	$\frac{7}{8}$	0.8750
15	3.500	$\frac{3}{4}$	0.750	$1\frac{1}{16}$	1.0625
20†	3.500	$\frac{7}{8}$	0.875	$1\frac{5}{16}$	1.3125
25	3.500	1	1.000	$1\frac{9}{16}$	1.5625
30†	3.500	$1\frac{1}{4}$	1.250	$1\frac{7}{8}$	1.8750
35	3.500	$1\frac{1}{2}$	1.500	$2\frac{1}{4}$	2.2500
40†	3.500	$1\frac{3}{4}$	1.750	$2\frac{11}{16}$	2.6875
45	3.500	$2\frac{1}{4}$	2.250	$3\frac{5}{16}$	3.3125
50†	3.500	$2\frac{3}{4}$	2.750	4	4.0000
55	3.500	$3\frac{1}{2}$	3.500	$5\frac{3}{16}$	5.1875
60†	3.500	$4\frac{1}{4}$	4.250	$6\frac{3}{8}$	6.3750

* The information in this table was extracted from *American Standard Machine Tapers* (ASA B5.10 — 1963) with the permission of the publisher, the American Society of Mechanical Engineers, 29 West 39th Street, New York, N. Y. 10018.

** This taper corresponds to an included angle of 16° 35′ 39.4″.

† The tapers with a dagger are designated as the "Preferred Series." The other tapers are designated as the "Intermediate Series."

25.3 Kinds of Tapers

Tapers in which the taper angle is small are called *self-holding* tapers. Tapers in which the taper angle is large are called *self-releasing* tapers. There are four kinds of standard tapers commonly used in industry. These are:

a) the Self-holding Tapers and Steep Machine Tapers,

b) the Brown and Sharpe taper,

c) the Morse taper,

d) the Jarno taper.

A brief description of each of these tapers follows.

The Self-Holding Tapers and Steep Machine Tapers. In this set of standard tapers are a self-holding series and a steep taper series. The self-holding series has 22 sizes. These are listed in Table IV.

The steep taper series is described in Table V. Ring gauge self-holding tapers are covered in Table VI.

The Brown and Sharpe Taper. This type of standard taper has 18 sizes, running from No. 1 to No. 18. The taper for this series is very close

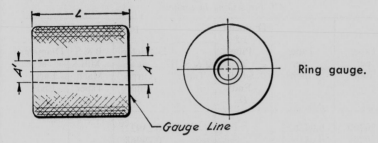

Ring gauge.

Gauge Line

TABLE VI

RING GAUGES, SELF-HOLDING TAPERS*

All dimensions in inches.

No. of Taper	Taper Per Foot (Basic)**	Diameter at Gauge Line** A	Diameter at Small End† A'	Length L
0.239	0.50200	0.23922	0.20000	$\frac{15}{16}$
0.299	0.50200	0.29968	0.25000	$1\frac{3}{16}$
0.375	0.50200	0.37525	0.31250	$1\frac{1}{2}$
1	0.59858	0.47500	0.36900	$2\frac{1}{8}$
2	0.59941	0.70000	0.57200	$2\frac{9}{16}$
3	0.60235	0.93800	0.77800	$3\frac{3}{16}$
4	0.62326	1.23100	1.02000	$4\frac{1}{16}$
$4\frac{1}{2}$	0.62400	1.50000	1.26600	$4\frac{1}{2}$
5	0.63151	1.74800	1.47500	$5\frac{3}{16}$
6	0.62565	2.49400	2.11600	$7\frac{1}{4}$
7	0.62400	3.27000	2.75000	10
200	0.750	2.0000	1.703	$4\frac{3}{4}$
250	0.750	2.5000	2.156	$5\frac{1}{2}$
300	0.750	3.0000	2.609	$6\frac{1}{4}$
350	0.750	3.5000	3.063	7
400	0.750	4.0000	3.516	$7\frac{3}{4}$
450	0.750	4.5000	3.969	$8\frac{1}{2}$
500	0.750	5.0000	4.422	$9\frac{1}{4}$
600	0.750	6.0000	5.328	$10\frac{3}{4}$
800	0.750	8.0000	7.141	$13\frac{3}{4}$
1000	0.750	10.0000	8.953	$16\frac{3}{4}$
1200	0.750	12.0000	10.766	$19\frac{3}{4}$

* The information in this table was extracted from *American Standard Machine Tapers* (ASA B5.10 — 1963) with the permission of the publisher, the American Society of Mechanical Engineers, 29 West 39th Street, New York, N. Y. 10018.
** Taper per foot and diameter at "Gauge Line" (Col. A) are basic dimensions.
† Dimensions in Column (A') calculated for reference only.

TABLE VII

BROWN AND SHARPE TAPERS*

All dimensions in inches.

No. of Taper	Taper per Foot[1]	Taper per Inch[2]	Diameter of Plug at Small End[1] D	B & S** Taper P	Diameter at Large End[2] A	B & S Mill. Mach. Taper P	Diameter at Large End[2] A
1	0.50200	0.041833			0.23922		
2	0.50200	0.041833			0.29968		
3	0.50200	0.041833			0.37525		
4	0.50240	0.041867	0.3500	$1\frac{1}{16}$	0.4206		
4	0.50240	0.041867	0.3500			$1\frac{1}{4}$†	0.4023
5	0.50160	0.041800	0.4500	$2\frac{1}{8}$	0.5388		
5	0.50160	0.041800	0.4500			$1\frac{3}{4}$†	0.5232
6	0.50329	0.041941	0.5000	$2\frac{3}{8}$†	0.5996		
7	0.50147	0.041789	0.6000	$2\frac{7}{8}$	0.7201		
7	0.50147	0.041789	0.6000			3†	0.7254
8	0.50100	0.041750	0.7500	$3\frac{3}{16}$†	0.8987		
9	0.50085	0.041738	0.9001	$4\frac{1}{4}$	1.0775		
9	0.50085	0.041738	0.9001			4†	1.0671
10	0.51612	0.043010	1.04465	5	1.2597		
10	0.51612	0.043010	1.04465			$5\frac{11}{16}$†	1.2893
11	0.50100	0.041750	1.24995	$5\frac{15}{16}$	1.4978		
11	0.50100	0.041750	1.24995			$6\frac{3}{4}$†	1.5318
12	0.49973	0.041644	1.5001	$7\frac{1}{8}$	1.7968	$7\frac{1}{8}$†	1.7968
13	0.50020	0.041683	1.75005	$7\frac{3}{4}$†	2.0731		
14	0.50000	0.041666	2.0000	$8\frac{1}{4}$	2.3438	$8\frac{1}{4}$†	2.3438
15	0.50000	0.041666	2.2500	$8\frac{3}{4}$†	2.6146		
16	0.50000	0.041666	2.5000	$9\frac{1}{4}$†	2.8854		
17	0.50000	0.041666	2.7500	$9\frac{3}{4}$†	3.1563		
18	0.50000	0.041666	3.0000	$10\frac{1}{4}$†	3.4271		

* Extracted from *American Standard Machine Tapers* (ASA B5.10 — 1963), with the permission of the publisher, The American Society of Mechanical Engineers, 29 West 39th Street, New York, N. Y. 10018.
** These depths are not used in all cases.
† These lengths are standard for shank cutters.
[1] Taper per foot and diameter of plug at small end are basic.
[2] Taper per inch and diameter at large end (Col's. A) are calculated for reference only.

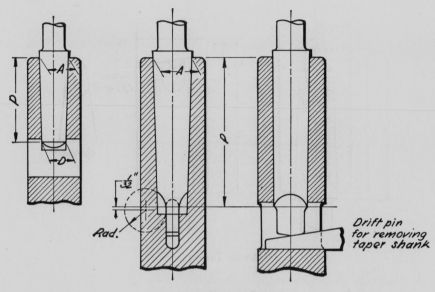

Brown & Sharpe Taper.

to $\frac{1}{2}$ in. per foot, with the exception of taper No. 10 which has a taper of 0.51612 in. per foot, and No. 6 which has a taper of 0.50329 in. per foot. The remaining 16 sizes have tapers which differ from $\frac{1}{2}$ in. per foot by less than 0.003 in. per foot. See Table VII.

Morse Taper. One of the most commonly used tapers is the Morse taper. Standard tapers of this type are used on shanks of twist drills, reamers, and many tools (Figs. 381 and 382). In this taper series there are nine sizes. These sizes are numbered 0, 1, 2, 3, 4, $4\frac{1}{2}$, 5, 6, and 7. The taper per inch and the diameter at the gauge line A are 0.052050 in. and 0.3561 in. for taper No. 0 and 0.052000 in. and 3.27000 in. for

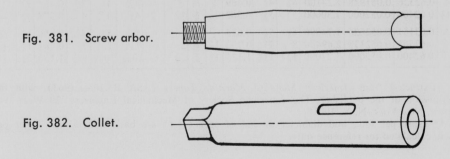

Fig. 381. Screw arbor.

Fig. 382. Collet.

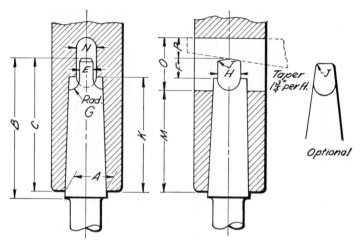

Morse Tapers.

TABLE VIII

MORSE TAPERS*

All dimensions given in inches.

No. of Taper	Taper per Foot**	Taper per Inch**	Diameter at End of Socket**	Shank: Total Length of Shank	Shank: Depth	Tang: Thickness	Tang: Length	Tang: Radius of Mill	Tang: Diameter	Tang: Radius	Socket: Min. Depth of Tapered Hole K, Drilled	Socket: Min. Depth of Tapered Hole K, Reamed	Socket: End of Socket to Tang Slot	Socket: Width	Tang Slot: Length	Tang Slot: Shank End to Back of Tang Slot
			A	B	C	E	F	G	H	J			M	N	O	P
0	0.62460	0.052050	0.3561	2 11/32	2 7/32	5/32	1/4	3/32	15/64	3/64	2 1/16	2 3/32	1 15/16	11/64	9/16	3/32
1	0.59858	0.049882	0.47500	2 9/16	2 7/16	0.203	3/8	3/16	11/32	3/64	2 1/16	2 3/32	2 1/16	0.218	3/4	3/8
2	0.59941	0.049951	0.70000	3 1/8	2 15/16	0.250	7/16	1/4	17/32	1/16	2 9/16	2 41/64	2 1/2	0.266	7/8	7/16
3	0.60235	0.050196	0.93800	3 7/8	3 11/16	0.312	9/16	9/32	23/32	3/64	3 5/16	3 1/4	3 1/16	0.328	1 3/16	7/16
4	0.62326	0.051938	1.23100	4 7/8	4 5/8	0.469	5/8	5/16	31/32	3/32	4 3/16	4 1/8	3 7/8	0.484	1 1/4	1/2
4½	0.62400	0.052000	1.50000	5 3/8	5 1/4	0.562	11/16	3/8	1 1/64	1/8	4 5/8	4 9/16	4 5/16	0.578	1 3/8	9/16
5	0.63151	0.052626	1.74800	6 1/8	5 7/8	0.625	3/4	3/8	1 3/32	1/8	5 5/16	5 1/4	4 15/16	0.656	1 1/2	7/16
6	0.62565	0.052138	2.49400	8 9/16	8 1/4	0.750	1 1/8	1/2	2	3/32	7 13/32	7 21/64	7	0.781	1 3/4	1/2
7	0.62400	0.052000	3.27000	11 5/8	11 1/4	1.125	1 3/8	3/4	2 5/8	3/16	10 5/32	10 5/64	9 1/2	1.156	2 5/8	7/8

* Extracted from *American Standard Machine Tapers* (ASA B5.10 — 1963), with the permission of the publisher, The American Society of Mechanical Engineers, 29 West 39th Street, New York, N. Y. 10018.

** Taper per foot, and diameter at end of socket (*A*) are basic dimensions. Taper per inch, calculated for reference only.

taper No. 7, respectively. The taper Nos. 1 through 6 have the same dimensions as those listed in Columns 2 and 3 of the table of American Standard Self-Holding Tapers. The nominal taper per foot of these tapers is ⅝ in. per foot. See Table VIII.

The Jarno Taper. The Jarno taper is a standard type of taper used in the headstock and tailstock of lathes and machine tools. See Table IX. This type of taper has 20 sizes, all of which have the same taper — 0.600 in. per foot. There are four factors which enter into a particular Jarno taper. These are:

a) the number of the taper,

Jarno Taper.

TABLE IX
JARNO TAPER*

All dimensions in inches.

No. of Taper	Taper per Foot	Taper per Inch	Diameter at Large End A	Diameter at Small End B	Length of Taper L
1	0.6	0.05	0.125	0.10	0.5
2	0.6	0.05	0.250	0.20	1.0
3	0.6	0.05	0.375	0.30	1.5
4	0.6	0.05	0.500	0.40	2.0
5	0.6	0.05	0.625	0.50	2.5
6	0.6	0.05	0.750	0.60	3.0
7	0.6	0.05	0.875	0.70	3.5
8	0.6	0.05	1.000	0.80	4.0
9	0.6	0.05	1.125	0.90	4.5
10	0.6	0.05	1.250	1.00	5.0
11	0.6	0.05	1.375	1.10	5.5
12	0.6	0.05	1.500	1.20	6.0
13	0.6	0.05	1.625	1.30	6.5
14	0.6	0.05	1.750	1.40	7.0
15	0.6	0.05	1.875	1.50	7.5
16	0.6	0.05	2.000	1.60	8.0
17	0.6	0.05	2.125	1.70	8.5
18	0.6	0.05	2.250	1.80	9.0
19	0.6	0.05	2.375	1.90	9.5
20	0.6	0.05	2.500	2.00	10.0

* Extracted from *American Standard Machine Tapers* (ASA B5.10 — 1963), with the permission of the publisher, The American Society of Mechanical Engineers, 29 West 39th Street, New York, N. Y. 10018.

b) the diameter of the large end of the taper,
c) the diameter of the small end of the taper,
d) the length of the taper.

These four factors are related to each other by the following formulas:

1. Length of Jarno taper in inches $= \dfrac{\text{Number of Jarno taper}}{2}$

2. Diameter of large end of Jarno

   taper in inches $= \dfrac{\text{Number of Jarno taper}}{8}$

3. Diameter of small end of Jarno

   taper in inches $= \dfrac{\text{Number of Jarno taper}}{10}$

25.4 American Standard Taper Machine Pins

These are used for keyway drivers, fastening collars to shafts, or any place where heavy work is not involved. Metal pins are frequently used in the fastening of metal parts. Several types of these pins are available, among which are straight pins, dowel pins, and taper pins. The taper pins have a taper of $\frac{1}{4}$ in. per foot. This is equivalent to $\frac{1}{48}$ in. per inch, or 0.02083 in. per inch.

There are 21 sizes of the American Standard taper pins. These run 7/0, 6/0, 5/0, 4/0, 3/0, 2/0, and 0, 1, 2, to 14. Sizes 11 to 14 are special sizes and have special lengths.

The general appearance of the taper pins is shown in Figure 383. See also Table X.

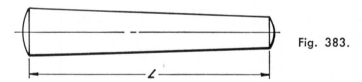

Fig. 383.

The diameter *d* at the small end of these pins can be found by using the formula:

$$d = D - 0.02083\ L$$

Here:

  d = diameter at small end of pin,
  D = diameter at large end of pin,
  L = length of pin along its axis.

These dimensions are in inches.

TABLE X
DIMENSIONS OF TAPER PINS*

All dimensions in inches.
(Taper $\frac{1}{4}$ in. per Foot)

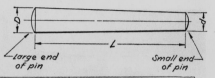

Large end of pin   Small end of pin

Taper Pin No.	Size (Dia.) of Large End	Length L**	Additional Lengths
7/0	0.0625	0.375 0.500 0.625	
6/0	0.0780	0.375 0.625 0.500 0.750	
5/0	0.0940	0.500 0.750 0.625 1.000	
4/0	0.1090	Same as 5/0	
3/0	0.1250	0.500 0.750 0.625 0.875 1.000	
2/0	0.1410	0.500 0.750 1.000 0.625 0.875 1.250	
0	0.1560	Same as 2/0	1.500
1	0.1720	0.750 1.000 0.875 1.250	1.500 2.000 1.750
2	0.1930	0.750 1.000 1.500 0.875 1.250	1.750 2.250 2.000 2.500
3	0.2190	0.750 1.000 1.500 0.875 1.250 1.750	2.000 2.500 3.000 2.250 2.750
4	0.2500	1.000 1.500 2.000 1.250 1.750	2.250 2.750 2.500 3.000
5	0.2890	1.000 to 2.250†	2.500 3.000 2.750
6	0.3410	1.250 to 3.000†	3.250 3.750 3.500 4.000
7	0.4090	2.000 to 3.750†	4.000
8	0.4920	2.000 to 4.500†	4.750 5.000
9	0.5910	2.750 to 5.250†	5.500 6.000 5.750
10	0.7060	3.500 to 6.000†	

* The information shown in this table was extracted from *American Standard Machine Pins* (ASA B5.20 — 1958), with the permission of the publishers, The American Society of Mechanical Engineers, 29 West 39th Street, New York, N. Y. 10018.

** Standard reamers available for pins listed in the column designated "Length L."

† In steps of 0.250 in. between these lengths.

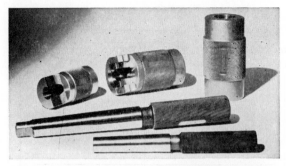

Standard Taper
Cylindrical Gauges.

Brown & Sharpe Mfg. Co.

25.5   Formulas Used in Calculating Tapers

The formulas used in the calculation of tapers are quite simple and easy to use.* Consider the simple taper plug shown in Figure 384.

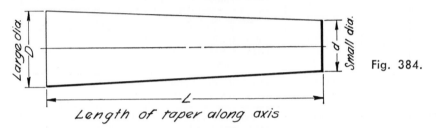

Fig. 384.

Length of taper along axis

In terms of the dimensions shown, we say that

$$\text{Taper per inch} = \frac{(\text{Large diameter} - \text{small diameter})}{\text{Length of taper in inches}}$$

> **Formula A**
>
> $$TPI = \frac{(D - d)}{L}$$

where the large diameter, the small diameter, and the length are expressed in inches also.

The taper per foot is found by multiplying the taper per inch by 12. Hence:

$$\text{Taper per foot} = \frac{(\text{Large diameter} - \text{small diameter}) \times 12}{\text{Length in inches}}$$

> **Formula B**
>
> $$TPF = \frac{(D - d) \times 12}{L}$$

* In all of these formulas, D = large diameter; d = small diameter; L = length of taper; TPI = taper per inch; TPF = taper per foot.

Here the large diameter and small diameter are expressed in inches as before.

These fundamental formulas may now be solved for each of the factors appearing on the right-hand side of the equals sign. Thus, from Formula A we obtain:

$$
\textbf{Formula C1} \\
L = \frac{(D - d)}{TPI}
$$

or if we know the taper per foot:

$$
\textbf{Formula C2} \\
L = \frac{(D - d) \times 12}{TPF}
$$

Using this formula we can compute the length of the taper when we know the diameter at the large end, the diameter at the small end, and the taper per inch.

From Formula A we can also obtain two more formulas. These are:

$$
\textbf{Formula D} \\
D = L \times (TPI) + d
$$

$$
\textbf{Formula E} \\
d = D - L \times (TPI)
$$

Formula D enables us to compute the large diameter when we know the length of the taper, the taper per inch, and the small diameter. Using Formula E, we can compute the small diameter when we know the large diameter, the length of the taper, and the taper per inch.

The use of these shop formulas is illustrated by the following problems:

■ **EXAMPLE 1:**

A piece to be turned in a lathe has the dimensions shown in Figure 385. Find the taper of the piece per inch and per foot.

Fig. 385.

Solution and Explanation:

Since we know the diameter at each end and the length of the piece, we can use Formula A to find the taper per inch.

$$\text{Taper per inch} = \frac{(\text{Large diameter} - \text{Small diameter})}{\text{Length of taper in inches}}$$

$$TPI = \frac{(D - d)}{L}$$

$$= \frac{(2.5 - 2)}{10} = \frac{0.5}{10}$$

$$TPI = 0.050$$

$$\text{The taper per foot} = \frac{(D - d)}{L} \times 12$$

$$= \frac{(2.5 - 2.0)}{10} \times 12$$

$$= \frac{0.5}{10} \times 12$$

$$= 0.600$$

Hence this piece has a taper of 0.050 in. per in. or 0.600 in. per foot. This is the amount of the Jarno taper.

■ EXAMPLE 2:

A No. 4 American Standard taper pin has a large diameter of 0.2500 in., a length of 2.000 in., and a taper of ¼ in. per foot (0.02083 in. per in). What is the diameter of this pin at the small end (Fig. 386)?

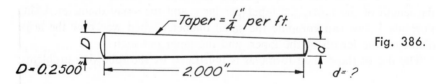

Fig. 386.

Solution and Explanation:

Since the diameter at the small end is to be determined, we use the formula:

$$d = D - L \times (TPI)$$

where D = diameter at large end = 0.2500 in.
         L = length of pin = 2.000 in.
      TPI = 0.02083 in. per inch

Substituting into the formula, we have:

$$d = 0.2500 - 2.000 \times 0.02083$$
$$d = 0.2500 - 0.04166$$

or d = 0.20834 in. or 0.2083 in. (to the same accuracy
         as the large diameter).

Hence the diameter of the small end is 0.2083 in.

■ EXAMPLE 3:

What must be the finished length of a piece of stock having a taper of 0.500 per foot if the large diameter is 1.875 in. and the small diameter is 1.500 in.?

Solution and Explanation:

For this problem substitute the known values in Formula C 2:

$$L = \frac{(D - d) \times 12}{TPF} \qquad \begin{array}{l} D = 1.875 \text{ in.} \\ d = 1.500 \text{ in.} \\ TPF = 0.500 \end{array}$$

$$L = \frac{(1.875 - 1.500) \times 12}{0.500}$$

$$L = \frac{0.375 \times 12}{0.500}$$

$$L = \frac{4.500}{0.500} = 9.000 \text{ in.}$$

Hence the finished length should be 9.000 in.

■ EXAMPLE 4:

A plug gauge has the dimensions shown in Figure 387. What is its diameter at the large end?

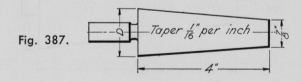

Fig. 387.

Solution and Explanation:

In this problem we know that $d = \frac{7}{8}$ in., $L = 4$ in., and the taper per inch $(TPI) = \frac{1}{16}$ in. Hence the large diameter D is obtained using Formula D:

$$D = L \times (TPI) + d$$
$$D = 4 \times \tfrac{1}{16} + \tfrac{7}{8}$$
$$D = \tfrac{1}{4} + \tfrac{7}{8} = 1\tfrac{1}{8} \text{ in.}$$

Hence the large diameter is $1\frac{1}{8}$ in.

25.6   Problems Involving Calculation of Tapers

1. A taper pin is 6 in. long and has a diameter at the large end of 0.706 in. If it has a taper of 0.02083 in. per inch, what is its diameter at the small end?

2. A taper shank has a length of 7 in. It has a diameter of 1.400 in. at the small end and a diameter of 1.750 in. at the large end. What is the taper per inch? What is the taper per foot?

3. If a plug gauge has a small diameter of 3.063 in., a diameter at the gauge line of 3.500 in., and a length (from gauge line to end) of 7 in., what is its taper per foot?

4. The lathe center shown in Figure 388 has a taper of 0.5986 in. per foot. Its small diameter $d = 0.369$ in. How big is the diameter D?

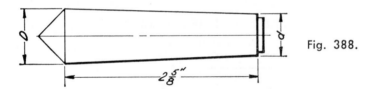

Fig. 388.

5. A lathe center has a small diameter of 0.500 in. At a distance of 3 in. from this end the diameter is 0.650 in. What is the taper per foot of this lathe center? Which of the standard tapers is this?

6. A tapered roller has the dimensions shown in the drawing (Fig. 389). What is its diameter at the large end?

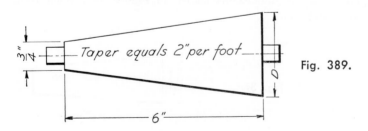

Taper equals 2" per foot

Fig. 389.

7. What is the length of the tapered section of the piece shown in Figure 390?

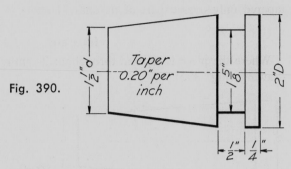

Fig. 390.

8. A taper shank has a length of 8⅞ in. Its large diameter is 2.3437 in. and its diameter at the small end is 2.2500 in. What is the taper of this shank per foot? Give answer to nearest fraction of an inch.

9. A round tapered bar has a small diameter of 1.250 in., a large diameter of 1.875 in., and a length of 5¾ in. What is the taper per inch? What is the taper per foot?

10. The tapered hole in a drill-press spindle measures 0.875 in. in diameter at a certain point. Three inches farther along its axis it measures 0.750 in. From these measurements what is the taper per foot of this hole?

25.7   How Tapers are Turned

In the machine shop, tapers may be turned by three commonly used ways. One of the most commonly used methods is by "setting over" the tailstock, or "offsetting" it, by a definite amount. This is done by turning the adjusting screws on the lower part of the tailstock until the tailstock has been moved "out of line" from the *true center line between the base and the tailstock body* by the required amount of setover (Fig. 391).

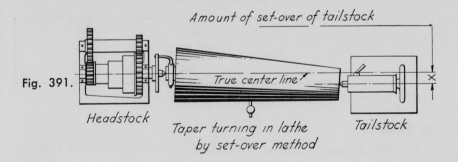

Fig. 391.

Amount of set-over of tailstock

True center line

Headstock

Taper turning in lathe by set-over method

Tailstock

The formulas used in computing the amount of offset depend on whether the tapered piece is tapered throughout its entire length or is tapered only over a part of its entire length.

1st Case

Where the piece is tapered throughout its entire length, as shown in the drawing (Fig. 392).

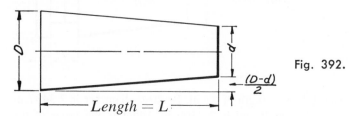

Fig. 392.

Since the diameter at the large end of the taper is D, and at the small end is d, the amount of offset is half the difference of the diameters. Hence the useful formula:

Formula F

$$\text{Offset} = \frac{(D - d)}{2}$$

In terms of the taper per foot, we know that

$$TPF = \frac{(D - d) \times 12}{L}$$

From this formula, we have:

$$(D - d) = \frac{TPF \times L}{12}$$

and

$$\frac{(D - d)}{2} = \frac{TPF \times L}{24}$$

Therefore the offset can also be determined from:

Formula G

$$\text{Offset} = \frac{TPF \times L}{24}$$

The following examples will illustrate these formulas:

■ EXAMPLE 1:

By what amount should the tailstock of a lathe be set over in order to cut a taper on a piece $7\frac{1}{2}$ in. long if the piece has a diameter of 1.875 in. on one end and a diameter of 1.500 in. at the other end?

Solution and Explanation:

Using Formula F, and substituting the known data, we find that:

$$\text{Offset} = \frac{(D - d)}{2}$$

$$\text{Offset} = \frac{(1.875 - 1.500)}{2}$$

$$= \frac{0.375}{2} = 0.1875 \text{ in. or } \tfrac{3}{16} \text{ in. if expressed in fraction form}$$

Hence the required offset is 0.1875 in.

This particular piece has a taper of 0.600 in. per foot. Using this fact and Formula G, we have:

$$\text{Offset} = \frac{TPF \times L}{24}$$

$$\text{Offset} = \frac{0.600 \times \tfrac{15}{2}}{24}$$

$$= \frac{4.5}{24} = 0.1875 \text{ in. or } \tfrac{3}{16} \text{ in., which gives the same amount of}$$

offset as Formula F

2nd Case

This is the case in which the tapered portion does *not* extend the full length of the piece, but only over a part of it, as illustrated by the examples in Figure 393.

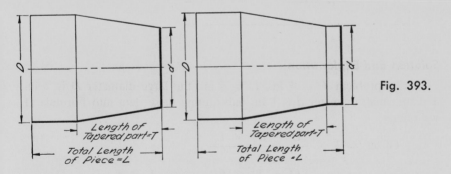

Fig. 393.

In the computation of the tailstock offset the *total length of the piece* is used. The practical shop formula for this computation is:

Formula H

$$\text{Offset} = \frac{1}{2} \times \frac{(D - d) \times L}{T}$$

---

where T is the length of tapered part and L is the total length of the piece, and all dimensions are in inches. It is interesting to note if the piece is tapered throughout its entire length, then $T = L$, and the formula above would become the same as Formula F:

$$\text{Offset} = \frac{(D - d)}{2}$$

Formula H can also be used in calculating tapers on pieces which are turned on *mandrels* or *arbors*. In this case, L in the formula is replaced by the length of the arbor.

The following problems illustrate the use of these formulas.

■ **EXAMPLE 2:**

By how much should the tailstock be set over to turn the taper on the nozzle shown in Figure 394?

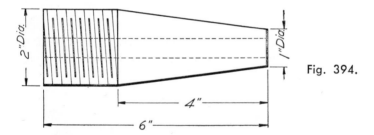

Fig. 394.

Solution and Explanation:

In this problem $T = 4$ in., $L = 6$ in., the large diameter D is 2 in., and the small diameter d is 1 in. Substituting these data into Formula H, we obtain:

$$\text{Offset} = \tfrac{1}{2} \times \frac{(D - d) \times L}{T}$$

$$\text{Offset} = \tfrac{1}{2} \times \frac{(2 - 1) \times 6}{4} = \tfrac{1}{2} \times \frac{1 \times 6}{4} = \tfrac{3}{4} \text{ in.}$$

Hence the tailstock should be offset $\tfrac{3}{4}$ in. for this taper.

■ **EXAMPLE 3:**

Compute the amount that the tailstock on a lathe must be set over in order to cut the taper on the arbor shown in Figure 395.

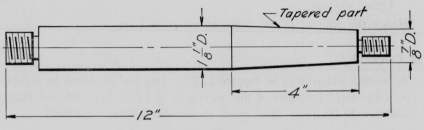

Fig. 395.

Solution and Explanation:

Using Formula H, we substitute the given values:

$$\text{Offset} = \tfrac{1}{2} \times \frac{(D - d) \times L}{T}$$

$D = 1\tfrac{1}{8}$ in.
$d = \tfrac{7}{8}$ in.
$T = 4$ in.
$L = 12$ in.

$$\text{Offset} = \tfrac{1}{2} \times \frac{(1\tfrac{1}{8} - \tfrac{7}{8}) \times 12}{4}$$

$$\text{Offset} = \tfrac{1}{2} \times \frac{(\tfrac{2}{8}) \times \overset{3}{\cancel{12}}}{\underset{1}{\cancel{4}}}$$

$$\text{Offset} = \tfrac{6}{16} = \tfrac{3}{8} \text{ in.}$$

Hence the tailstock should be set over $\tfrac{3}{8}$ in.

■ **EXAMPLE 4:**

A spindle is 2 ft. long and has a taper of $\tfrac{1}{4}$ in. per ft. What should be the offset of the tailstock on the lathe on which this spindle will be turned?

Solution and Explanation:

Here we can use Formula G:

$$\text{Offset} = \frac{TPF \times L}{24}$$

$TPF = \tfrac{1}{4}$ in.
$L = 24$ in.

$$\text{Offset} = \frac{\frac{1}{4} \times \overset{1}{\cancel{24}}}{\cancel{24}}$$

$$\text{Offset} = \frac{1}{4} \text{ in.}$$

Hence the amount of the tailstock offset is $\frac{1}{4}$ in.

■ **EXAMPLE 5:**

A bearing which is to be tapered is 2 in. long and is placed on a 6-in. arbor. The large diameter of the bearing is to be $2\frac{1}{4}$ in., while the small diameter is to be $2\frac{1}{8}$ in. How much should the tailstock be offset?

Solution and Explanation:

In this problem the known data are:

$$D = 2\frac{1}{4} \text{ in.}$$
$$T = 2 \text{ in.}$$
$$d = 2\frac{1}{8} \text{ in.}$$
$$L = 6 \text{ in. (length of the arbor)}$$

When these numbers are substituted into Formula H, we get:

$$\text{Offset} = \frac{1}{2} \times \frac{(D - d) \times L}{T}$$

$$\text{Offset} = \frac{1}{2} \times \frac{(2\frac{1}{4} - 2\frac{1}{8}) \times 6}{2}$$

or: $$\text{Offset} = \frac{1}{2} \times \frac{\frac{1}{8} \times \overset{3}{\cancel{6}}}{\underset{1}{\cancel{2}}} = \frac{1}{2} \times \frac{1}{8} \times 3 = \frac{3}{16} \text{ in.}$$

Hence the required tailstock offset is $\frac{3}{16}$ in.

25.8 Turning Tapers by Use of a Taper Attachment

Although the "offset method" is one of the most commonly used methods of turning a taper on a lathe, another common method makes use of the taper attachment (Fig. 396). The use of this lathe attachment simplifies the turning of the taper and avoids moving the tailstock off center. The taper attachment is provided with a guide bar which is graduated in degrees at one end and in taper per foot at the other end. In turning a taper with this device, the operator sets the taper attachment to the proper taper per foot. The cutting tool is guided over the work at the proper angle to cut the taper.

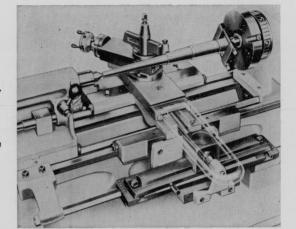

Fig. 396. Using a taper
attachment.

Clausing

When the taper attachment is used, the taper per foot can be computed
from the previous formula

$$TPF = \frac{(D - d) \times 12}{L}$$

where D, d, and L are in inches.

■ EXAMPLE 1:

The lathe center shown in the drawing (Fig. 397) is to be turned on
a lathe equipped with a taper attachment calibrated in taper per foot.
How should this attachment be set in order to turn the tapered portion
of the lathe center? All dimensions are in inches.

Fig. 397.

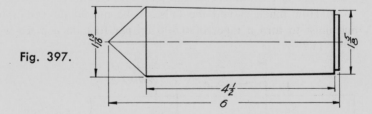

Solution and Explanation:

Since the taper attachment is calibrated in taper per foot, this must be
computed. From the drawing, $D = 1\frac{13}{16}$ in., $d = 1\frac{5}{8}$ in., and $L = 4\frac{1}{2}$ in.
Hence, using Formula B:

$$TPF = \frac{(D - d) \times 12}{L}$$

$D = 1\frac{13}{16}$ in.
$d = 1\frac{5}{8}$ in.
$L = 4\frac{1}{2}$ in.

$$TPF = \frac{(1\frac{13}{16} - 1\frac{5}{8}) \times 12}{4\frac{1}{2}}$$

$$TPF = \frac{(1\frac{13}{16} - 1\frac{10}{16}) \times 12}{\frac{9}{2}} = \frac{(\frac{1}{\cancel{3}}) \times \cancel{12}^{4} \times 2}{\cancel{\frac{9}{3}}_{1}}$$

$$TPF = \frac{8}{16} = \frac{1}{2} \text{ in.}$$

Hence the taper attachment should be set to a taper of $\frac{1}{2}$ in. per foot.

25.9 Turning Tapers by Use of the Compound Rest

A third method, which is applicable chiefly to the cutting of steep tapers, utilizes the compound rest on the lathe. The compound rest is turned about a vertical axis through the proper number of degrees as required by the angle of the taper. The cutting tool, which is mounted in the toolholder on the compound rest, is then fed by hand into the piece to be tapered.

For complete details, the reader should consult books on machine shop techniques.*

25.10 Problems Involving Calculations Relating to Taper Turning

1. What should the tailstock offset be to turn the taper on a piece $9\frac{7}{8}$ in. long having a large diameter of $3\frac{3}{8}$ in. and a small diameter of $2\frac{3}{4}$ in?

2. A tapered piece is 9 in. long and has a taper of 0.500 in. per foot. What is the amount of tailstock offset to turn this taper?

3. How much should the tailstock be moved off center to permit a machinist to turn a taper of 0.600 in. per foot on a piece whose length is $7\frac{1}{2}$ in.?

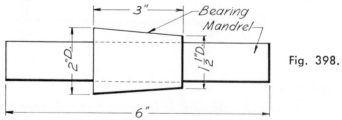

Fig. 398.

---

* C. A. Felker, *Machine-Shop Technology* (Milwaukee: The Bruce Publishing Co., 1962), pp. 241–242.

4. What is the offset of the tailstock required to turn a taper 6 in. long on a piece 12 in. long if the taper is 0.500 in. per foot?

5. A tapered bearing is to be turned on a mandrel as illustrated in Figure 398. What is the setting for this job if it is done on a lathe having a taper attachment?

6. A special brass plug 6 in. long is to be turned with a taper of $\frac{1}{2}$ in. to the foot. What would be the tailstock offset for this?

7. Determine the taper per foot in the lathe center (Fig. 399). What setover is necessary in turning this taper if made from a piece of stock 5 in. long?

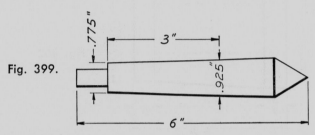

Fig. 399.

8. Calculate the setover of the tailstock on a lathe in order to turn a taper of 0.250 in. per foot on a piece that measures 6 in. long.

9. Determine the taper per foot of the lathe center in Figure 400. What should be the setting of the taper attachment in turning this taper?

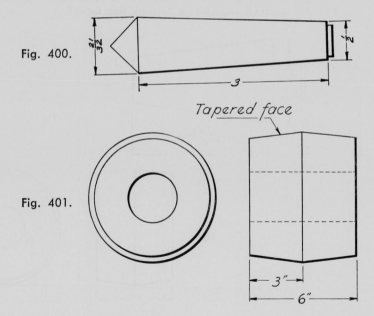

Fig. 400.

Fig. 401.

10. The pulley sketched in Figure 401 is to be given a tapered crown of ¾ in. to the foot. To do this job the pulley is forced on a 10-in. mandrel and is then turned on a lathe. Calculate the amount of offset necessary for this job.

11. Calculate the taper per foot of the piece in the drawing (Fig. 402). If this is cut on a 9-in. mandrel for taper turning, what is the amount that the tailstock is set over?

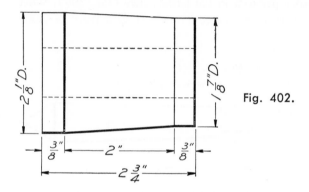

Fig. 402.

12. A special milling-machine arbor 20 in. long is tapered $5\frac{1}{4}$ in. on one end with a taper of 0.600 in. per foot. How much should the tailstock be set over in order to turn this taper?

13. What is the taper per foot on the plug gauge (Fig. 403)? How much is the tailstock set over in turning this taper?

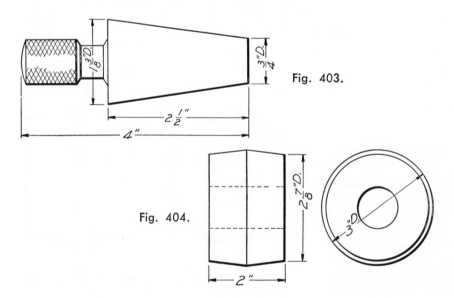

Fig. 403.

Fig. 404.

14. With a taper per foot of 0.600 in., what would be the setover required to make a tapered shank on a piece 10 in. long?

15. In order to turn the crown on the 3-in. pulley as illustrated in Figure 404, it is mounted on a 9-in. mandrel. Calculate the taper per foot and the amount of tailstock setover needed in turning the taper. A rule of thumb for tapering a crown on a pulley of this size is 2.5 deg. off center using the compound rest or taper attachment.

SUMMARY OF
TABLES AND FORMULAS

Linear Measure

12 inches (in.) ($''$)	= 1 foot (ft.) ($'$)	
3 feet	= 1 yard (yd.) = 36 in.	
$5\frac{1}{2}$ yards	= 1 rod (rd.) = $16\frac{1}{2}$ ft. = 198 in.	
320 rods	= 1 mile (mi.) = 1760 yd. = 5280 ft.	
1 meter (m.)	= 39.37 inches = 3.28 ft. = 1.09 yd.	

Square or Surface Measure

144 square inches (sq. in.) ($\square''$) = 1 square foot (sq. ft.)
9 square feet = 1 square yard (sq. yd.) = 1296 sq. in.
$30\frac{1}{4}$ square yards = 1 square rod (sq. rd.) = $272\frac{1}{4}$ sq. ft.
160 square rods = 1 acre (A) = 4840 sq. yd. = 43,560 sq. ft.
640 acres = 1 square mile (sq. mi.) = 102,400 sq. rd. = 3,097,600 sq. yd. = 27,878,400 sq. ft.
1 square meter = 1.196 sq. yd. = 10.764 sq. ft.

Cubic Measure

1728 cubic inches (cu. in.) = 1 cubic foot (cu. ft.)
27 cubic feet = 1 cubic yard (cu. yd.)
1 cubic meter = 1.308 cu. yd. = 35.314 cu. ft.

Avoirdupois Weight

16 ounces (oz.) = 1 pound (lb.)
100 pounds = 1 hundredweight (cwt.)
20 hundredweight = 1 ton (T) = 2000 pounds
2240 pounds = 1 long ton

Dry Measure

2 pints (pt.) = 1 quart (qt.)
8 quarts = 1 peck (pk.) = 16 pt.
4 pecks = 1 bushel (bu.) = 32 qt. = 64 pt.
1 bushel = 2150.4 (cu. in.), 1.244 or $1\frac{1}{4}$ (cu. ft.)
1 bushel corn = 56 lb.
1 bushel potatoes = 60 lb.
1 bushel wheat = 60 lb.
U. S. dry quart = $67\frac{1}{5}$ cu. in.

Liquid Measure

4 gills	= 1 pint (pt.)
2 pints	= 1 quart (qt.)
4 quarts	= 1 gallon (gal.) = 8 pt.
$31\frac{1}{2}$ gallons	= 1 barrel (bbl.) = 126 qt. = 252 pt.
2 barrels	= 1 hogshead (hhd.) = 63 gal. = 252 qt. = 504 pt.
1 gallon	= 231 cu. in. or 0.134 cu. ft.
7.48 gallons	= 1 cu. ft. or $7\frac{1}{2}$ gal. approx.
U. S. liquid quart	= $57\frac{3}{4}$ cu. in.
1 gallon water	= 8.34 lb. or $8\frac{1}{3}$ lb. approx.
1 gallon gasoline	= 6.32 lb.
1 gallon linseed oil	= 7.84 lb.

Formulas Pertaining to Geometric Figures

For all flat figures: A = area; P = perimeter

Name of Figure   **Formulas**

Square

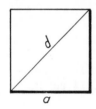

a = side
d = diagonal
$A = a^2$
$$A = \frac{d^2}{2}$$
$P = 4a$
$d = 1.4142a$

Rectangle

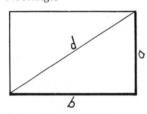

b = base
a = altitude
d = diagonal
$A = ab$
$P = 2a + 2b$
$d = \sqrt{a^2 + b^2}$

Parallelogram

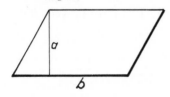

b = base
a = altitude
$A = ab$

The diameter of the largest circle within an equilateral triangle.

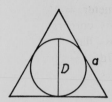

a = side of triangle

$$D = \frac{\sqrt{3}}{3}a = 0.5774a$$

The diameter of the largest circle which will enclose a given equilateral triangle.

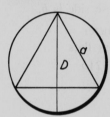

a = side of triangle

$$D = \frac{2\sqrt{3}}{3}a = 1.1547a$$

The side of the largest square inside a circle of a given diameter.

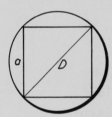

D = diameter of circle

$a = 0.7071D$

$D = 1.4142a$

Regular Hexagon

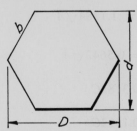

A = area of hexagon
d = distance across flats
D = distance across corners
b = side of hexagon

$$A = \frac{3\sqrt{3}}{2}b^2 = 2.5981b^2$$

$d = \sqrt{3}\,b = 1.7321b$

$D = 2b = 1.1547d$

Diameter of circle that will enclose a regular hexagon whose side is b.

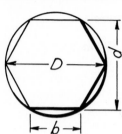

D = required diameter =
distance across corners
d = distance across flats
$D = 2b = 1.1547d$

Diameter of circle enclosed by a regular hexagon whose side is b.

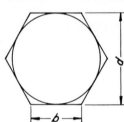

d = required diameter =
distance across flats

$d = \sqrt{3}\,b = 1.7321b$

Circle

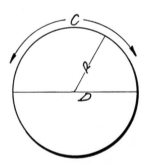

D = diameter
R = radius
C = circumference
$A = \pi R^2 = 3.1416R^2$

$A = \dfrac{\pi D^2}{4} = 0.7854D^2$

$C = 2\pi R = 6.2832R$
$C = \pi D = 3.1416D$

$D = \sqrt{\dfrac{4A}{\pi}} = 1.1284\sqrt{A}$

$R = \sqrt{\dfrac{A}{\pi}} = 0.5642\sqrt{A}$

$D = \dfrac{C}{\pi} = 0.3183C$

$R = \dfrac{C}{2\pi} = 0.1592C$

Sector of Circle

Angle of sector
in degrees

$$A = \frac{(\text{Angle of sector in degrees}) \times \pi R^2}{360°}$$

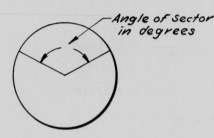

Circular Ring

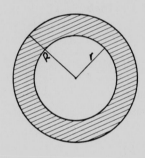

A = shaded area

π = 3.1416; $\dfrac{\pi}{4}$ = 0.7854

A = area of outer circle minus area
of inner circle

$A = \pi R^2 - \pi r^2 = \pi(R^2 - r^2)$

$A = \pi(R + r)(R - r)$

A = 3.1416 (sum of radii) ×
(difference of radii)

$A = \dfrac{\pi D^2}{4} - \dfrac{\pi d^2}{4} = \dfrac{\pi}{4}(D^2 - d^2)$

$A = \dfrac{\pi}{4}(D + d)(D - d)$

A = 0.7854 (sum of diameters) ×
(difference of diameters)

Scalene Triangle

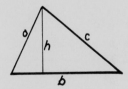

b = base
h = altitude
$A = \dfrac{bh}{2}$
$P = a + b + c$

Equilateral Triangle

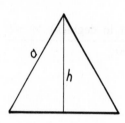

h = altitude

$$h = \frac{a\sqrt{3}}{2} = 0.8660a$$

$$A = \frac{ah}{2}$$

$$A = \frac{\sqrt{3}}{4}a^2 = 0.4330a^2$$

$$A = \frac{\sqrt{3}}{3}h^2 = 0.5774h^2$$

$$P = 3a$$

Ellipse

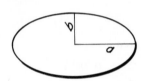

A = area
a = half of major axis
b = half of minor axis
$A = \pi ab = 3.1416ab$

Trapezoid

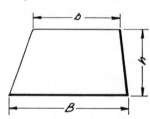

A = area
B = large base
b = small base
h = altitude

$$A = \frac{h}{2}(B + b)$$

Right Triangle

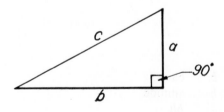

a and b = sides or legs
c = hypotenuse
A = area
P = perimeter

$$A = \frac{ab}{2}$$

$$P = a + b + c$$

$$c = \sqrt{a^2 + b^2}$$

$$a = \sqrt{c^2 - b^2}$$

$$b = \sqrt{c^2 - a^2}$$

Geometric Solids

Cube

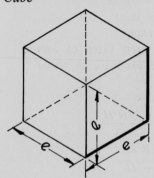

e = edge of cube
V = volume
S = surface area
$V = e \times e \times e = e^3$
$S = 6 \times e \times e = 6e^2$

Rectangular Solid

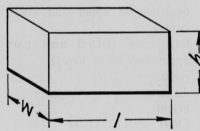

l = length
w = width
h = height or depth
V = volume
S = surface area
$V = lwh$
$S = 2(hw + hl + lw)$

Pyramid

B = area of base
H = altitude
$V = \dfrac{Bh}{3}$

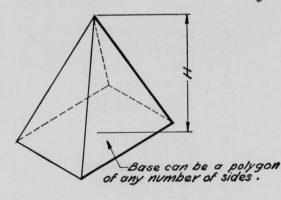

Base can be a polygon of any number of sides.

Right Circular Cone
Base is a circle. Axis perpendicular to base.

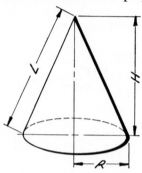

R = radius of base
B = area of base
L = slant height
S = lateral area (area of curved surface exclusive of base)
H = height
$S = \pi R L$

$$V = \frac{BH}{3} = \frac{\pi R^2 H}{3}$$

$V = 1.0472 R^2 H$
$l = \sqrt{R^2 + H^2}$

Right Circular Cylinder
(Bases perpendicular to curved surface.)

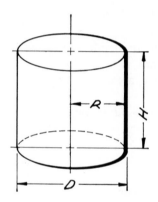

S = lateral area (area of vertical part exclusive of upper and lower bases)
T = total area (lateral area plus upper and lower bases)
R = radius
D = diameter
H = height
$V = \pi R^2 H = 3.1416 R^2 H$

$$V = \frac{\pi D^2}{4} H = 0.7854 D^2 H$$

$S = 2\pi RH = 6.2832 RH$
$S = \pi DH = 3.1416 DH$
$T = 2\pi RH + 2\pi R^2$
$T = 2\pi R (H + R) =$
$\qquad\qquad 6.2832 R (H + R)$

Sphere

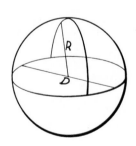

R = radius
D = diameter
V = volume
S = surface area

$$V = \frac{4}{3}\pi R^3 = 4.1888 R^3$$

$$V = \frac{\pi}{6} D^3 = 0.5236 D^3$$

$S = 4\pi R^2 = 12.5664 R^2$
$S = \pi D^2 = 3.1416 D^2$

Hollow Right Circular Cylinder

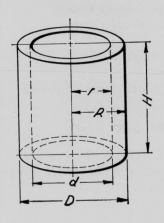

V = net volume = volume of outer cylinder minus volume of inner cylinder

R = large radius

r = small radius

H = height

$V = \pi H \ (R^2 - r^2)$

$V = \pi H \ (R + r) \ (R - r)$

$V = 3.1416H$ (sum of radii) $\times$ (difference of radii)

$$V = \frac{\pi D^2 H}{4} - \frac{\pi d^2 H}{4}$$

$$V = \frac{\pi}{4} H \ (D^2 - d^2)$$

$$V = \frac{\pi}{4} H \ (D + d) \ (D - d)$$

$V = 0.7854H$ (Sum of dia.) $\times$ (difference of dia.)

Frustum of Pyramid

B = area of lower base

b = area of upper base

H = height

V = volume

$$V = \frac{H}{3}(B + \sqrt{Bb} + b)$$

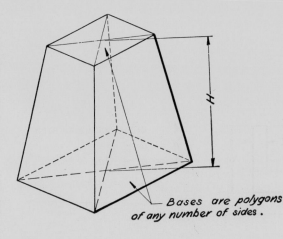

Bases are polygons of any number of sides.

Frustum of Right Circular Cone

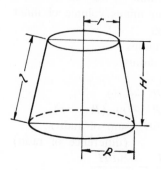

R = radius of lower base
r = radius of upper base
H = height
l = slant height
V = volume
S = lateral area (area of curved surface)

$$V = \frac{\pi}{3}H(R^2 + Rr + r^2)$$
$$V = 1.0472H(R^2 + Rr + r^2)$$
$$S = \pi l(R + r) = 3.1416l(R + r)$$
$$l = \sqrt{H^2 + (R - r)^2}$$

Simple Structural Steel Shapes
(Simplified Form)

I Beams and H Beams

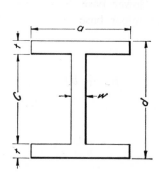

A = cross sectional area
$A = 2at + cw$
$d = c + 2t$

Channel

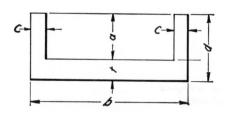

A = cross sectional area
$a = d - t$
$A = bt + 2ac$

Angle Iron

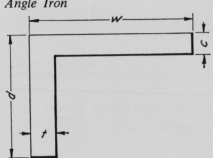

A = cross sectional area

$A = cw + t(d - c)$

Speeds

Surface speed of pulley in feet per minute =
Circumference of pulley in feet $\times$ RPM

$$RPM = \frac{\text{Surface speed of pulley in feet per minute}}{\text{Circumference of pulley in feet}}$$

$$\text{Circumference of pulley in feet} = \frac{\text{Surface speed of pulley in feet per minute}}{RPM}$$

Cutting speed of circular saws, band saws, swing saws in feet per minute
= Circumference of saw in feet $\times$ RPM

Cutting speed of lathe tool in feet per minute =
Circumference of piece being turned in feet $\times$ RPM of piece

Cutting speed of grinding wheels in feet per minute =
Circumference of wheel in feet $\times$ RPM

Belt speed in feet per minute = Circumference of pulley in feet $\times$ RPM

Length of belt in coil in feet $=0.131(D + d) \times$ number of laps

(D = outer diameter in inches)
(d = inner diameter in inches)

Taper Formulas

D = diameter of tapered piece at large end in inches
d = diameter of tapered piece at small end in inches

$$\text{Taper per inch} = \frac{(D - d)}{\text{Length in inches}}$$

$$\text{Taper per foot} = \frac{(D - d)}{\text{Length in inches}} \times 12$$

Tailstock setover for taper turning

$$= \tfrac{1}{2} \frac{(\text{Length of piece in inches} \times \text{taper per foot})}{12}$$

$$= \tfrac{1}{2} \frac{(D - d) \times \text{length of piece in inches}}{\text{Tapered length}}$$

Screw Thread Formulas

Unified and American Threads

$$\text{Pitch in inches} = \frac{1}{\text{number of threads per inch}} \qquad p = \frac{1}{n}$$

Number of threads per inch

$$= \frac{1}{\text{pitch in inches}} \qquad n = \frac{1}{p}$$

Height (or depth) of sharp V thread in inches

$$= 0.86603 \times \text{pitch in inches} \qquad H = 0.86603 \times p$$

$$= \frac{0.86603}{\text{number of threads per inch}} \qquad H = \frac{0.86603}{n}$$

Height of external thread in inches

$$= 0.61343 \times \text{pitch in inches} \qquad H = 0.61343p$$

$$= \frac{0.61343}{\text{number of threads per inch}} \qquad H = \frac{0.61343}{n}$$

Minor diameter of external thread in inches (root diameter)

= Nominal diameter of screw in inches minus $1.22687 \times$ pitch in inches $\qquad K_s = D_s - 1.22687 \times p$

= Nominal diameter of screw in inches minus $\dfrac{1.22687}{\text{number of threads per inch}} \qquad K_s = D_s - \dfrac{1.22687}{n}$

American National Threads

Pitch in inches — same as for Unified and American Threads
Number of threads per inch — same as for Unified and American Threads
Basic depth of American National form of thread in inches

(Crest to root height)

$$= 0.64952 \times \text{pitch of thread in inches} \quad h_S = 0.64952p$$

$$= \frac{0.64952}{\text{number of threads per inch}} \qquad h_S = \frac{0.64952}{n}$$

Minor diameter of external thread in inches (root diameter)

= Nominal diameter of screw in inches minus $1.29904 \times$ pitch in inches $\quad K_S = D_S - 1.29904p$

= Nominal diameter of screw in inches minus
$$\frac{1.29904}{\text{number of threads per inch}} \qquad K_S = D_S - \frac{1.29904}{n}$$

Useful Constants

$$\sqrt{2} = 1.4142$$

$$\sqrt{3} = 1.7321$$

$$\frac{1}{\sqrt{2}} = 0.7071$$

$$\frac{1}{\sqrt{3}} = 0.5774$$

$$\pi = 3.1416$$

$$\frac{\pi}{4} = 0.7854$$

$$\frac{\pi}{3} = 1.0472$$

$$\frac{\pi}{6} = 0.5236$$

$$\frac{1}{\pi} = 0.3183$$

$$\frac{1}{\sqrt{\pi}} = 0.5642$$

Weight of water in a tank (in lb.)
= Volume of water in tank in cubic feet $\times$ 62.425

Weight of iron castings as made from pine patterns without cores (in lb.)
= Weight of pine pattern $\times$ 16

Weight of iron castings as made from mahogany patterns without cores
= Weight of pattern $\times$ 12

Weight of timbers = Volume in cubic feet $\times$ Weight per cubic foot

Weight of building materials
= Volume in cubic feet $\times$ Weight per cubic foot

Table of Squares, Square Roots, Areas, and Circumference

Number N	Square of Number N^2	Square Root of Number $\sqrt{N}$	Area of Circle If N = Dia.*	Circumference of Circle If N = Dia.*
1	1	1.00000	0.7854	3.1416
2	4	1.4142	3.1416	6.283
3	9	1.7321	7.0686	9.425
4	16	2.0000	12.5664	12.566
5	25	2.2361	19.6350	15.708
6	36	2.4495	28.2743	18.850
7	49	2.6458	38.4845	21.991
8	64	2.8284	50.2655	25.133
9	81	3.0000	63.6173	28.274
10	100	3.1623	78.5398	31.416
11	121	3.3166	95.033	34.558
12	144	3.4641	113.097	37.699
13	169	3.6056	132.732	40.841
14	196	3.7417	153.938	43.982
15	225	3.8730	176.715	47.124
16	256	4.0000	201.062	50.265
17	289	4.1231	226.980	53.407
18	324	4.2426	254.469	56.549
19	361	4.3589	283.529	59.690
20	400	4.4721	314.159	62.832
21	441	4.5826	346.361	65.973
22	484	4.6904	380.133	69.115
23	529	4.7958	415.476	72.257
24	576	4.8990	452.389	75.398
25	625	5.0000	490.874	78.540
26	676	5.0990	530.929	81.681
27	729	5.1962	572.555	84.823
28	784	5.2915	615.752	87.965
29	841	5.3852	660.520	91.106
30	900	5.4772	706.858	94.248
31	961	5.5678	754.768	97.389
32	1024	5.6569	804.248	100.531
33	1089	5.7446	855.299	103.673
34	1156	5.8310	907.920	106.814
35	1225	5.9161	962.113	109.956
36	1296	6.0000	1017.88	113.097
37	1369	6.0828	1075.21	116.239
38	1444	6.1644	1134.11	119.381
39	1521	6.2450	1194.59	122.522
40	1600	6.3246	1256.64	125.664

* $\dfrac{\pi}{4}$ = 0.785398 π = 3.141593

Number N	Square of Number N^2	Square Root of Number $\sqrt{N}$	Area of Circle If $N =$ Dia.*	Circumference of Circle If $N =$ Dia.*
41	1681	6.4031	1320.25	128.81
42	1764	6.4807	1385.44	131.95
43	1849	6.5574	1452.20	135.09
44	1936	6.6332	1520.53	138.23
45	2025	6.7082	1590.43	141.37
46	2116	6.7823	1661.90	144.51
47	2209	6.8557	1734.94	147.65
48	2304	6.9282	1809.56	150.80
49	2401	7.0000	1885.74	153.94
50	2500	7.0711	1963.50	157.08
51	2601	7.1414	2042.82	160.22
52	2704	7.2111	2123.72	163.36
53	2809	7.2801	2206.18	166.50
54	2916	7.3485	2290.22	169.65
55	3025	7.4162	2375.83	172.79
56	3136	7.4833	2463.01	175.93
57	3249	7.5498	2551.76	179.07
58	3364	7.6158	2642.08	182.21
59	3481	7.6811	2733.97	185.35
60	3600	7.7460	2827.43	188.50
61	3721	7.8102	2922.47	191.64
62	3844	7.8740	3019.07	194.78
63	3969	7.9373	3117.25	197.92
64	4096	8.0000	3216.99	201.06
65	4225	8.0623	3318.31	204.20
66	4356	8.1240	3421.19	207.35
67	4489	8.1854	3525.65	210.49
68	4624	8.2462	3631.68	213.63
69	4761	8.3066	3739.28	216.77
70	4900	8.3666	3848.45	219.91
71	5041	8.4261	3959.19	223.05
72	5184	8.4853	4071.50	226.19
73	5329	8.5440	4185.39	229.34
74	5476	8.6023	4300.84	232.48
75	5625	8.6603	4417.86	235.62
76	5776	8.7178	4536.46	238.76
77	5929	8.7750	4656.63	241.90
78	6084	8.8318	4778.36	245.04
79	6241	8.8882	4901.67	248.19
80	6400	8.9443	5026.55	251.33
81	6561	9.0000	5153.00	254.47
82	6724	9.0554	5281.02	257.61
83	6889	9.1104	5410.61	260.75
84	7056	9.1652	5541.77	263.89
85	7225	9.2195	5674.50	267.04

Number N	Square of Number N^2	Square Root of Number $\sqrt{N}$	Area of Circle If $N = $ Dia.*	Circumference of Circle If $N = $ Dia.*
86	7396	9.2736	5808.80	270.18
87	7569	9.3274	5944.68	273.32
88	7744	9.3808	6082.12	276.46
89	7921	9.4340	6221.14	279.60
90	8100	9.4868	6361.73	282.74
91	8281	9.5394	6503.88	285.88
92	8464	9.5917	6647.61	289.03
93	8649	9.6437	6792.91	292.17
94	8836	9.6954	6939.78	295.31
95	9025	9.7468	7088.22	298.45
96	9216	9.7980	7238.23	301.59
97	9409	9.8489	7389.81	304.73
98	9604	9.8995	7542.96	307.88
99	9801	9.9499	7697.69	311.02
100	10000	10.0000	7853.98	314.16

Weights of Materials in Pounds Per Cubic Foot

(*Approximate*)

Aluminum	165	Maple	43
Birch	40	Mercury	849
Brass	534	Oak (white)	46
Brick (common)	120	Oak (red)	41
Brick work (ordinary)	120	Pine (southern, yellow, dry)	41
Bronze	510	Platinum	1340
Chestnut	41	Plutonium (at 0° C)	1239
Cobalt	544	Sand (dry)	100
Copper	555	Silicon	145
Concrete	145	Silver	655
Earth (loose)	75	Spruce (eastern, dry)	28
Hemlock	30	Snow	8
Hickory	50	Steel	489.6
Ice	57	Tungsten	1204
Iron (cast)	442	Walnut (black)	38
Iron (wrought)	484	Water (fresh)	62.4
Lead	710	Water (sea)	64
Limestone	160	Zinc	440
Mahogany	56		

Weights of Flat Steel Bars in Pounds Per Linear Foot

(*Width and Thickness in Inches*)

Thickness of Bar	Width of Bar						
	$\frac{1}{2}$	$\frac{3}{4}$	1	$1\frac{1}{4}$	$1\frac{1}{2}$	$1\frac{3}{4}$	2
$\frac{1}{8}$	0.213	0.319	0.425	0.531	0.638	0.744	0.850
$\frac{3}{16}$	0.319	0.478	0.638	0.797	0.956	1.116	1.275
$\frac{1}{4}$	0.425	0.638	0.850	1.063	1.275	1.488	1.700
$\frac{5}{16}$	0.531	0.797	1.063	1.328	1.594	1.859	2.125
$\frac{3}{8}$	0.638	0.956	1.275	1.594	1.913	2.231	2.550
$\frac{7}{16}$	0.744	1.116	1.488	1.859	2.231	2.603	2.975
$\frac{1}{2}$	0.850	1.275	1.700	2.125	2.550	2.975	3.400
$\frac{9}{16}$	0.956	1.434	1.913	2.391	2.869	3.347	3.825
$\frac{5}{8}$	1.063	1.594	2.125	2.656	3.188	3.719	4.250
$\frac{11}{16}$	1.169	1.753	2.338	2.922	3.506	4.091	4.675
$\frac{3}{4}$	1.275	1.913	2.550	3.188	3.825	4.463	5.100
$\frac{13}{16}$	1.381	2.072	2.763	3.453	4.144	4.834	5.525
$\frac{7}{8}$	1.488	2.231	2.975	3.719	4.463	5.206	5.950
$\frac{15}{16}$	1.594	2.391	3.188	3.984	4.781	5.578	6.375
1	1.700	2.550	3.400	4.250	5.100	5.950	6.800

Weight of bar $=$ Cross-sectional area of bar $\times$ 3.400
Weight of steel $=$ 489.6 lb. per cubic foot

Weights of Steel Bars

D = Diameter or Distance Across Flats in Inches	Weight in lb. per Foot of Bar Length			
	Round Bars	Square Bars	Hexagon Bars	Octagon Bars
$\frac{1}{8}$	0.042	0.053	0.046	0.044
$\frac{1}{4}$	0.167	0.213	0.184	0.176
$\frac{3}{8}$	0.376	0.478	0.414	0.396
$\frac{1}{2}$	0.668	0.850	0.736	0.704
$\frac{5}{8}$	1.043	1.328	1.150	1.100
$\frac{3}{4}$	1.502	1.913	1.656	1.584
$\frac{7}{8}$	2.044	2.603	2.254	2.156
1	2.670	3.400	2.945	2.817
$1\frac{1}{8}$	3.380	4.303	3.727	3.565
$1\frac{1}{4}$	4.172	5.313	4.601	4.401
$1\frac{3}{8}$	5.049	6.428	5.567	5.325
$1\frac{1}{2}$	6.008	7.650	6.625	6.337
$1\frac{5}{8}$	7.051	8.978	7.775	7.438
$1\frac{3}{4}$	8.178	10.413	9.017	8.626
$1\frac{7}{8}$	9.388	11.953	10.352	9.902
2	10.681	13.600	11.778	11.267
$2\frac{1}{4}$	13.519	17.213	14.906	14.259
$2\frac{1}{2}$	16.690	21.250	18.403	17.604
$2\frac{3}{4}$	20.195	25.713	22.268	21.301
3	24.033	30.600	26.500	25.350

In computing this table of weights, the constants used were: $\frac{\pi}{4} = 0.785398$; $\sqrt{3} = 1.7320508$; $\tan 22\frac{1}{2}° = 0.41421$; weight of steel $= 489.6$ lb./cu. ft.

Decimal Equivalents of Fractional Parts of One Inch

Fraction	Decimal		Fraction	Decimal
$\frac{1}{64}$	.015625		$\frac{33}{64}$	.515625
$\frac{1}{32}$	.031250		$\frac{17}{32}$	.531250
$\frac{3}{64}$	.046875		$\frac{35}{64}$	.546875
$\frac{1}{16}$	.062500		$\frac{9}{16}$	.562500
$\frac{5}{64}$	.078125		$\frac{37}{64}$	.578125
$\frac{3}{32}$	.093750		$\frac{19}{32}$	.593750
$\frac{7}{64}$	.109375		$\frac{39}{64}$	.609375
$\frac{1}{8}$	.125000		$\frac{5}{8}$	.625000
$\frac{9}{64}$	.140625		$\frac{41}{64}$	.640625
$\frac{5}{32}$	.156250		$\frac{21}{32}$	.656250
$\frac{11}{64}$	.171875		$\frac{43}{64}$	.671875
$\frac{3}{16}$	.187500		$\frac{11}{16}$	.687500
$\frac{13}{64}$	.203125		$\frac{45}{64}$	.703125
$\frac{7}{32}$	.218750		$\frac{23}{32}$	.718750
$\frac{15}{64}$	.234375		$\frac{47}{64}$	.734375
$\frac{1}{4}$	.250000		$\frac{3}{4}$	.750000
$\frac{17}{64}$	.265625		$\frac{49}{64}$	.765625
$\frac{9}{32}$	.281250		$\frac{25}{32}$	.781250
$\frac{19}{64}$	.296875		$\frac{51}{64}$	.796875
$\frac{5}{16}$	.312500		$\frac{13}{16}$	.812500
$\frac{21}{64}$	.328125		$\frac{53}{64}$	.828125
$\frac{11}{32}$	.343750		$\frac{27}{32}$	.843750
$\frac{23}{64}$	.359375		$\frac{55}{64}$	.859375
$\frac{3}{8}$	.375000		$\frac{7}{8}$	.875000
$\frac{25}{64}$	.390625		$\frac{57}{64}$	.890625
$\frac{13}{32}$	.406250		$\frac{29}{32}$	.906250
$\frac{27}{64}$	.421875		$\frac{59}{64}$	.921875
$\frac{7}{16}$	.437500		$\frac{15}{16}$	.937500
$\frac{29}{64}$	.453125		$\frac{61}{64}$	.953125
$\frac{15}{32}$	.468750		$\frac{31}{32}$	.968750
$\frac{31}{64}$	.484375		$\frac{63}{64}$	.984375
$\frac{1}{2}$	.500000		1	1.000000

Areas and Circumferences of Circles

Dia.	Area	Circum.		Dia.	Area	Circum.
$\frac{1}{16}$	0.0031	0.1963		$\frac{15}{16}$	0.6903	2.9452
$\frac{1}{8}$	0.0123	0.3927		1	0.7854	3.1416
$\frac{3}{16}$	0.0276	0.5890		$1\frac{1}{8}$	0.9940	3.5343
$\frac{1}{4}$	0.0491	0.7854		$1\frac{1}{4}$	1.2272	3.9270
$\frac{5}{16}$	0.0767	0.9817		$1\frac{3}{8}$	1.4849	4.3197
$\frac{3}{8}$	0.1105	1.1781		$1\frac{1}{2}$	1.7671	4.7124
$\frac{7}{16}$	0.1503	1.3744		$1\frac{5}{8}$	2.0739	5.1051
$\frac{1}{2}$	0.1963	1.5708		$1\frac{3}{4}$	2.4053	5.4978
$\frac{9}{16}$	0.2485	1.7671		2	3.1416	6.2832
$\frac{5}{8}$	0.3068	1.9635		$2\frac{1}{4}$	3.9761	7.0686
$\frac{11}{16}$	0.3712	2.1598		$2\frac{1}{2}$	4.9087	7.8540
$\frac{3}{4}$	0.4418	2.3562		$2\frac{3}{4}$	5.9396	8.6394
$\frac{13}{16}$	0.5185	2.5525		3	7.0686	9.4248
$\frac{7}{8}$	0.6013	2.7489				

Lumber Table
Board-Foot Measure of Standard Sizes for Given Lengths

Size in Inches	Length in Feet			
	10	12	14	16
1 × 6	5	6	7	8
1 × 8	$6\frac{2}{3}$	8	$9\frac{1}{3}$	$10\frac{2}{3}$
1 × 10	$8\frac{1}{3}$	10	$11\frac{2}{3}$	$13\frac{1}{3}$
1 × 12	10	12	14	16
1 × 14	$11\frac{2}{3}$	14	$16\frac{1}{3}$	$18\frac{2}{3}$
$1\frac{1}{4}$ × 4	$4\frac{1}{6}$	5	$5\frac{5}{6}$	$6\frac{2}{3}$
$1\frac{1}{4}$ × 6	$6\frac{1}{4}$	$7\frac{1}{2}$	$8\frac{3}{4}$	10
$1\frac{1}{4}$ × 8	$8\frac{1}{3}$	10	$11\frac{2}{3}$	$13\frac{1}{3}$
$1\frac{1}{2}$ × 4	5	6	7	8
$1\frac{1}{2}$ × 6	$7\frac{1}{2}$	9	$10\frac{1}{2}$	12
$1\frac{1}{2}$ × 8	10	12	14	16
2 × 4	$6\frac{2}{3}$	8	$9\frac{1}{3}$	$10\frac{2}{3}$
2 × 6	10	12	14	16
2 × 8	$13\frac{1}{3}$	16	$18\frac{2}{3}$	$21\frac{1}{3}$

American Standard Regular Hexagon and Square Bolts and Nuts*

(All dimensions in inches.)

Thread shall be coarse-thread series, class 2A for bolts.
Thread shall be coarse-thread series, class 2B for nuts.

Nominal Size or Basic Major Dia. of Thread	Hexagon						Square					
	Width of Head		Height of Head	Width of Nut		Thickness of Nut	Width of Head		Height of Head	Width of Nut		Thickness of Nut
	Across Flats Max. (Basic)	Across Corners Max.	Nom.	Across Flats Max. (Basic)	Across Corners Max.	Nom.	Across Flats Max. (Basic)	Across Corners Max.	Nom.	Across Flats Max. (Basic)	Across Corners Max.	Nom.
$\frac{1}{4}$	$\frac{7}{16}$	0.505	$\frac{11}{64}$	$\frac{7}{16}$	0.505	$\frac{7}{32}$	$\frac{3}{8}$	0.530	$\frac{11}{64}$	$\frac{7}{16}$	0.619	$\frac{7}{32}$
$\frac{5}{16}$	$\frac{1}{2}$	0.577	$\frac{7}{32}$	$\frac{9}{16}$	0.650	$\frac{17}{64}$	$\frac{1}{2}$	0.707	$\frac{13}{64}$	$\frac{9}{16}$	0.795	$\frac{17}{64}$
$\frac{3}{8}$	$\frac{9}{16}$	0.650	$\frac{1}{4}$	$\frac{5}{8}$	0.722	$\frac{21}{64}$	$\frac{9}{16}$	0.795	$\frac{1}{4}$	$\frac{5}{8}$	0.884	$\frac{21}{64}$
$\frac{7}{16}$	$\frac{5}{8}$	0.722	$\frac{19}{64}$	$\frac{3}{4}$	0.866	$\frac{3}{8}$	$\frac{5}{8}$	0.884	$\frac{19}{64}$	$\frac{3}{4}$	1.061	$\frac{3}{8}$
$\frac{1}{2}$	$\frac{3}{4}$	0.866	$\frac{11}{32}$	$\frac{13}{16}$	0.938	$\frac{7}{16}$	$\frac{3}{4}$	1.061	$\frac{21}{64}$	$\frac{13}{16}$	1.149	$\frac{7}{16}$
$\frac{5}{8}$	$\frac{15}{16}$	1.083	$\frac{27}{64}$	1	1.155	$\frac{35}{64}$	$\frac{15}{16}$	1.326	$\frac{27}{64}$	1	1.414	$\frac{35}{64}$
$\frac{3}{4}$	$1\frac{1}{8}$	1.299	$\frac{1}{2}$	$1\frac{1}{8}$	1.299	$\frac{41}{64}$	$1\frac{1}{8}$	1.591	$\frac{1}{2}$	$1\frac{1}{8}$	1.591	$\frac{41}{64}$
$\frac{7}{8}$	$1\frac{5}{16}$	1.516	$\frac{37}{64}$	$1\frac{5}{16}$	1.516	$\frac{3}{4}$	$1\frac{5}{16}$	1.856	$\frac{19}{32}$	$1\frac{5}{16}$	1.856	$\frac{49}{64}$
1	$1\frac{1}{2}$	1.732	$\frac{43}{64}$	$1\frac{1}{2}$	1.732	$\frac{7}{8}$	$1\frac{1}{2}$	2.121	$\frac{21}{32}$	$1\frac{1}{2}$	2.121	$\frac{7}{8}$
$1\frac{1}{8}$	$1\frac{11}{16}$	1.948	$\frac{3}{4}$	$1\frac{11}{16}$	1.949	1	$1\frac{11}{16}$	2.386	$\frac{3}{4}$	$1\frac{11}{16}$	2.386	1
$1\frac{1}{4}$	$1\frac{7}{8}$	2.165	$\frac{27}{32}$	$1\frac{7}{8}$	2.165	$1\frac{3}{32}$	$1\frac{7}{8}$	2.652	$\frac{27}{32}$	$1\frac{7}{8}$	2.652	$1\frac{3}{32}$
$1\frac{3}{8}$	$2\frac{1}{16}$	2.382	$\frac{29}{32}$	$2\frac{1}{16}$	2.382	$1\frac{13}{64}$	$2\frac{1}{16}$	2.917	$\frac{29}{32}$	$2\frac{1}{16}$	2.917	$1\frac{13}{64}$
$1\frac{1}{2}$	$2\frac{1}{4}$	2.598	1	$2\frac{1}{4}$	2.598	$1\frac{5}{16}$	$2\frac{1}{4}$	3.182	1	$2\frac{1}{4}$	3.182	$1\frac{5}{16}$

* Extracted (and adapted) from *American Standard Square and Hexagon Bolts and Nuts* (ASA B18.2 — 1960) with the permission of the publisher, The American Society of Mechanical Engineers, 29 West 39th Street, New York, N. Y. 10018.

Cap Screws*

(*All dimensions in inches.*)

Nominal Size or Basic Major Dia. of Thread	Hexagonal Head**			Fillister Head	
	Width Across Flats, Max.	Width Across Corners, Max.	Height of Head, Nominal	Diameter of Head, Max.	Total Height of Head, Max.
$\frac{1}{4}$	$\frac{7}{16}$	0.505	$\frac{5}{32}$	0.375	0.216
$\frac{5}{16}$	$\frac{1}{2}$	0.577	$\frac{13}{64}$	0.437	0.253
$\frac{3}{8}$	$\frac{9}{16}$	0.650	$\frac{15}{64}$	0.562	0.314
$\frac{7}{16}$	$\frac{5}{8}$	0.722	$\frac{9}{32}$	0.625	0.368
$\frac{1}{2}$	$\frac{3}{4}$	0.866	$\frac{5}{16}$	0.750	0.413
$\frac{9}{16}$	$1\frac{3}{16}$	0.938	$\frac{23}{64}$	0.812	0.467
$\frac{5}{8}$	$1\frac{5}{16}$	1.083	$\frac{25}{64}$	0.875	0.521
$\frac{3}{4}$	$1\frac{1}{8}$	1.299	$\frac{15}{32}$	1.000	0.612
$\frac{7}{8}$	$1\frac{5}{16}$	1.516	$\frac{35}{64}$	1.125	0.720
1	$1\frac{1}{2}$	1.732	$\frac{39}{64}$	1.312	0.803
$1\frac{1}{8}$	$1\frac{11}{16}$	1.949	$\frac{11}{16}$	....	....
$1\frac{1}{4}$	$1\frac{7}{8}$	2.165	$\frac{25}{32}$	....	....
$1\frac{3}{8}$	$2\frac{1}{16}$	2.382	$\frac{27}{32}$	....	....
$1\frac{1}{2}$	$2\frac{1}{4}$	2.598	$\frac{15}{16}$	....	....

* Extracted from *American Standard Hexagon Head Cap Screws,* etc. (ASA B.18.6.2 — 1956) with the permission of the publisher, The American Society of Mechanical Engineers, 29 West 39th Street, New York, N. Y. 10018.

** Threads shall be coarse, fine, or 8-thread series, class 2A for plain (unplated) cap screws.

Straight Shank Twist Drills (Wire Gauge Sizes)

Diameter of Drill D	Decimal Equivalent, Inches	Diameter of Drill D	Decimal Equivalent, Inches
80	0.0135	38	0.1015
79	0.0145	37	0.104
78	0.016	36	0.1065
77	0.018	35	0.110
76	0.020	34	0.111
75	0.021	33	0.113
74	0.0225	32	0.116
73	0.024	31	0.120
72	0.025	30	0.1285
71	0.026	29	0.136
70	0.028	28	0.1405
69	0.0292	27	0.144
68	0.031	26	0.147
67	0.032	25	0.1495
66	0.033	24	0.152
65	0.035	23	0.154
64	0.036	22	0.157
63	0.037	21	0.159
62	0.038	20	0.161
61	0.039	19	0.166
60	0.040	18	0.1695
59	0.041	17	0.173
58	0.042	16	0.177
57	0.043	15	0.180
56	0.0465	14	0.182
55	0.052	13	0.185
54	0.055	12	0.189
53	0.0595	11	0.191
52	0.0635	10	0.1935
51	0.067	9	0.196
50	0.070	8	0.199
49	0.073	7	0.201
48	0.076	6	0.204
47	0.0785	5	0.2055
46	0.081	4	0.209
45	0.082	3	0.213
44	0.086	2	0.221
43	0.089	1	0.228
42	0.0935		
41	0.096		
40	0.098		
39	0.0995		

* Extracted from *American Standard Twist Drills* (ASA B5.12 — 1958), with permission of the publisher, The American Society of Mechanical Engineers, 29 West 39th Street, New York, N. Y. 10018.

Straight Shank Twist Drills—Fractional Sizes

Diameter of Drill D	Decimal Equivalent, Inches	Diameter of Drill D	Decimal Equivalent, Inches
$\frac{1}{64}$	0.0156	$\frac{17}{64}$	0.2656
$\frac{1}{32}$	0.0312	$\frac{9}{32}$	0.2812
$\frac{3}{64}$	0.0469	$\frac{19}{64}$	0.2969
$\frac{1}{16}$	0.0625	$\frac{5}{16}$	0.3125
$\frac{5}{64}$	0.0781	$\frac{21}{64}$	0.3281
$\frac{3}{32}$	0.0938	$\frac{11}{32}$	0.3438
$\frac{7}{64}$	0.1094	$\frac{23}{64}$	0.3594
$\frac{1}{8}$	0.1250	$\frac{3}{8}$	0.375
$\frac{9}{64}$	0.1406	$\frac{25}{64}$	0.3906
$\frac{5}{32}$	0.1562	$\frac{13}{32}$	0.4062
$\frac{11}{64}$	0.1719	$\frac{27}{64}$	0.4219
$\frac{3}{16}$	0.1875	$\frac{7}{16}$	0.4375
$\frac{13}{64}$	0.2031	$\frac{29}{64}$	0.4531
$\frac{7}{32}$	0.2188	$\frac{15}{32}$	0.4688
$\frac{15}{64}$	0.2344	$\frac{31}{64}$	0.4844
$\frac{1}{4}$	0.250	$\frac{1}{2}$	0.5000

* Extracted from *American Standard Twist Drills* (ASA B5.12 — 1958), with permission of the publisher, The American Society of Mechanical Engineers, 29 West 39th Street, New York, N. Y. 10018.

Straight Shank Twist Drills—Letter Sizes

Diameter of Drill D	Decimal Equivalent, Inches	Diameter of Drill D	Decimal Equivalent, Inches
A	0.234	S	0.348
B	0.238	T	0.358
C	0.242	U	0.368
D	0.246	V	0.377
E	0.250	W	0.386
F	0.257	X	0.397
G	0.261	Y	0.404
H	0.266	Z	0.413
I	0.272		
J	0.277		
K	0.281		
L	0.290		
M	0.295		
N	0.302		
O	0.316		
P	0.323		
Q	0.332		
R	0.339		

* Extracted from *American Standard Twist Drills* (ASA B5.12 — 1958), with permission of the publisher, The American Society of Mechanical Engineers, 29 West 39th Street, New York, N. Y. 10018.

SUMMARY OF TABLES AND FORMULAS

Tap Drill Sizes

Probable Percentage of Full Thread Produced in Tapped Hole Using Stock Sizes of Drill

Tap	Tap Drill	Decimal Equiv. of Tap Drill	Theo- retical % of Thread	Probable Oversize (Mean)	Probable Hole Size	Percent- age of Thread
0-80	56	.0465	83	.0015	.0480	74
	$\frac{3}{64}$	.0469	81	.0015	.0484	71
1-64	54	.0550	89	.0015	.0565	81
	53	.0595	67	.0015	.0610	59
1-72	53	.0595	75	.0015	.0610	67
	$\frac{1}{16}$	.0625	58	.0015	.0640	50
2-56	51	.0670	82	.0017	.0687	74
	50	.0700	69	.0017	.0717	62
	49	.0730	56	.0017	.0747	49
2-64	50	.0700	79	.0017	.0717	70
	49	.0730	64	.0017	.0747	56
3-48	48	.0760	85	.0019	.0779	78
	$\frac{5}{64}$	.0781	77	.0019	.0800	70
	47	.0785	76	.0019	.0804	69
	46	.0810	67	.0019	.0829	60
	45	.0820	63	.0019	.0839	56
3-56	46	.0810	78	.0019	.0829	69
	45	.0820	73	.0019	.0839	65
	44	.0860	56	.0019	.0879	48
4-40	44	.0860	80	.0020	.0880	74
	43	.0890	71	.0020	.0910	65
	42	.0935	57	.0020	.0955	51
	$\frac{3}{32}$	.0938	56	.0020	.0958	50
4-48	42	.0935	68	.0020	.0955	61
	$\frac{3}{32}$	.0938	68	.0020	.0958	60
	41	.0960	59	.0020	.0980	52
5-40	40	.0980	83	.0023	.1003	76
	39	.0995	79	.0023	.1018	71
	38	.1015	72	.0023	.1038	65
	37	.1040	65	.0023	.1063	58
5-44	38	.1015	79	.0023	.1038	72
	37	.1040	71	.0023	.1063	63
	36	.1065	63	.0023	.1088	55
6-32	37	.1040	84	.0023	.1063	78
	36	.1065	78	.0026	.1091	71
	$\frac{7}{64}$	.1094	70	.0026	.1120	64
	35	.1100	69	.0026	.1126	63
	34	.1110	67	.0026	.1136	60
	33	.1130	62	.0026	.1156	55
6-40	34	.1110	83	.0026	.1136	75
	33	.1130	77	.0026	.1156	69
	32	.1160	68	.0026	.1186	60
8-32	29	.1360	69	.0029	.1389	62
	28	.1405	58	.0029	.1434	51

Tap Drill Sizes (Cont.)

Tap	Tap Drill	Decimal Equiv. of Tap Drill	Theo-retical % of Thread	Probable Oversize (Mean)	Probable Hole Size	Percent-age of Thread
8-36	29	.1360	78	.0029	.1389	70
	28	.1405	68	.0029	.1434	57
	$\frac{9}{64}$	.1406	68	.0029	.1435	57
10-24	27	.1440	85	.0032	.1472	79
	26	.1470	79	.0032	.1502	74
	25	.1495	75	.0032	.1527	69
	24	.1520	70	.0032	.1552	64
	23	.1540	67	.0032	.1572	61
	$\frac{5}{32}$	.1563	62	.0032	.1595	56
	22	.1570	61	.0032	.1602	55
10-32	$\frac{5}{32}$	.1563	83	.0032	.1595	75
	22	.1570	81	.0032	.1602	73
	21	.1590	76	.0032	.1622	68
	20	.1610	71	.0032	.1642	64
	19	.1660	59	.0032	.1692	51
12-24	$\frac{11}{64}$	.1719	82	.0035	.1754	75
	17	.1730	79	.0035	.1765	73
	16	.1770	72	.0035	.1805	66
	15	.1800	67	.0035	.1835	60
	14	.1820	63	.0035	.1855	56
12-28	16	.1770	84	.0035	.1805	77
	15	.1800	78	.0035	.1835	70
	14	.1820	73	.0035	.1855	66
	13	.1850	67	.0035	.1885	59
	$\frac{3}{16}$	.1875	61	.0035	.1910	54
$\frac{1}{4}$-20	9	.1960	83	.0038	.1998	77
	8	.1990	79	.0038	.2028	73
	7	.2010	75	.0038	.2048	70
	$\frac{13}{64}$	.2031	72	.0038	.2069	66
	6	.2040	71	.0038	.2078	65
	5	.2055	69	.0038	.2093	63
	4	.2090	63	.0038	.2128	57
$\frac{1}{4}$-28	3	.2130	80	.0038	.2168	72
	$\frac{7}{32}$	.2188	67	.0038	.2226	59
	2	.2210	63	.0038	.2248	55
$\frac{5}{16}$-18	F	.2570	77	.0038	.2608	72
	G	.2610	71	.0041	.2651	66
	$\frac{17}{64}$	.2656	65	.0041	.2697	59
	H	.2660	64	.0041	.2701	59
$\frac{5}{16}$-24	H	.2660	86	.0041	.2701	78
	I	.2720	75	.0041	.2761	67
	J	.2770	66	.0041	.2811	58
$\frac{3}{8}$-16	$\frac{5}{16}$	.3125	77	.0044	.3169	72
	O	.3160	73	.0044	.3204	68
	O	.3230	64	.0044	.3274	59
$\frac{3}{8}$-24	$\frac{21}{64}$	.3281	87	.0044	.3325	79
	Q	.3320	79	.0044	.3364	71
	R	.3390	67	.0044	.3434	58

Tap Drill Sizes (Cont.)

Tap	Tap Drill	Decimal Equiv. of Tap Drill	Theoretical % of Thread	Probable Oversize (Mean)	Probable Hole Size	Percentage of Thread
$\frac{7}{16}$-14	T	.3580	86	.0046	.3626	81
	$\frac{23}{64}$	.3594	84	.0046	.3640	79
	U	.3680	75	.0046	.3726	70
	$\frac{3}{8}$	.3750	67	.0046	.3796	62
	V	.3770	65	.0046	.3816	60
$\frac{7}{16}$-20	W	.3860	79	.0046	.3906	72
	$\frac{25}{64}$	.3906	72	.0046	.3952	65
	X	.3970	62	.0046	.4016	55
$\frac{1}{2}$-13	$\frac{27}{64}$	.4219	78	.0047	.4266	73
	$\frac{7}{16}$	.4375	63	.0047	.4422	58
$\frac{1}{2}$-20	$\frac{29}{64}$	.4531	72	.0047	.4578	65
$\frac{9}{16}$-12	$\frac{15}{32}$	.4688	87	.0048	.4736	82
	$\frac{31}{64}$	.4844	72	.0048	.4892	68
$\frac{9}{16}$-18	$\frac{1}{2}$	.500	87	.0048	.5048	80
	$\frac{33}{64}$	.5156	65	.0048	.5204	58
$\frac{5}{8}$-11	$\frac{17}{32}$	.5313	79	.0049	.5362	75
	$\frac{35}{64}$	.5469	66	.0049	.5518	62
$\frac{5}{8}$-18	$\frac{9}{16}$	.5625	87	.0049	.5674	80
	$\frac{37}{64}$	.5781	65	.0049	.5831	58
$\frac{3}{4}$-10	$\frac{41}{64}$	.6406	84	.0050	.6456	80
	$\frac{21}{32}$	.6563	72	.0050	.6613	68
$\frac{3}{4}$-16	$\frac{11}{16}$	.6875	77	.0050	.6925	71
$\frac{7}{8}$-9	$\frac{49}{64}$	.7656	76	.0052	.7708	72
	$\frac{25}{32}$	.7812	65	.0052	.7864	61
$\frac{7}{8}$-14	$\frac{51}{64}$	.7969	84	.0052	.8021	79
	$\frac{13}{16}$	.8125	67	.0052	.8177	62
1″-8	$\frac{55}{64}$	.8594	87	.0059	.8653	83
	$\frac{7}{8}$	.875	77	.0059	.8809	73
	$\frac{57}{64}$	.8906	67	.0059	.8965	64
	$\frac{29}{32}$	.9063	58	.0059	.9122	54
1″-12	$\frac{29}{32}$	.9063	87	.0060	.9123	81
	$\frac{59}{64}$	.9219	72	.0060	.9279	67
	$\frac{15}{16}$	.9375	58	.0060	.9435	52
1″-14	$\frac{59}{64}$	.9219	84	.0060	.9279	78
	$\frac{15}{16}$	.9375	67	.0060	.9435	61
$1\frac{1}{8}$-7	$\frac{31}{32}$	.9688	84	.0062	.9750	81
	$\frac{63}{64}$	.9844	76	.0067	.9911	72
	1″	1.000	67	.0070	1.007	64
	$1\frac{1}{64}$	1.0156	59	.0070	1.0226	55
$1\frac{1}{8}$-12	$1\frac{1}{32}$	1.0313	87	.0071	1.0384	80
	$1\frac{3}{64}$	1.0469	72	.0072	1.0541	66
$1\frac{1}{4}$-7	$1\frac{3}{32}$	1.0938	84	No Test Results Available		
	$1\frac{7}{64}$	1.1094	76			
	$1\frac{1}{8}$	1.125	67			
$1\frac{1}{4}$-12	$1\frac{5}{32}$	1.1563	87			
	$1\frac{11}{64}$	1.1719	72			
$1\frac{3}{8}$-6	$1\frac{3}{16}$	1.1875	87	Reaming Recommended		
	$1\frac{13}{64}$	1.2031	79			

Tap Drill Sizes (Cont.)

Tap	Tap Drill	Decimal Equiv. of Tap Drill*	Theoretical % of Thread	Probable Oversize (Mean)	Probable Hole Size	Percentage of Thread
	$1\frac{7}{32}$	1.2188	72			
	$1\frac{15}{64}$	1.2344	65			
$1\frac{3}{8}$-12	$1\frac{9}{32}$	1.2813	87		No Test	
	$1\frac{19}{64}$	1.2969	72		Results	
$1\frac{1}{2}$-6	$1\frac{5}{16}$	1.3125	87		Available	
	$1\frac{21}{64}$	1.3281	79			
	$1\frac{11}{32}$	1.3438	72		Reaming	
	$1\frac{23}{64}$	1.3594	65		Recommended	
$1\frac{1}{2}$-12	$1\frac{13}{32}$	1.4063	87			
	$1\frac{27}{64}$	1.4219	72			

* Extracted from "Drilled Holes For Tapping," published by the Drill and Reamer Division and the Tap and Die Division of the Metal Cutting Tool Institute, 405 Lexington Ave., New York, N. Y. 10017.

Bibliography

Books and Handbooks

American Institute of Steel Construction, Inc., *Manual of Steel Construction,* 6th ed., New York, 1963.

American Society of Tool and Manufacturing Engineers, F. W. Wilson ed., *Tool Engineers Handbook,* 2nd ed., McGraw-Hill Book Co., Inc., 1959.

Anderson, L. D., and Heyer, O. C., *Wood-Frame House Construction,* U. S. Dept. of Agriculture Handbook No. 73, 1955, Superintendent of Documents, Washington, D. C. 20025.

Bureau of Naval Personnel, *Machinery Repairman 3 & 2,* Navpers 10530-B, Superintendent of Documents, Washington, D. C. 20025.

Buckingham, B. R., *Elementary Arithmetic — Its Meaning and Practice,* Ginn & Co., New York, 1953.

Burghardt, H. D., *et al.,* Machine Tool Operation, Part I, 5th ed., 1959; Part II, 4th ed., 1960, McGraw-Hill Book Co., Inc., New York.

Dallavia, Louis, *Estimating General Construction Costs,* 2nd ed., McGraw-Hill Book Co., Inc., New York, 1957.

Dalzell, J. R., *Simplified Masonry Planning and Building,* McGraw-Hill Book Co., Inc., New York, 1955.

Dalzell, J. R., and Townsend, G., *Masonry Simplified,* Vol. I, 1956; Vol. II, 1957, American Technical Society, Chicago, Ill.

Diehl, J. R., *Manual of Lathing and Plastering,* MAC Publishers Association, Washington, D. C. 20006, 1960.

Dietz, A. G. H., *Dwelling House Construction,* 2nd ed., D. Van Nostrand Co., Inc., New York, 1954.

Feirer, J. L., and Tatro, E. E., *Machine Tool Metalworking,* McGraw-Hill Book Co., Inc., New York, 1961.

Felker, C. A., *Shop Mathematics,* The Bruce Publishing Co., Milwaukee, Wis., 1965.

Ford Trade School, *Shop Theory,* 4th ed., McGraw-Hill Book Co., Inc., New York, 1955.

Giesecke, F. E., *et al., Technical Drawing,* 4th ed., The Macmillan Co., New York, 1958.

Hague, C. W., *Printing and Allied Graphic Arts,* The Bruce Publishing Co., Milwaukee, Wis., 1957.

Hoelscher, R. P., and Springer, C. H., *Engineering Drawing and Geometry,* 2nd ed., John Wiley and Sons, New York, 1961.

Hoelscher, R. P., *et al., Basic Drawing for Engineering Technology,* John Wiley and Sons, New York, 1964.

Huntington, W. C., *Building Construction: Materials and Types of Construction,* 3rd ed., John Wiley and Sons, New York, 1963.

Kepler, F. R., and Bettencourt, Wm., *Mechanical Drafting Handbook,* The Bruce Publishing Co., Milwaukee, Wis., 1963.

Lair, E. A., *Carpentry for the Building Trades,* 2nd ed., McGraw-Hill Book Co., Inc., New York, 1953.

LeGrand, R., editor, *The New American Machinist's Handbook,* McGraw-Hill Book Co., Inc., New York, 1955.

Nordhoff, W. A., *Machine-Shop Estimating,* 2nd ed., McGraw-Hill Book Co., New York, 1960.

Oberg, E., and Jones, F. D., *Machinery's Handbook,* 16th ed., The Industrial Press, New York, 1964.

Peurifoy, R. L., *Construction Planning, Equipment, and Methods,* McGraw-Hill Book Co., Inc., New York, 1956.

———— *Estimating Construction Costs,* 2nd ed., McGraw-Hill Book Co., Inc., New York, 1958.

Pulver, H. E., *Construction Estimates and Costs,* 3rd ed., McGraw-Hill Book Co., Inc., New York, 1960.

Rosenberg, R. R., and Lewis, H., *Business Mathematics Principles and Practice — Complete,* 5th ed., Gregg Publishing Division, McGraw-Hill Book Co., Inc., New York, 1958.

Spencer, H. C., *Basic Technical Drawing,* The Macmillan Co., New York, 1956.

Underwood, G., *House Construction Costs,* McGraw-Hill Book Co., Inc., 1950.

Walker, F. R., *The Building Estimator's Reference Book,* 15th ed., Frank R. Walker Co., Chicago, Ill., 1963.

White, R. W., *Building Practice Manual,* D. C. Heath and Co., Boston, 1952.

Wilson, J. D., *Practical House Carpentry,* McGraw-Hill Book Co., Inc., New York, 1957.

The American Society of Mechanical Engineers, 345 East 47th Street, New York, N. Y. 10017 (ASME) Publications Catalog AM-3 Fall, 1963. Contains American Standards Listing.

U. S. Department of Commerce, National Bureau of Standards, *Screw-Thread Standards for Federal Services 1957 Handbook H 28 (1957) — Part I and Part II.* Superintendent of Documents, Washington, D. C. 20025.

Magazines

American Builder
American City
American Machinist
Building Construction
Civil Engineering
Construction Methods and Equipment
Engineering News Record
Excavating Engineer
Modern Machine Shop

Index

Addition, of decimals, 62 f; of fractions and mixed numbers, 27 f; of mixed numbers, 18 f; of similar fractions, 18; of units of length, 154 f; of whole numbers and fractions, 18; of whole numbers, mixed numbers, and similar fractions, 20 f
Algebraic forms, 110, 127
American National Thread, 401
Angle, acute, 183; how generated, 182 f; how read, 183; obtuse, 184; parts of, 183; right, 183; straight, 184
Areas, computation of, 182 ff; of roofs, 282 ff; unit of, 188

Belt, crossed, length of, 355 f; lengths, problems on computation of, 358 ff
Belt speed formulas, 352
Belting, length of, in coil, 357; open, formulas for length of, 352 f
Belts, pulley, kinds of, 348
Board feet, 172
Board lath, estimating cost of, 265
Bolts, 426 ff; table of, 426 f
Brick, cost of, 274; estimating quantities of, 275 f; kind and sizes of, 273; Roman, 276
Brick bonds, kinds of, 274
Brickwork, 273 f
Building, costs of home, 263
Building trades, mathematics applied to, 263 ff

Chain drives, 391 f; standards relating to, 391 f
Circle, computation of areas of, 199; definition of, 197; formulas for area of, 198
Circumference, of circle, formulas for, 202
Compound gear trains, 377 ff
Cone, formula for lateral area of, 220; parts of, 220
Constants, table of, 475
Cubic measure, 227 ff; computations of, 229 f; how determined, 227; dimensions of, 228
Cutting, paper stock, 223 f

Cutting speeds, 340 ff
Cylinders, 234; formulas for areas of, 217; formulas for volumes of, 235; hollow, 242 f; lateral area of, 216

Decimal fractions, 59
Decimal notation, 59
Decimal numbers, 61; reading of, 61
Decimals, addition of, 63; applications, 77 f; changed to common fractions, 93 ff; converted from fractions, 91; division of, 83 ff; multiplication of, 75 f; subtraction of, 69
Degree, definition of, 182; how indicated, 182; subdivisions of, 183
Denominator, least common, 22 f
Dimensions, on shop drawings, 9
Division, of decimals, 83 ff; of fractions, 53 f; involving money, 102; of mixed numbers, 54; of units of two or more denominations, 166 f
Drills, 414 ff

Efficiencies, determining, 117
Ellipse, computation of area of, 201; formulas for area of, 200
Ems, how computed, 308 f; in width and depth of leaded type, 313 ff

Factor, largest common, 10
Formula, definition of, 122, 337
Formulas, American National thread form, 401 f; for areas of simple steel shapes, 422 f; for compound gear train, 381 ff; evaluation of, 122 ff, 132 ff; for gear drives, 363; for hexagon bolt heads, 428 f; how written, 338 f; for length of crossed belt, 355 f; letters appearing in, 127; list of, 128 ff; for plane geometric figures, 464 ff; reading of, 124 ff; and plane figures, 128 ff; and solid figures, 130 ff; for screw threads, 474 f; shop, 337 f; for solid geometric figures, 468 ff; for speeds, 473; for square and hexagon nuts, 431 f; for square bolt heads, 429 f; subjects of, 127; table of, for hexagon and square bolt heads, 427 f; table of, for nuts,